The Cross of Lassitude

THE CROSS OF LASSITUDE

PORTRAITS OF FIVE DELINQUENTS

Joan Colebrook

ANDRE DEUTSCH

FIRST PUBLISHED 1968 BY
ANDRE DEUTSCH LIMITED
105 GREAT RUSSELL STREET
LONDON WC1
COPYRIGHT © 1967 BY JOAN COLEBROOK

PRINTED IN GREAT BRITAIN BY
LOWE & BRYDONE (PRINTERS) LTD
LONDON
ISBN 0233 96070 8

600205863x

I am indebted to

F R A N K I E

for the generosity and zest

with which she cooperated in this research,

as also to the other young men and women

who willingly shared with me

the experiences of their lives.

"The American girls carried babies and coins in their bellies

And the boys fainted stretched on the cross of lassitude."

—FEDERICO GARCÍA LORCA

Author's Note

In all essentials this book is not a work of fiction, although some fictional devices have been used. It is a narrative—'reformed' from the life stories of prison inmates—supplemented by detailed information given me by the inhabitants of ghettos and the habitués of vice and crime areas. It is the result of four years of work and observation in urban slums, and of three years of research in various Eastern prisons, but all names and places have been changed, and the life stories—in an attempt to present typical sequences—have been generalized and simplified, each story including material from several informants. Conversations, where possible, have been reported verbatim, or reconstructed from descriptions of informants. Episodes have been written only after careful research, consultation with official records, repeated interviews, and wherever possible the cooperation of all those who—in real life—took part in the episodes described. No part of the plot has been changed to increase drama (the author feels in fact that in this account violence, action, the rapidity of the sequence of events, sexual turnover, etc., have been underemphasized).

The personnel in the prison scenes are fictional, drawn from the author's observation, and from information given by officers willing to be interviewed for this purpose. The author wishes to state that it was not her intention to describe these officers in depth, nor to present a complete picture of the day-to-day life in institutions. It was rather to give some account of formative emotional influences in the lives of the main characters: 'Frankie,' 'Baby,' 'Harry,' 'Pug Nose,' 'Beppo,' and 'Loper.'

Contents

I

Henry Street—The County Jail

The children are like shadows of those adults who pass by in the eternal theater of the slum streets. They stand in the wings watching the play with eager eyes—they dog footsteps—ape expressions—listen enraptured—seem to stand absorbing through thirsty pores the juices of life itself. They are insatiable, and their tiny jaws masticate with relish whatever food comes their way. Their unformed limbs perform constantly an imitative ballet. They are indiscriminate, and as ready to see glory on the forehead of a stranger as they are to gather filth from the rubbish-choked gutter.

And they are always prepared to love. Sometimes when a single tree, starved and blackened, buds forlornly in a back yard, they will adore it so much that they will kill it with kindness, pelting it with balls and tin cans, breaking its boughs, and burying beebees into its misused bark. For this tree has become, through their breaking, their cutting, their bruising of it—through their very acting upon it—part of them.

Seated on the steps of the monotonous houses, they store up the hours. Their infantile eyes (as if they were magic rays, capable of breaking down walls, and penetrating into every corner of every house) absorb with unappeasable hunger the final object in each room, the stain upon each ceiling, the blush upon the skin of a woman, the hair upon the hand of a man. These cruelly efficient X-ray eyes bear to the frontiers of memory a surging and darkened tide, afloat with flotsam and jetsam.

Among these children both sexes are represented, but the spotlight of the times focuses momentarily upon the female who, stepping out of a traditional role, appears for a moment (wearing what has become almost a uniform, a straight short coat and narrow hip-hugging pants) lit up by the neon light which blazes coldly from the shop at the corner. This "little woman" who once, even here, was respected for her probable chastity, now in chilly illumination, and rocking on her heels with the openly fondling Lotharios of the corner, is forced to claim a dangerous equality, and learn through the exercise of it new ways to outdo the slower male. Like primitive brides allotted in childhood and prematurely caressed into womanhood, these female children are exposed to a heat which—almost as soon as their eyes are opened —bursts upon their senses, burning away vegetative innocence, and penetrating like a corrosive acid the defenses with which nature has equipped them. Just as they have so often participated vicariously in the rites of the bed itself, so in the too-much-slept-in bedrooms, half-naked and aping seduction, they have pirouetted before the bulging wardrobes with their spotted mirrors, or stumbled in the high heels and dress-up clothes of their mothers. As they have been illogically slapped for using obscene words, by the same token they have been shaken for joining, in a night of drunken, fornicating, window-breaking darkness, their screaming to the violent screaming of parents and partners.

Deer stand hypnotized on the highways by the glare of headlights, and in the same way these children stand transfixed by the mesmeric power of lights too strong for them, pure bewilderment inducing them to give themselves up to a death not yet conceived of or explained. And in the case of girl-children, primed for a fate which by its very nature is associated with pleasure, the bewildering glare illuminates an area filled with seductive knowledge, seemingly separated from death itself, as music is from the instrument which makes it.

Perhaps it is for these reasons that one finds such children in the cellblock of North City's Henry Street Jail and catches between the rusted bars, once white-painted, glimpses of faces which have been changed before growth with its leisured laws could place some harmony upon them. Their very names (although all of them are girls, half of them have the names of boys) —'Frankie' (Francesca) in Cell I—'Baby' (Brenda) in Cell 2— 'Harry' (Harriet) in Cell 3—'Pug Nose' (Ana) in Cell 4—and

'Beppo' (Beulah) in Cell 5—suggest this hothouse development. Their accouterments, too, are like those which old soldiers carry around to remind themselves of battle—for Frankie, who is Negro, her belt (to accentuate maleness), for Baby a sharpened file (to defend herself with), for Harry a spoon (to open locks), for Pug Nose a stuffed panda (to keep her company), and for 'Portygee' Beppo various tools essential to her success in the field of love. This equipment resembles that adopted by older criminals, for the strictly utilitarian purposes of the trade. But it does not quite deceive anyone, not even the matrons who at once control and serve their young prisoners, nor its owners least of all, who only in hours of desperation can conjure themselves into a position of strength. The equipment acts as a protective fetish, however, and its possession suggests futures of great efficiency.

At nine o'clock at night, after the lights have been dimmed (in the open and alert world of the transient jail, light is never entirely absent) a new relationship blossoms between the officers and those who have been placed in captivity. For these particular matrons—some of whom, had it not been considered inappropriate, might have turned themselves into mothers—the faces of the girls on the narrow cots glow at this particular hour of the night with a certain essential radiance, like the phosphorescence of tropical plants, illuminating the shadows of a jungle. As the ingroup of society, they (the matrons) might wish to exchange information with the outgroup (the girls), but since open exchange would be perilous, it takes place in secret, by nods of sympathy, by haphazard murmurs of confidence, and by subtle extensions of privilege, all of which form a precarious bridge along which members of these two groups progress toward understanding.

The county jail, like a bus depot or a railway station, is considered a stopping-off place for Paragoula, the State Reformatory for Women. But this fact is not seriously considered by the five girls in the cells, who are restless and uneasy, perhaps a little bewildered, looking sadly for Fate to settle all questions, but none of whom, not even the comparatively worldly Beppo, sees her life as a matter of growth or deterioration. Nor are they unduly indignant because they are in *prison* (which they call familiarly 'the joint'). Only Frankie indeed, whose mind is naturally alert and whose nature is rebellious, has thought to protest. But perhaps this is because they do not understand that the jail in which they are housed is bound by cords of a steely strength to those other prisons, reformatories, and mental hospitals scattered about the state. So it might be said that the girls, willing or unwilling, at fault or not at fault, have had their names entered in the kindergarten of an institution from which they will probably, if one can believe the statistics, graduate at some future date. They are, therefore, almost innocents, aware that it is not quite the thing to be imprisoned, but inured to the thought of it, most of them having heard since babyhood (and as if in opposition to the threat of the good middle-class parent, "Mummy and Daddy will go away and leave you") that if they are not good they "will be put away." In Cell I, Frankie thinks that she has found a friend in 'Wally' (Miss Walton), the officer on night duty, and to obtain what she wants she utilizes, ironically enough, that respect for achievement which she has always found so effective when she is trying to 'beat a rap' in high school. She is like some apt pupil who secretly longs to play hooky but knows that only by asking for her school books will she gain the respect she desires.

"Miss Walton," she whispers through the bars, her dark eyes glowing with a stealthy illumination, "Miss Walton—d'you have any drawing paper—I wanta do a drawing." And then as Miss Walton brings her mountainous form close to the bars, "P-l-e-a-s-e bring me some paper, honey . . . any kinda paper."

"*Paper*," repeats Miss Walton, "paper?"

"Yes, paper, honey—paper to draw a picture."

"Office paper?" questions Miss Walton, "That's all I've got."

"*Anything*, honey," answers Frankie in desperation, "*anything*." She stands in her narrow blue short-legged pajamas, from which extend her thin black legs, with, on the crown of her head, the little peacock-like crest of hair shooting up from the white bandanna wound carefully to keep down the process which had been done a week ago. Her face is dark, not only because it is a Negro's face (the skin is the clear brown of coffee berries) but because it holds inside it a gloom, a twilight, which makes more profound the heavy curved fleshy lids falling over the eyes. It is only when a smile breaks over her face that Miss Walton sees the light rise like a slow retarded illumination. As she is to see it later in the prison passage as the girl walks in unobtrusive clothes, her face, her hair, her skirt, drowned in neutrality; and then, as someone catches her attention, that smile, like light rising on a lunar landscape.

"I'll get you paper," Miss Walton promises in a low tone. "Why not? . . . But no funny business."

"I wanta *draw*," Frankie insists. "Who can go to sleep like a baby at nine o'clock? At school I'm the best in art. My art teacher, Miss Donneville, she's my heart!"

"There's nothing wrong with *that*," Miss Walton emphasizes in a whisper, as if to indicate that Frankie isn't in Henry Street because of her artistic inclinations. "But you quiet down now, before the whole block wants paper."

. . . And the block is stirring, sleep far from it, or from all but Pug Nose, who like Frankie is not yet fifteen and who lies on her back on her narrow mattress in Cell 4, snoring gently through her once-broken nose, clutching her panda, her long rope of reddish hair dangling almost to the floor. In Cell 2, next to Frankie, Baby sits cross-legged on her bed, a heavy girl, with short luxurious bangs growing low on her forehead and giving with her thick dark brows a look both helpless and threatening, a look of everything being too much for her, her black hair almost on top of her eyebrows with their male heaviness, and her blue eyes puzzled and her mouth with its sullenness, and the out-of-proportion size of her thighs which now protrude, clumsily pink, from the edge of her cotton nightdress. Every now and then, in a kind of a panic, as if just to assure herself that someone is close to her, she taps with the end of the sharp little file on the wall of the cell, and Frankie, if not too preoccupied with her drawing, taps back, or else calls to her, "Hiya Baby," in a low voice, musical and throaty. In Cell 3, Harry signals to no one, calls to no one, but paces to and fro with a regularity which is only matched by the gentle snores of Pug Nose in the next cell. In Henry Street to await trial for stealing and burning cars, this tall, tawny-haired, crop-headed eighteen-year-old has lived in silence for most of her life, and it has now become a habit with her, a habit which she may never be able to break. Her rounded face pale in the dim light which washes the edge of her cell, her blue eyes fixed, she treads rapidly and almost silently to and fro, occasionally flexing her arm as a boy might and making a soundless lunge at the wall.

In the last cell, number 5, separated from Harry's pacing by the passed-out, cot-reclining figure of Pug Nose, Beppo (Beulah, who actually has two nicknames, one of them being 'Man') sensibly prepares for bed. She has a little Indian blood mixed with her Portuguese-American inheritance, and as a result short hair breaks dark, straight, and heavy over a broad-nosed, mat-skinned intelligent face, and she needs no scarf to keep it in order.

All she does at this hour is to put on a pair of man's socks and a slightly oversize man's shirt, which comes well down over her muscled thighs and so gives her the appearance of a rather attractive street boy, distracting the onlooker from her blank, level, and sometimes frightening gaze. Beppo (Harry's age) has already a formidable reputation as a 'Butch,' but unlike Harry, she has been too clever to be picked up for robbery; therefore, she is in Henry Street for thirty days only, on a charge of L and L (Lewd and Lascivious conduct), a charge which suggests that she is more sophisticated than the occupants of the neighboring cells. This hint of sophistication does not imply, however, that she is in control of her destiny. It does not record those long-buried rages and resentments, which are to drive her in the future to stab one of her own girls, to assault a policeman, to allow her narcotics habit to grow inordinately large. But at the present moment she finds it easiest to forget past emotional lapses and to vow that she will think of the future, that she will cut out the petty stuff, that she will 'cop' every girl she can—a resolve that urges her in the first flush of enthusiasm to attempt to wake up the sleeping Pug Nose.

Miss Walton, who has given Frankie her paper, has a feeling of creativity, treading the block with the thick crepe soles of her shoes, and conscious of the bunch of keys, held by a black leather strap to her belt and jingling faintly in the pocket of her uniform. She sees that Harry lies silently, that Beppo is lost in thought, that

Brenda is filing her nails, that the sleeping Pug Nose turns sadly on her three-inch mattress, seeming to offer herself to a rejecting world, to implore the night with her pale open mouth. She peers in again at the little Negro girl, who sits crouched by the bars of the cell, sketching in the dim light, and because she has seen the record, she knows that this fourteen year old, who has been committed to Henry Street for three months while she awaits trial, is the niece of Jeanette Tobey, a notorious and beautiful prostitute, at present in one of the cells upstairs. From the vantage point of thirteen years of work in a penal institution, Miss Walton recognizes the familiar pattern. A mother—an aunt—in the cells. A little later, a daughter—a niece. And, if one worked for enough years, then a granddaughter—a grand niece. In this particular case, the mantle of inheritance seems to have fallen upon an unusually intelligent girl. "How's that pencil?" she asks, going back to Frankie's cell. "Do you want a better one?"

"A better one? Oh, *honey*," the girl raises her eyes again and directs that radiant smile upon her benefactress. "I'd love some *colors*. Some real *bright* colors."

"I'll get you some tomorrow," promises Miss Walton, smiling herself. "Anything to keep you quiet."

Upstairs in the staff room, she stresses the increase in juvenile admissions this summer, and Miss McVee, an officer on duty in the block, murmurs an automatic surprise, as though not aware that aspirants for the underworld are turned out with the same regularity with which public schools turn out graduates. Could some hole have been bored in the thick brick wall of the jailhouse tower (where the staff room is situated) and equipped with a long-distance telescope, would she not have been able to put her eye to it and see such training—in homes, streets, school playgrounds, in neighborhood corner and store? Would her conversation with Miss Walton then not have been rather like the bored remarks which couples long married direct toward each other, as if to assure themselves of their own reality?

. . . From Miss McVee: "They seem to get younger and younger."

. . . From Miss Walton: "I don't know about that new one, Harriet Brun. She's eighteen or older and she doesn't talk much . . . but the little one, that Ana, with the broken nose, she's only fifteen and I swear she looks younger."

"Ana—the redhead? The one with the long rope of hair?"

"Yes. We're only keeping her overnight, I guess. She's got a VD test."

"Well," said Miss McVee hopefully, "if that's the case, she can't be so innocent."

"Innocent?" Miss Walton wedges herself into the narrow space between the table and the cupboard, and stretches up for a cup and saucer, the shoulders of her nylon uniform cracking ominously. "What's innocent? Can a girl of fifteen know *everything?*"

"They can know a lot," Miss McVee says cautiously. "Besides, they were brought in here because they *broke* the law."

But Miss Walton is bent on analysis. "Francesca Ford—she's down there drawing as if she's in art class. She's the niece of Jeanette Tobey, which speaks for itself, doesn't it?"

"Sure does," agrees Miss McVee. "What's she in for?"

"Stubborn-child complaint—truant, promiscuous, and so on . . . The judge put her on probation for three years on $500 bail, and then she jumped the bail. When they get around to hearing the case they'll probably send her to Wentworth, but I bet we'll have her here for at least two months. She's a pretty girl, medium brown, and she's got the cutest little white beauty spot."

Miss McVee slowly washes and wipes the teacups, and says in her conscientious schoolteacher's voice: "They oughtn't to leave her here so long."

"I know it." Miss Walton sinks into a chair and eases off her shoes. "I know it, but that's how it goes . . ."

"Well . . ." Miss McVee, who tries to feel that those in charge know more than she does, hangs up the dish towel with exaggerated care. "Perhaps they think it's a *deterrent* . . ."

"She'll learn more here than she'll ever forget." Miss Walton's small eyes look sad, as if some graceful spirit were struggling to free itself from her heavy body. "She'll pick up from everyone around her, that's the kind of child she is . . . and she *idolizes* that aunt. The aunt came here in a brocade coat trimmed with mink."

"*Mink!*" exclaims Miss McVee in horrified surprise . . . Their conversation goes on, while the telescope's eye focuses on Darlenton, not more than forty miles from North City, where a young curly-haired girl, just graduated from the 'streets' to the 'houses,' finds herself on the luxurious strip of Highway C 20, where she can take in $200 to $400 a day and split with the house —and be treated, as she says, like a "queen." "*It's fabulous in Darlenton,*" she proclaims as if on a closed TV circuit, "*Mass and New Hampshire can't do nothing for me no more—not even New York City can't—I'm used to drinking champagne and sparkling burgundy, because I believe I'm qualified to have the finer things in life . . .*" She preens herself with conscious pride, admitting with a charming smile, "*I think something's wrong with me . . . A man can't do nothing for me but put money in my pocket . . . Here in Darlenton, it's tops!*"

But in the staff room at Henry Street Jail the two officers have their eye on the immediate. Miss Walton's sense of humor is reasserting itself.

"Her pimp came and got the coat and put it in cold storage."

"What a nerve!" Miss McVee gasps.

"He's one of the most competitive men on the Avenue . . . and with a property like that he can certainly afford to pay off . . . Doubt if we'll see *her* here again in a hurry . . ."

Miss McVee looks embarrassed. It is hard for her to believe that policemen take bribes, or that courts operate without complete justice, and the thought that a prostitute could avoid prison sentences by rising from a streetwalker to a call girl hurts her, so that now she feels uncomfortable. But when Miss Walton asks idly: "What's the count today?" she reverts to briskness and accuracy—this at least she knows about. "Twenty-nine," she says promptly.

Down in the cellblock there has already been a change in the delicate balance of human relations. The relieving officer is particularly busy because the absence of a co-worker has left her to deal with an addict just now placed in the padded treatment cell. During the officer's absence, Beppo has suceeded in waking Pug Nose, who has then been induced to crouch on the floor in a position close to the open end of Beppo's cell, but well hidden from a passing officer, too busy to check with a flashlight to see that all the prisoners are in bed with some part of their anatomy showing ('to see flesh' as the institution phrase has it). Pug Nose had confided that she would like Beppo to call her Ana, and Beppo has realized that this ninety-four-pound little girl, with the long rope of hair, wants to be treated like a lady.

"How old are you?" she whispers, taking a cigarette, lighting it slowly, and rolling it carefully along the stone floor, until Ana can reach it and put it in her own mouth.

"Sixteen," lies Ana.

"What you doin' here, Baby?" Beppo's whisper is filled with sexual mockery.

"They took me in for vagrancy and then they put a VD on me . . ." Large pale-green eyes fringed with long black lashes are suddenly filled with tears. "I was only hanging on the common and that Big Guinea on the beat he got a curse on me—you could be coming out of a nun's convent and he'd say you was a whore! Well, he was on the beat on Evans and he chased me in the cruiser and caught up with me. Margie, that's my best girl friend, she's at Wentworth now, 'n' I wish they'd of taken me there . . ."

"Wentworth . . . that's a rap of a year . . . What you want to be put away like *that* for?"

Ana looks doubtful. "I wanta be with Margie—tomorrow I go in court I think, or the next day. The Youth Board's had me, but I truanted twice . . . Last time I was away three months," she adds boastfully.

"Doing?" questions Beppo, who is lying on her back on the floor, staring at the high ceiling and the great barred windows at the end of the passage. She hears the little Polish girl pouring out a torrent of inaccurate information, naïve boasting, excited description, while her small flat-nosed face is pressed eagerly against the bars, with Beppo able to see through the V of her pajamas the dead-white blue-veined skin of her throat. ". . . you think I ever was able to stop running . . . you're kidding! There was the cruiser on one side 'n' the wagon on the other . . . Honest to God, I'd just come back from California from my sister Millicent's . . ."

"How'd you get *there?*" Beppo asks.

"Hitch-hike . . ." Ana's voice is breathless with haste. "We girls went right acrosst the country and slept in cars and things, and then at Millicent's she was real bad because she'd left her husband when he was taking dope and punching the walls and breaking his hands and all that, so we didn't stay long, but when I got back they were out for me because I'm the leader. —Did they take up Jennie Lane or Bertha?—I hope to *tell* you they didn't! They just took *me* . . ." Her tone expresses self-importance. "My mother thinks the cops planned it with my girl friends, so I could get the blame . . . My mother says I sure got the Big Guinea's ego. He came along and said: 'All right you bunch of tramps get the hell off the corner!' And then in front of Perry's drugstore—that's the place where all the addicts and hustlers and AWOL sailors hang out—he ran into us again, and he sure took off after *me*. I pulled away and he twisted my arm and slapped me, and they took off my heels to stop me kicking . . ." Ana takes a quick puff of her cigarette, and adds in a drawling self-important voice: "I gotta be a witness in a rape charge, too—"

"Rape *and* VD," comments Beppo, "you *are* something!"

"That VD—that's a lie," Ana says stoutly. "The boys'll just say anything so they say some *name*. In the Navy they've got to tell a name if they're sick, or they put them in the brig. So one of them told *mine* . . . That's a lie all right . . . but it's true I was raped . . ."

"When, Baby?"

"Las' April, 'fore I went to California . . . Daisy was raped, too."

"Daisy's your sister?" questions Beppo. She is conning the girl skillfully and lovingly.

"No, Millicent's my sister, and Rosie. Daisy's really my niece, isn't that funny? . . . But I call her my sister because she's my older sister Rosie's daughter—but Rosie wasn't married, you see, so Daisy's not 'legit' and that's why my mother has no authority over her. And Daisy was in the Vice-Roys, and you have to go to bed with the guys when you're in *that* club . . . You know the Vice-Roys, don't you?"

"Sure I do." Beppo is scornful. "A lily-white gang . . ." "So you decided to get raped because Daisy was raped!"

"*Decided!* Nothing . . ." Ana's tough little voice becomes tearful again. "It's just that I go with the girls, and the girls got more power on me than I got on *them* . . . An' one night Carol asked me to a party and I got there and I said: 'Where's the party?' because there was only two guys and her and me—so I said: 'Where's the party?' and Carol said: 'Never mind, let's have a drink.' And they all had a drink and I had two beers. Carol and her boyfriend were making out, see, and the other guy said: 'Come in here, those two want to talk,' and we went in this little room and sat on the edge of the bed, and suddenly he knocked me down on the bed, and he gave me a black eye and my tooth cut my lip and the blood was streaming, and he said: 'You're not going to be no Virgin Mary any more.' I had bruises all along my thighs, and I screamed and I screamed . . ."

"What a jerk," Beppo murmurs into the prison night. "So you got the cops on him?"

"No-o-o." Ana is still not sure whose side she is on—her own, or the side of the boy who raped her. Because it has been firmly fixed in her mind, that the code of 'the girls,' who consider themselves outside of society and therefore fit for all kinds of violence, must be *her* code. "He drove me home and he said he was sorry, that he lost his head . . . It was my mother got the cops on him." Ana imitates the hysterical falsetto of her mother: "My baby . . . oh my baby . . . oh my baby . . ." Then her voice trails off. "I don't think they have no right," she mutters, ". . . that's the reason people turn queer . . . someone hurts them . . . but I didn't turn queer yet."

"Maybe you don't know what's what," Beppo says. "Maybe that's why you didn't turn queer . . . yet . . ."

Across the distance between them, Ana shoots her a quick, slightly shocked look, and gives a tiny shrug to her shoulders, even as a self-satisfied smile touches the edges of her coarse pink little mouth. Then she cracks back carelessly: "Who're *you* kidding?"

Beppo laughs. She sits up a little, her St. Christopher's medal swinging forward on its silver chain, her gamin face screwed up in a teasing manner. "It's lovely in here, Pug," she says with a mocking intonation, "wish you was here."

At the other end of the cell row, Frankie is sketching a girl getting out of the wagon to enter the Henry Street Jail, but she has grown tired of trying to get the right perspective and put the half-finished picture on the floor. . . . There is the sound of the buzzer. The chain-link fence opens, and the wagon is driven through —outside, the river and the grass under the hot sun; here, the darkness of the closed wagon and the knowledge that she is going to prison for the first time in her life. She wears her tight dungarees and an orange-colored shirt with short sleeves, and there is a cigarette behind her ear under the flopping parrot-like crest of processed hair. Shadows deepen her eyes. She jolts to and fro in the wagon, not trying to hold on to the seat. The driver calls out. Another chain-link fence opens, and now they are in a courtyard with a high wall of damp grayish stone, a courtyard too narrow to let in much of the outside sun. Frankie gets out of the wagon. She is motioned forward. She swaggers in her tight dungarees. Some of the girls look out of the window from the second tier of cells. "Hiya—" someone calls. It is as if she has been recognized.

She feels that this place has been long expecting her . . . that she has come to her second home.

In the office, two tired-looking girls are being processed: the white girl wears a flowered blouse and black pants, and the Negro girl wears a short blue cotton suit and carries an umbrella. They slump on the bench together, occasionally shifting their positions, or answering the officer's questions in lethargic and disillusioned voices.

Another officer is turning out the girl's pocketbooks, making a record of the contents, putting money and valuables into sealed envelopes, removing contraband, and returning the innocuous pocketbooks to the girls. Her face noncommital, she works swiftly and efficiently, every now and then impatiently pushing back a loose strand of hair.

"Who's the bondsman?" asks the officer at the desk as she begins to fill in two blue cards.

"Mr. Corelli," someone replies.

"Idle and Disorderly," the officer says. Then, "Did you say Pelham Street?"

"Yes," the Negro girl replies.

"Religion?"

"Baptist."

"Place of birth?"

"Jackson, Mississippi."

The officer looks up with a quick glance of appraisal.

"Date of coming to North City?"

"1959," the girl answers.

"Did you do all of this in *one* year?" the officer questions with a smile, not unkind, but seeming in a superior Northern way to comment upon the whole Southern system. The girl looks away and does not answer.

Frankie stands waiting at the back of the room, feeling an echo of the girl's shame. Isn't she too a Negro, and here she is in with no-good trash from the South? The question hovers for a moment, the question which is to be, for her, perpetually unanswered. Does she *have* to be here? Her lips frame the words. "I wouldn't be here if Mama hadn't taken me downtown in the first place . . ."

As she is motioned forward to the desk to take the place of the girl in the flowered blouse, she sees a male officer come in from the passage, ushering another prisoner, a full-figured, heavy-browed girl, with coarse glossy black hair—a girl who looks as if she didn't know what to do with her limbs, who seems ready to burst out of her clothes.

This is Brenda 'Baby' O'Reilly, and she is to inhabit the cell next to Frankie's. Baby is seventeen, just slightly retarded, and at the present moment her brother, Dennis (eighteen), waits in a cell over on the 'male' side, not more than 200 feet away from her. It is of Dennis she is thinking now, because her real trouble seems to have run parallel with Dennis's trouble, although Dennis, who is soon to be sent to the state hospital for a psychiatric evaluation, has always been a little moody and strange, and it is because of this that she feels she has to support him. If her mother and father had helped him, if they'd got him out on bail the first time he was in, then perhaps he would be straight now . . . Anyway, *she* isn't going to let him down . . . her own brother! To let anyone down, that is the worst thing in the world!

She is ten years old and her family has just moved into the Project. She is running home from school with her bag bouncing on her shoulders, when suddenly someone trips her. A group attack her and begin to beat her and to pull at her hair. "Smarty Irish," someone calls. "Let's pull off her shoes and socks." While one girl does this, and throws her shoes over the fence, another threatens to cut her long plaits with a knife. "An' that's for what Dennis did to my brother," a third girl calls, giving her a solid thump in the ribs . . . Brenda does not know why this happens. She does not know why she is a "smarty Irish," or what Dennis has done. She only knows that when she tries to explain to her father, he tells her to keep away from the 'Polacks' and the 'colored!' or he'll break every bone in her body. "I'll *scar* you," he threatens her, and she goes to bed with a vague terror that somehow or other, someone will catch her unawares.

At thirteen she is feminine and heavy, with bright blue eyes, a slight red flush in her broad cheeks, and a rough shine to the coarse hair which hangs like a waterfall down her back. She likes to play active games, especially basketball, where most of the best players are colored, and where she feels relaxed and at ease—and although she hides it, she doesn't like to go with her mother to visit middle-class Irish families where she has to behave well and say "Yes—that's nice!" when the girls in the family tell her about church on Sunday and the Sodality, "Yes—isn't that nice!" "Why don't you go with Kathleen," her mother prompts her, "she's a lot better than those damn half-breeds you play basketball with? I tell you, Brenda, I don't want you with them. Be with your own kind!"

Brenda knows that Dennis doesn't like the colored either, but she can't take that seriously until—when she is fifteen—he is accused of beating up a Negro preacher on the Commons and stealing a wallet. When she hears the news she screams, and her father promptly slaps her and tells her to keep it quiet, that Dennis has been picked up on Mercer Avenue and that there is no proof he is guilty . . . But already the kids know about it and they are chanting down in the street, "O'Reilly's in jail—O'Reilly's in jail . . ."

Brenda has got a sharp knife from the kitchen and she approaches the boys on the corner and asks them belligerently: "You got something to say about my brother?"

"Yeah," one of the boys answers, "he's nothin' but a jailbird!"

"D'you wanta be in a pine box?" Brenda asks, advancing on him and showing her knife.

"What you gonna do with *that?*" asks one of the boys incredulously. "Are you a *girl* or what? Want that another O'Reilly goes to jail?"

Brenda throws away the knife and bursts into tears . . . She knows the laws of the street and she tells her father that they'll jump her. "I'm scared," she repeats monotonously. "I'm warning you," her father tells her, "don't carry no weapons," but he doesn't explain to her what he hopes to do for Dennis, nor how he hopes to protect her from those who may be lying in wait downstairs. That night, as she goes fearful and unarmed, to the corner store, three of the girls jump her and beat her up. "If you ever hurt Joe, or any of the boys on the corner," they threaten her, "we'll kill you and you'll be under the ground." . . . Weeping and disheveled, she bangs on the wall of the apartment and implores her mother to get Dennis out on bail. "I can't take it, Ma," she cries. "Please get him out—please get him out. I don't want them to keep talking about it."

"Don't pay them no mind," her mother is saying.

"I got to. Don't you see? It'll effect the boys . . . Larry comes home from school crying . . . What you gonna do . . . ? Everyone's tellin' us we got a jailbird for a brother . . ."

"Don't pay them *mind*, Brenda," her mother begs. "Don't you see what we're goin' through?"

Wild-eyed, Brenda thinks of weapons again. She gets her father's gun, goes downstairs at midnight, and climbs on the back of King's motorbike (King is a colored boyfriend of whom her mother doesn't approve). "Which ones jumped you?" he asks her as they watch the group on the corner, lit up by the white light from the store. "Which ones? . . ." The motorcycle charges the group, gunning its motor, riding up on the pavement. The screaming boys and girls scatter in all directions. Victoriously Brenda waves the gun, and someone shrieks out: "She's got a gun . . . she's got a gun . . . I hope she goes to jail like her brother . . ."

By the time that the store owner has called the station and the paddy wagon has arrived, Brenda and King have 'got on the wind' and are rocketing along the dark, empty streets.

———————

Frankie hears the tap tap on her wall again, and she repeats like a charm the "Hiya Baby" with which she has been soothing Brenda for the last few days. She gets up, and like a shadow slips over to the bars. "It's all right now . . . You hear me . . . don't worry."

"Frankie."

"Yes, Baby."

"I built up a complex."

"A complex about what, honey?"

"About being loud and crazy."

"You're not loud and crazy, Baby. You're fine."

"I'm scared I'm goin' crazy. I don't want to be like her."

"Like who?"

"Like that girl down in the common room yesterday that was yelling."

"Oh she was just excited, Baby."

"I'll get like that if they keep me shut up. It's getting next to me, Frankie."

"Okay now, Baby, occupy your mind."

"If I can't get loud and silly, then I'm scared of getting crazy," Baby explains, tapping in a sort of panic with her file on the wall. "It gets next to me. I don't know why my mother doesn't come see me . . . Sometimes I think I hate her, she turned me in so many times . . ."

"She'll come, Baby. She's like my mother. I done all that time at St. Ursula's in back of *my* mother."

"I hate her," Baby says, leaning against the wall and letting the tears run down her face.

———————————

Frankie, chilly now in her pajamas, tiptoes back to bed, but Baby stays, remembering. She remembers Rachel, who had had an apartment in the Project and had been, in some way, her first real friend. When she was only thirteen and in the eighth grade, while she was baby-sitting for Rachel's two children, she was visited by a colored boy three years older than she was, who seduced her on Rachel's sofa and then kissed away her tears and told her that it was 'nothing' . . . Surely it had not been from this time that she had associated the colored with sexual caresses. Because for a long time afterwards she had withdrawn from boys altogether and from life itself, feeling uneasy and finding it hard to concentrate, sitting there in school, her eyes heavy, her pencil not moving . . .

Yet it was as if something had remained from that incident, not only the sensation of being quickly and abruptly penetrated by the boy, but the feeling of a pattern of familiarity being set up, of something being spread over her, a fine invisible mesh, so that a color of skin, a way of walking, a sound of talking hemmed her in . . . In the first grade a little cinnamon-skinned girl had held her hand in all the round-games, and put her arms about her and told her that she loved her. Now she remembered it . . .

She is lonely. She shrinks against the wall of her cell, arranging and rearranging her heavy rounded thighs, crying a little and experiencing a sensuous confusion. She is lonely for her mother who hates the colored; she is lonely for the long-fingered, dark-skinned King, who *is* colored. She wishes that she were in Frankie's cell, beside her on the narrow mattress, close twined to her sinewy dark body.

She is fifteen and it is after Dennis has gone to jail, and King is persuading her to be 'in his corner,' leaning over her in Rachel's room, watching her as she changed the baby's diaper, and teasing her about the way she put the safety pin in. "How are you doin' it?" he scolds her. "You're real tardy."

"It'll stay, handsome." She rolls the baby over and puts him on his stomach. "So long as it's fastened."

"Why you tellin' me fine things?" he questions, lolling on Rachel's double bed.

"Fine things?"

"Like 'handsome'?"

"You *are* handsome." Brenda laughs in the warm sunlight pouring through the open window of the fifth floor of the Project. "You're handsome, all right."

"I know where you're at," King is saying. He is holding her and playing with her. "I know where you're at."

Brenda is aware that she doesn't really know where she is at herself. In fact, she is genuinely puzzled. "You're eighteen and you're not in school," she says, "and you don't work . . ."

She sees herself in the mirror, broad-faced, sturdy, with the slender black hand on her white neck, and now boldly making its way downward.

"You wouldn't understand . . . you're a square," King says, turning her around so he can kiss her.

"Would you please run it down for me?"

But King only laughs and pushes her onto Rachel's bed and makes out with her, telling her all the time that she is *his* woman, and that he'll take care of her and that he'll show her how to have a fine time and fine things. "You're the best, Baby," he says in his easy gentle hypnotic way. "You're absolutely the best."

Later on, the question of how King makes his living again comes up, and he tells her that he sings with the "Blue Notes."

"They only sing once in three weeks," Brenda objects.

"Well, I got something working for me on the side."

"On the side?"

King runs his hand down her spine, and watches the fond and confused look which spreads like a film over her eyes. Again he tells her that she wouldn't understand.

"You're square, Baby, 'n' your family's square."

"I'm not square . . ." Brenda maintains stoutly.

"Yes, you're square, Baby . . ."

"I'm more or less by myself in my own home," Brenda says in sudden loneliness. She clings to King, who withdraws himself a little, and makes her feel that she must fight to keep him.

"I've got these women out on the Avenue," he tells her, "and they bring in a good 'yard' a night." He tries to convince her that this is the life for the adventurous and the ambitious, for those who want fun and money, for those who aren't square. He recounts the names of girls who are out on the street—and who are all of them friends of Rachel—Julia and Blossom, Petra and Angel. "Angel is 'tight' with Rich," he informs her. "She gets everything for Rich. How'd you think he gets those sixty-dollar shoes?" Then he pushes her away a little, impressing upon her the fact that she's going to lose him. "It's a different life—you can't keep up, Baby."

"I'm gonna try it," she says bravely.

. . . There follows a period of anguish and embarrassment, a time when the hours suddenly grow long, as she stands on a corner under a light and King waits some distance away from her, ready to direct customers, to stiffen her resolve, to trail her for safety to LeRoi's house. (Because Baby is white in an all-Negro neighborhood and likely to be picked up by the police, it seems wiser to go to LeRoi's house than to the three-dollar 'trick' house on the block.) This time is a long time, short as it is, a time of constant bewilderment. Amateur himself, King is not adamant enough to drive her as if she were a hardened prostitute, and soon she is weeping in his arms and saying: "King, I can't do it no

more . . . I can't go with nine hundred and ninety men and
come home to you . . . I jumped into it, King . . . I jumped
into it without understanding . . ." And King is smoothing her
long black hair and saying: "All right, Baby . . . all right . . .
There's nothing to worry about . . . It's all right."

———————————

In the comparative quiet of the prison night a sound comes: a
moaning and crying which swells up from the basement, a sound
which is countered by the pad pad of rubber-soled shoes hastening down the ramp, and turning into the section where the addicts
and alcoholics are shut up, and where against the stained and
darkened canvas padding so many heads have beaten in vain.

"A-a-aah . . . a-a-aah . . ." come the long quivering cries,
forcing out an inarticulate passionate message. Pug Nose is asleep
again, and Beppo is on the edge of sleep, so that for her the noises
come vaguely and are woven back and forth, to and fro, into a
tapestry of uneasy dreams. If Harry hears these sad and unex-
plained noises, she makes no signal, for long ago she has learned to
accept in silence the whole crazy pattern of her life, to absorb
without a word abuses from a fate never understood. But when
the noises start, Frankie and Baby are immediately out of bed,
pressing themselves against the bars closest to the ramp, and waiting in shivering silence for some climax to that unhappy orches-
tra, shaking in panic and terror, each in her own separate way
asking herself what part these sounds play in her own fate, what
such sounds mean to *her?*

When for a moment there is silence again, Frankie hears
Brenda's shocked whisper on the other side of her cell: "What
was it? . . . Frankie, can you hear? . . . What *was* it?" even
while a door is opened below and there comes a wild crescendo, a
tormented wailing and crying, a sound of retching, a beating as if
a body or bodies were being thrown to and fro, out of control,
like heavy birds in captivity.

A door closes . . . There is silence again . . .

"Frankie? . . ."

"Yes, Baby . . ."

"What *was* it?"

"I don't know, honey . . ."

"Were they *beating* them? . . ."

"I don't *know*, honey . . . I don't know *what* it was . . ." Her voice is anguished. She leans her face against the bars and stares into the darkness, and she hears, like some terrible fore-warning, her mother's favorite quotation—"MANY THINGS MUST BE FULFILLED."

It can't be like that! . . . It can't be like that! She flings her-self against the bars, calling out and frightening Baby so much that she, too, begins to call out.

"Do something," Frankie shrieks. "Do something . . . do something . . ."

A chemist might call it diacetylmorphine, and say that it is a synthetic alkaloid made by heating morphine and acetic acid. "It is more potent than morphine," the medical student recites, ". . . a superior analgesic. Its effects include freedom from pain, sedation, relaxation, hypnosis, euphoria . . . ," and his voice is unmoved, as are the voices of the healthy and the free. Another voice, how-ever, murmurs from a Lexington bed, low-toned, passive, filled with that strange quiet of acceptance. "My wife left me behind the drugs," it says, and then a few moments later it scatters sen-tences, as if across a devastated terrain, littered with remnants of what had once been whole. ". . . the more you use, the less you have . . . the more you have, the more you use." ". . . in total need . . . an addict is in total need." "My body crawls for it . . . my body is drawn to it, as iron is drawn to a magnet . . ."

When some well-meaning visitor drops a book upon the bed, his sunken face is lifted and a faint light shows in his eyes. He is turning the book in his hands and remarking that it is con-cerned with history. "I like to read," he says mildly, "about coun-tries that are occupied by the *enemy* . . ."

Dressed in a white blouse and pleated skirt, wearing the knee socks which she hates, she cannot wait to go to school, and follows her cousin Opaline along the familiar street and presses her body against those bars calculated to keep intruders out of the school playground. While Opaline's figure crosses the yard, proceeds up the cement steps, and is received into the school's dark mysteries, Francesca, with inconsolable anguish, presses and presses her thin and pliable body between the cruel bars. She is scarcely aware of what she is doing, so that as the days pass she makes the imprint of the iron upon her flesh. Accompanied by her own improvised lunch box—a crumpled paper bag holding a slice of bread and an apple—she manages at last, in what can only be described as a psychological euphoria and a physical melting of bones, to pass through the excluding bars and to enter alone—a tiny Negro child, with enormous, thirstily shining eyes—into the school's kingdom.

Here she wanders up and down what seem to her vast corridors. She is lost for moments beneath a dark forest of caps and coats. At one point she shrinks inside the doors of a washroom where, in a desert of hygienic white, she hears the endless tread of feet go by in the passage outside. And at another point, when she has somehow found her way into the basement, which is filled with pipes larger than any she has seen in her life, she is aware, in that hushed warmth, of the rush of life flowing over her head, as if she had put her ear to the pulse of a great beast. When at last, upstairs again, in the passage near the principal's office, a tall lady with hard-tapping heels finds her staring with concentrated attention at a colored map of the world and meets her with a surprised exclamation of "Where did *you* come from, little girl?" it seems to Francesca that she had already passed through the necessary tests and ordeals and that she is now ready, like Opaline, to be accepted; therefore, she feels no distrust as she lifts her solemn eyes to the lady's face (all these white women from the other world are 'ladies') and says with confidence: "I'm Francesca—I got my lunch—I just came to school."

In the prison she wakes to being 'Frankie,' as she wakes also to the eternal electric light, to the rubber-soled tread of the matrons, to the activities of this crossroads of justice (where prisoners pass and repass to other prisons, to courts, to mental institutions, to freedom). She wakes to a day already stale, controlled, previsioned, wakes to the thin mattress, the absent pillow, the stripped cell.

Yet she is not alone for she is convinced that she is one of God's elect, that she is born to deal with words, to make them obey her. She is a prophet, she thinks, and one day she will open her mouth and prophesy. So she stretches out her hand toward the only book she has with her, *Leaves of Grass*, and her hand closes over the cover, as if by holding it some of the words may enter into her soul. Since her mother has always sought counsel from the Bible, she now pushes a muscular brown finger between the pages, and makes a mark upon the page. She reads:

My flesh and blood playing out lightning to strike what
    is hardly different from myself,
On all sides prurient provokers stiffening my limbs,
Straining the udder of my heart for its withheld drip.

Clasping her hands on her breast, the book between them, lying with her head swathed like a mummy, her feet stretched out like a little corpse, she feels in her laid-out body a fatal and purifying yeast. She scarcely knows what the words mean, but still she shudders with delight.

At 31 Moon Street, her father, William Ford, the Negro from Georgia, has just finished telling her mother, Alva, that "if it hadn't been for that thing in your belly . . . I wouldn't have married you." Francesca's eyes, the questioning eyes of an intelligent child, search out an implicit threat. Her father is laughing, but he is also calling her mother a bitch, and the mere raising of his dark hand against the white walls, fills his child with anxiety . . . Nothing happens, her eyes only seem to grow larger and larger in an effort to draw everything into her small body. She waits. She searches patiently for an answer of some sort. She waits for her mother to laugh as her father laughs . . . she waits and waits . . .

Alva is on the phone. Trained in the passionate and verbal school of her own Evangelist mother, and having graduated from high school as well, Alva is now caught up in a desire to have the middle-class status which her light skin seems to deserve. "I am interested in biology, and taking night classes along with being a nurse's aide. I feel I would really like to make a career of this, and it's something that would go along with the children, you know . . . William could look after them nights. William resists this . . . it distresses him. He's apt enough, but he don't want me to be interested . . . He's not realizing that this is something that has to be *fulfilled* in me . . ."

Alva has adopted a veneer of her mother's religious attitude, but has somehow combined this with more contemporary idioms and aims. She speaks of God and his prophecies with a strange affectless air, as if they were as everyday as the violence and ignorance and crime of the surrounding slum. "Yes," she goes on in a slightly important voice, "I'd attend the night course at the hospital . . . also take physiology, biology, and an outline of sociology . . ."

"Alva," roars William, who is listening uneasily. "Stop talking on that phone! Stop thinkin' you're so damn smart! Why don't you put that phone down now an' cease usin' those big words." When he gets angry, William stutters. "T-t-t-tryin' to impress that all y-y-y-y-you doin'."

Alva does not respond, but eventually she puts down the phone and goes quietly about her housework. She wears a pink dress with a wide black belt, and because of her tall figure she seems as erect and as unnaturally elongated as certain African sculptures, although her whole moving body—as well as her face with its tight-stretched skin and intensely curved mouth and nose —gives rather the impression of a graceful but jerkily moving doll, tuned to a formal ballet. Sometimes her expression—aided by the slightest possible cast to the left eye—is touched with the glittering fanatacism of the prophet.

"You hear me," says the frustrated William, "I don' want you going out this house nights . . . and I don' want you gettin' smart."

"Even to the hospital . . . ?" questions Alva, sorrowfully. "Why are you so distrustful? Jesus warned men against all manner of distrustfulness." She is going through a religious period and seeks eagerly to include her husband in it. "If you, too, could be convicted, William . . . if you, too, could tarry . . . ?"

"Ef Jesus come down here," William claims, shifting uneasily again, "I'd tell him get outa my *face.*"

Francesca is sorry for her father, who seems to be, with his bull-like solidity, beating ineffectually against the fluid power of Jesus—but she is captured by the poetic idea that God himself could 'tarry' amongst men, and she absorbs her mother's ambition, her mother's need to advance, preparing to amaze the kindergarten teacher with her skill at reading about "Dick and Jane," feeling that the words of the Scriptures are akin to the words in the schoolbook, and all equally sacred. *"Run* Dick . . . Run *Jane,"* she intones, in broad adoration of the whole system of hieroglyphics.

In the ghetto of North City, the houses seem old indeed. But here on Moon Street steps sag, paint peels, windows are boarded up, and at night the fronts step back into shadow—leaving the streets alone, the rare pale lights picking out wan pools of illumination across which pass, from time to time, mysterious figures, dark-coated, dark-skinned, bent upon dark errands. If the bell rings for one of the houses, there comes a silence, as if the occupant, letting the sound of the bell reverberate, waits, questioning . . .

This bell rings for Frankie. At nine years old she knows without fully regaining consciousness, that her father is re-entering the house. Hugging her thin body in the darkness, she relaxes into sleep with the relieved sense that while her mother is on the night shift at the hospital, her erring and stumbling father, his breath heavy with whisky, is making his way up the stairs. Now she can sleep more deeply, more securely; yet she has absorbed, too, young as she is, the aura of her father as a lover of women, of someone who leans over her mother near the stove, questioning, demanding, with a clumsy, tender haste . . . "How is it, baby?

. . . eh baby?"—and as well, leans with the same question over a certain white woman who tends bar at Forley's Tap around the corner (breathing, demanding, asking questions with his eyebrows, sketching in the air that outline of need and urgency). It is slowly that she combines the two attitudes, learning somehow with fear and anger that the bell which tinkles faintly on the wicket gate at the foot of the stairs is not always tinkling to let in her father but also to let out that white woman, who wrongly and incredibly usurps her mother's bed. Once when hearing those unmistakable sounds (her mother at work at the hospital) and trying to piece together the broken whispered conversation flung jaggedly into the night, she gets up out of her own bed, tiptoes downstairs, puts on her sneakers and her coat, and runs through the dark streets to the hospital entrance, where she crouches on the steps in the thinning light, her head on her knees, her eyes closed, waiting for her mother to come, waiting only to say in a numb childish way—looking up at her mother with pity and horror. "No, I didn't come for nothing . . . only to walk you home, Mama."

Tears squeeze between Francesca's tight-closed eyes, and run down her face onto the mattress. The room is dark . . . A hand descends upon her . . . it is the hand of her father . . . Again the tears well out of her and wet the mattress, but this time effortlessly, like water through sand. In uneasy dreams she moves looking for love, and in dreams the finger of prophecy gropes until the pages open again, and she can read . . .

. . . you do not know how longingly I look upon you.
You must be he I was seeking, or she I was seeking (it comes
    to me as of a dream).
. . . I do not doubt I am to meet you again,
I am to see to it that I do not lose you.

In the officers' room upstairs, Miss Walton and Miss McVee are ready to go off duty, but the superintendent has asked Miss Walton to stay on for two hours because they are short-handed, and she has acquiesced with the calm satisfaction of one who feels herself needed. Now after fifteen years of working in prisons, the prison is her life, the inmates her friends, and the whole correctional setup is her world. She feels herself indeed part of a subterranean garden, where huge—dank—fleshy—she grows like a plant in fertile soil, her roots penetrating into its mystery. So slow has been the encroachment of the prison that she has lost all sense of differentiation and forgotten that it has ever been otherwise, that once she has had friends who inhabited a different universe, that once she has been, like Miss McVee, shocked and dismayed by the attitude of her charges, that once she has stood apart from them . . . As with the changes in her body, which have come so subtly that she has not been aware of them but has only woken up to their encroachments when the extra sluggish flesh already binds her, she has not known that her psyche too is changing, that she is slowly becoming a prisoner. Yet of this mysterious metamorphosis she does not speak, expatiating aloud about more practical things: "Those toilets in the cells are backing up again . . . How many times have we had to call the engineer this week? How long will it be before we give up this medieval system?"

Miss McVee has put on a light-blue coat over her uniform, touched up her pale narrow mouth with Wild Rose lipstick, washed her hands, and carefully tied a blue scarf under her pointed chin. Now she changes her shoes, places the rubber-soled work shoes in a box marked with her name, and stows them in the crowded closet shared by all the officers. She scarcely knows what Miss Walton says. She is ready to descend the steel staircase, to pass through the gates and the passages, to emerge into the free world again and take up what she considers her real life (shopping at the local A & P, a quiet lunch by her TV, a good sleep, and an evening's bridge in the apartment upstairs).

"Good-bye-ee" she calls to Miss Walton. "Good-bye-ee . . . Don't work too hard now, dear . . . See you tomorrow . . ."

"Good-bye," Miss Walton calls more briefly. "I'll see you."

She settles back with relief in the creaking cane chair and shuts her eyes.

Unconsciously William is afraid that his children will repeat his own history, that they will be tough, wild street children as he was, that they will have tempers as bad as his own, and be violent, drunken, and lustful, as he knows himself to be. He centers his fears upon Francesca, the first-born, the love child, the child about whose existence he has so many doubts. The little white spot on her brown cheek for instance, the small round perfectly formed circle where the pigmentation has unaccountably failed; this white spot represents to him a brand which singles her out, as if he himself—her own father—had placed a curse upon her.

Sometimes when he sees her looking up at him, her eyes wide open, her round brown childish face swimming in light, that special spot seems to gather a radiance about it and to draw his attention with its symbolic quality, as if it were the mark of God or the devil. At such moments he feels trapped—not only by Alva's pretty angular body and light-skinned face with the deep-set eyes and the mouth curved like a scimitar, but by the religious gospel which he half believes to be powerful. When he has served short sentences for drunkenness, for knocking down and half killing a man in a quarrel, for cooperating in painting a car which turns out to be stolen, he has thought of this gospel, which, from behind bars and appearing in the person of a loving woman, has a siren's effectiveness. But in real life always, returned to the temptations of the street, the Niagara of holy words and prophecies passes over his head as something to be endured and survived, an element which must occasionally half drown him, but with which he must never come to terms.

It is evening, and Francesca is resplendent in new bobby socks (her mother has shamed her by insisting on knee socks).

"What you got?" Alva asks with a puzzled frown.

"Bobby socks," she answers.

"Where you get them?"

"I bought them."

"Where you get the money?" her mother insists.

"Miss Mandeville got a lot o' pennies in a jar," Francesca answers, aware at last of disturbance, but remembering how her mother comes home from the hospital sometimes with sheets and pillowcases secreted under her coat.

"There was a *lot* o' pennies," she reiterates.

"She *give* you them," her mother asks ominously, "or you take them?"

"I take them," Francesca murmurs.

"Your father gonna know when he gets home," Alva says, and then she adds as if she sees the words written in flame above her daughter's head, *"Thou shalt not steal!"*

Francesca trembles. She has heard these scriptural admonitions while she was still in the womb and she does not doubt their power. To give and to withhold life, that is the power of the WORD, and now, from the somber tone of her mother's voice, she knows that the matter is out of her hands, that somehow she, Frankie, has placed herself in the power of the Scriptures, and that her father will be the instrument chosen to carry out the punishment of God.

Yet her instinct for self-preservation drives the words out of her.

"Don't let Daddy do it . . ."

"God speaks through whom he will," is all her mother replies.

William Ford has only had two drinks, but the effort it has cost him to leave the bar and mount the steps to his house has robbed him of the rest of his patience. His eyes smolder. His strong arms ache. He fears the God who has become powerful in his kitchen and who speaks now in the soft appealing voice of his slender neat-waisted wife (that waist so closely confined by the black leather belt, he would feel at times like breaking it in half with his joined hands—"You can't hurt me now, William . . . There is someone stronger than you," or else, "The Scripture will be fulfilled, and we must submit to him who created us").

"Where she at?" he demands.

"In the back room." Alva's voice is dry because she knows that her daughter must be punished. Yet she draws Bobo to her, as if in instinctive self-defense.

In the other room William is taking off his belt.

"Get your clothes off," he says to the nine-year-old Francesca, "get your clothes off, I said."

There is too much anger, thinks Alva, standing pressed against the wall and holding her hand over Bobo's eyes. *Too much anger . . . Yet it is the anger of God*, she answers herself, as she hears the heavy garrison belt fly through the air onto her daughter's naked body.

Francesca has determined not to cry, and this strengthens her against the bitter onslaught which burns and tears at the flesh of her buttocks.

"No . . . no . . ." she whispers to herself.

But the quieter she is, the harder her father beats her.

Submit to him, prays Alva on the other side of the wall. *Submit to him.*

Suddenly, Francesca, her body shaking, has risen to her feet and jumped over the bed in a frantic effort to escape. Her screams shake the father to his most turgid depths, so that he longs for her to be quiet and beats her still harder, crying with each blow.

"Shut up . . . shut up . . . shut up . . ."

On the other side of the impeding wall, Alva moaning, and clasping Bobo to her, now whispers: "This is what you get, Bobo, if you steal," and she feels as in her own body how Francesca's bends like a bow from the last savage blow, and like a bow recoils, and bounds down the stairs into the yard. In one moment she is at the window and crying, from her knowledge of her husband who has death in his heart, "Don't run, Francesca . . . don't run . . ."

She sees William pursuing the child in the yard and, then thrusting Bobo from her, she dashes down the steps, seizes Francesca in her arms, and leads her back into the house. "Don't resist him," she whispers to the panting body she holds. "Don't resist him." But Francesca, whose nature loves resistance as it loves life, is beyond hearing. Longing for safety, she bursts from her mother's hands, and rushing into the far bedroom presses herself under the bed, as if she would make herself part of the wall or the floor.

In the other room Alva is talking to William.

"You *mad*, beat the child like this?" she asks, remembering how he had beaten her sometimes, demanding an obedience beyond reason, and his eyes as they are now, set like stone.

"She stealing, weren't she? Want that everyone know we have a child who steal?"

"Don't beat her more," Alva begs, conscious of the eyes of Bobo, wandering from one face to the other.

"She stealing." His short powerful arms break from her grasp. "She stealing."

"You beat her *enough*," begs Alva frantically, and even as he pushes her away and is in the other room dragging Francesca from under the bed, she stands looking down at her hands, wondering dimly why they are so sticky.

"No . . . no . . . no Daddy," cries Francesca in terror. She sees the belt lifted in the air, the bronze buckle swinging, and feels it descend upon her legs and knees. Something runs down both her legs, clear rivers of red, which spread and stain the floor. The red covers her like a garment as she squirms naked before her father, so that she appears to be a victim, painted for a ceremony.

"William . . ." Alva screams, "you'll kill her."

Francesca feels her face and arms smeared with blood, feels her whole life changed, hears her mother's cry and thinks of it as truth.

He wants to kill me, she thinks clearly, . . . *he wants me to die* . . .

When the mail is given out in the jail, the opened and censored letters are pushed through the bars of the cells into eager hands.

The fingers shut over the envelopes and draw them slowly into the closed prison world.

Sometimes their content gives little comfort, as on this particular morning when Frankie finds that she cannot tune herself to the long slanted lines of her mother's writing, which flows as evenly as her voice, and lulls her daughter into the same comfortable stupor in which she had once attended the church meetings on Moon Street.

"*Christ is coming,*" she reads, "*and where will you be when he comes? Will you be ready and waiting, or will you be left behind? Forget what others think of you. They can't stand before God and do you any good. Why pay attention to them now? The angel Gabriel is scheduled to blow the last trumpet. . . . then babies will be missing from their mothers' arms. Teen-agers will be running through the halls in schools looking for their Christian friends. The radio will be buzzing about the mysterious disappearance of people from every nation . . . There is only one way to be ready to face the dark future; give yourself to Jesus Christ . . . The day of the Lord will come as a thief in the night.*"

Anxiously Frankie reads, feeling somewhat cheated, hoping to find some proof of the humanity she shares with her family. "*. . . and I see that you had some illness. It was something to do with your arm and I fear that God is punishing you. Now more than ever you must be saved because something tells me that you will be chosen to further the word of God. Which way are you going in that place? That's the first step. You can't use angles with God. If you're neither hot nor cold you're not with him. Read* REVELATIONS *3, verses, 15, 16, 17, 19–22. You will see that there's work for you to do—others to be helped.*"

The voice of the letter fades into empty exhortations; and the day closes down upon her again without hope of further development. Like a caged dog she presses her face against the bars.

At twelve she has reached the summit of achievement as the acknowledged leader of a gang of small boys—the 'Vivaldos.' For them, Frankie adjusts the cigarette butt she wears behind her ear, gives a hitch to her jeans, and sits like a queen on broken door-steps and piles of old bricks.

"What we gonna do?" reiterates Bird.

"What we gonna do? What we gonna do?" mocks Frankie. They are "gonna do" whatever she is "gonna do"; just as they are going to copy her new insolent way of walking with her non-existent stomach sticking out and a toothpick rolling round and round on her tongue, and her manner of flipping a card, so that it will rise in the air, turn around, and settle firmly, face up, on the whisky box used for a table.

"Stretch is comin'," Frankie says at last, casting her beautiful dark eyes toward the patient 'Bird,' and rewarding him with a dazzling smile.

Bird is a thin, nervous, flaxen-haired creature whose elbows and knees seem to break through his clothes; but, like most of the other boys, he is taller than Frankie, whose lustrous teeth, shining in her dark, intent face, act like a beacon for him along life's road.

Now he is glad to be able to report: "Here Stretch fuckin' along."

"Hi Stretch, what's the word?"

Stretch Pérez, a Puerto Rican boy whose name is expressive of his wandering elongated figure, pulls out from under his jacket two old gun stocks and several thick blocks of drilled wood. From his trouser pocket emerge rubber bands and old firing pins—all of which are handed to Frankie. From the tops of his socks several pieces of sulfuric rag . . . from another pocket a handful of bee-bees.

"All I could collec'," he says glumly. "Pop come along and whip the work on, and I had to git out the back."

"Those Green Hill boys think they got it made . . ." Ripper warns. "We'll fight it out in the playground, end to end."

" 'N' if they don't c-c-c-come . . . t-t-t-t-t-tomorrer?" Bird stutters excitedly.

Frankie glances at him with her glance of a somber fanatic.

"Don' *worry*, Bird."

"W-w-w-what . . . ?" he begins to ask.

"Then we turn out the beach."

"Turn out the beach?" Stretch inquires with faint disbelief.

"Inside out," Frankie says with satisfaction. She gets up. She crosses the street like a warrior. She is running. The pure arc of her brows is winged with the violet glow of the evening light, and her tight hips swing to a rhythm as swift as the broken dance she makes with Charlie on a cleared space of the dusty pavement. The handkerchief tied flat across her forehead acts like a helmet. The little zip gun in her hand, with its intricate mechanism, is tribal as well as of the turf. She is blessed by her father's kin as well as by her own gang, by the neighborhood's pride as against the Green Hill Avenue boys, as well as by the "Bang—Bang—Bang" of TV. In fact, her speed is the spinning speed of the times, and as she waves above her swathed head, her bare brown arm—painted with the red, green, violet of the neon signs on the liquor shop—boys emerge from all the crevices of the playground, like twilight creatures who have waited only for this moment. Colly and Angelface, the elongated Stretch, the best gunman of them all, timid Big Ben and sharp-elbowed Bird, José, and Ripper and Spitfire, and Ronnie 'Loper' Robinson, whose eleven-year-old ambition is to be a big pimp, and get him a Cadillac.

"Why you standin' there fat-mouthin'?" she cries in sheer exuberance, as life wells in her, sending her legs, encased in tight jeans, pumping the length of the playground. "Why you fatmouthin'?"

The twilight casts its long wavering light shot with color along the street; it encloses them tenderly and without prejudice as their heads knot together only long enough to hear Frankie's rallying cry: "To the beach . . . to the beach . . ."

She becomes adept at transition, passes, one might say, into a role made traditional. She graduates from the boys' gang, to a lower echelon in the girls' gang (the 'Floricettes'), whose activities rock the rafters in the high school and lead its members through the windy tunnels of the subway as far afield as the university city, where they gather in laughing, screaming groups on the corners, or attend the big teen-age dances—all dressed alike in black skirts and coal-black sweaters. At first it is just to be, along with Charlie, the mascot of the group, so that she can jitterbug herself into a state of exhaustion, or dance back with a grace unmatched in the vast adolescent-packed halls. And only after that is it to be one of the favored ones, one of these (dark most of them, but white some) whose wildness is touched with poetry, whose loneliness is melted down into an instinct of ceaseless movement, an ambulatory anxiety as strong as the instinct of migratory animals . . . She embraces this desire: it is her "heart," as she says. She has discovered the great secret of the loveless, that from the next house, around the next corner, in the rhythm of the future dance, in the sterility of the next street, the future will find her.

The folded notes pass to and fro under the desks.

"Can I borrow your loafers?"

"Yes. Meet me after school on the corner."

"What we going to do?"

"We're going up to Wal's."

"You told your mother?"

"Yes—but don't tell *yours*."

It was agreed between them that Frankie should tell her mother only what was necessary. Opaline's mother, on the other hand, might know *everything*, because in her capacious body there was an equally capacious acceptance of the fact that a young Negro girl had better make the most of herself while she had the chance. "You goin' to Wal's?" she would ask, looking with a certain satisfaction at her seventeen-year-old daughter, who now wore silk stockings to school and slashed her wide mouth with a purplish lipstick. "Well, girl . . . I guess you know what you *at?*" In the question there was an unspoken comment, a sense of relief that Opaline was not going to waste her youth, as her mother had, being a domestic for white families.

Beside Opaline, who stalked along in heels, Frankie felt an ill-dressed midget, in spite of the fact that she wore now the envied black shirt and coal-black sweater of the Floricettes.

"Why you *need* me?" she asked for reassurance.

"I need you."

"What we gonna do?"

"I'll show you."

Opaline, swinging her schoolbag by its handle, turned Frankie in the direction of the hill behind their houses. "We gonna *walk*, Man?" inquired Frankie in disbelief.

"We gonna walk."

After ten minutes of silent walking, they entered a street unknown to Frankie, and lined with old houses recently converted into apartments, but still retaining what Opaline called style, so that, with a sense of importance, she informed Frankie: "They rent for $100." Opaline's magnificent dark hair, half curly like her mother's, half straight like her white father's, was piled upon her head, her purplish lips pouted and smiled. She seemed to be telling her little cousin that if she had worshipped her in the past, now this worship would be rewarded.

"What we doin'?" urged Frankie as they stood in front of the door of one of the big houses.

"I gotta meet this 'trick,'" murmured Opaline as they waited outside. "We gonna get us some 'cakes.'"

"Huh? Cakes?"

The door clicked to let them in, and they proceeded up a carpeted stairway to a second door, which was opened by a very tall, very slender, very black young man, who wore splendidly creased pants, a navy-blue waistcoat, and a scarlet blazer, later identified for Frankie as that of the college in the West Indies, where young men as black as this, learned to speak good English by imitating instructors who had graduated from Cambridge or Oxford. Opaline took it all as a matter of course. She had apparently been to this apartment before, had lounged on the electric-green sofa, played the expensive phonograph, and read the copies of *The Illustrated London News* which were strewn around on the tables. She even knew where the liquor was, and now prepared Frankie a long drink and established her safely on the sofa with cushions behind her, before she disappeared into the bedroom with the impatient young man.

That she should be able to sit in such a smart $100 apartment and drink real liquor while Opaline "did it" with an esoteric foreigner in the next room was of interest in itself, Frankie thought. And that later Opaline, not only of her blood, but still a schoolgirl like herself, should be able to hand her $3.00 with such an air of carelessness, and that Freddie, the young West Indian student, should compliment her, Frankie, on her style (when warmed by liquor and music, she executed a few steps in the middle of the room)—all this stacked up for Frankie. And easily now she could make the link with her Aunt Jeanette, who on the other side of the fence, the not-so-holy side, was still the one who seemed to make out best, with her cars and her clothes and her money, and even one might say—this Frankie felt was most precious of all— her independence. "Aunt Jeanette can tell anyone to go shit," she said to Opaline afterwards.

"Oh *Jeanette*," agreed Opaline, "*she* make out all right." She did not explain to Frankie that it was Jeanette who had got her this trick in the first place, and had promised her more in the future, nor that Jeanette (Aunt in name, but *de facto* teacher in the trade) had even hinted as well that Beryl, Opaline's younger sister, was not too inexperienced to pick up a little extra money.

"Anyone that look as good as *she* does," Frankie said. "It's not right of course," she added hastily, "it's against God's word . . .'

"What feed *you* don't feed *me*," Opaline remarked yawning, being careful not to show Frankie too clearly that flaunting God's word didn't worry *her*. "With Jeanette it's easy come, easy go."

"Boy, she do all right," drawled the studiously sophisticated Frankie, a little uneasy, but anxious not to appear square.

"She got herself a *Cadillac*," Opaline stressed, and they both paid silent tribute to Aunt Jeanette, the top call girl on the Hill, who wore her mink stole, was covered with a chinchilla robe, and rode in her passionately purple Cadillac.

Suddenly Opaline warned: "Don't tell Aunt Alva about this afternoon. She don't think *anything* of how Ma brings up Beryl and me."

"Oh Mama . . ." dismissed Frankie rebelliously, "she just can't *see* it . . . Man, when I get to be eighteen," and this comment seemed to sum up the afternoon's activities, "it'll be a case of 'Move over Aunt Jeanette, here I come.'"

Since more than one adolescent girl in this area is stirred to emulation of Aunt Jeanette and her colleagues in the profession, it is proper that a school friend of Frankie's (a girl so thin, so ugly, and so unpromising that the whole class pities her) should find status by describing regularly a vision she had once had at dusk—that of a slim and very beautiful prostitute, dressed in black, and melting into the walls of the neighborhood Catholic Church . . . It is surely as natural for a believer, especially a teen-age girl, to see prostitutes in this part of the city, as it is to see saints or holy visions . . .

The souls of dead men haunt the streets in any case, and in the practical sense, and during Frankie's formative years there have been at least twenty unsolved murders in this particular square mile (ten direct killings, and eight deaths tied to the activities of loan sharks). Bullet-riddled and wire-strangled bodies have been found in dumps and hallways, on pavements, and in the trunks of abandoned cars. A key witness to a state crime commission conveniently fell down an elevator shaft in a factory, and two of the witnesses, their legs swathed in cement, disappeared just as conveniently, into the depths of the North City Bay. Here in the little park, its grass sodden with the tears of alcoholic mothers, the vomit of old winos, drippings from pint bottles, the blood of the murdered and the wounded, and the surreptitious sperm of hasty love-making—philosophy has its place. "I wonder how pure and dainty other places are" is what one aspiring politician said, from the hood of his car one hot summer's day, as, true to his promise to campaign in every corner of his constituency, he spoke at the edge of this quarter acre, so gloomily green, so redolent with memory. And oldsters born in the district, and learning to philosophize in a different way are still ready to agree that you might take a child out of Moon Street, but you couldn't take Moon Street out of a child. Nor could the Negro singer (confident enough to resist unwarranted arrest as he returned one night from a command performance in the North City town hall, and so having his nose broken because he was mistaken for 'an ordinary Negro') doubt this last statement, though still smiling tenderly from his battered face upon countless brothers and sisters who had tormented the cops by their busy forging of licenses, their swift stealing of cars, their agility at shoplifting and running for the numbers, their readiness to play chicky for the pusher, their acceptance of trying pot, stuff, coke, greenies, acid, or beauties— and by all it is agreed, although this is the area where the action is, this maze of streets so penetrated by violence and inadequately publicized happenings, that here there is also unfinished business, a sort of vacuum, an unanswered question, which hangs above a way of life, static, dark, and empty.

———————

In the dusk things lost their clarity. The kitchen with only one light burning. The bowed head of her mother. The tense attention of her father.

"I tried to bring her to God . . . she would be whole if she would stay in Christ." Alva's voice was low as if her faith weakened.

"Don't put it on yourself," William urged.

"She my own sister, William . . ."

"What they do?"

"They got her to a hospital, an' used the stomach pump . . . I been with her most all day . . ." Alva's cheeks, generally as modeled as those on dusky polished masks, seemed hollowed now, her eyes burning in their deep sockets.

"God strike her hard this time," she said.

"She don't care about God, baby." William gave a brief disbelieving laugh. "*That* girl made her bargain long ago." He was nervous and moved around the kitchen aimlessly. "What happened to Aunt Jeanette . . . ?" Frankie burst out. "What . . . ?"

"I'll tell you later," her mother said wearily. "Don't ask me now . . . Go to your brother and tell him come eat . . ."

"Aunt *Jeanette* . . ."

"Shut your mouth," her father said briefly.

In the vague light of the yard Frankie saw Bobo, her brother, playing, but beyond, out on the street, she fantasied the shadow of her aunt . . . a slight, tall, well-turned figure, fragile, beautiful, and wearing an orchid-colored wool dress. Curiously like her mother—almost a twin, but better-looking and better-dressed—she passed to and fro, as if in endless survey of this street from which she had long ago drawn her first customers, and from which had come the expensive apartment on the Hill where Frankie had seen her once or twice (clad in shaped dresses, fluted like ancient vases; or tights of soft black leather, low-cut and skin-tight; or period costumes finished off by colored wigs . . .).

. . . There was a noise in the bedroom, shouts and the sound of blows, and her father, with a bag in his hand, smoothing his cheek ashamedly, was leaving hurriedly, taking two steps at a time. "Where has Papa gone?" Frankie asked her mother's hurt and severe face, and her mother said: "He's gone, and I hope for good," and that night slept alone in the big double bed. Dark, thin, alone . . . Which of these sisters was the woman, Frankie would ask, the one who in disgust refused to share the bed with her husband, or the one who had three ultra-feminine wigs, one brown, one red, one blond?

". . . Mama," Frankie is asking into the void, "can Opaline come over?"

"Opaline yes, but not Beppo—not that Portygee girl."

"Beppo's all right. She's nice," Frankie coaxed.

"I don't like her."

"Why don't you like her, Mama?"

"Opaline'll do time behind her yet."

". . . Mama . . ."

"She's no woman at least," said her mother, sure in her own femininity and thus mocking the Portuguese girl with her strong arms and boyish clothes.

"She's my heart," cried Frankie, "why does she have to be all dressed up like a broad? . . . And I want to be with Opaline."

"Be with Opaline, she's your own blood."

"Not without Beppo," said Frankie wisely. "She won't come without Beppo."

But later when Opaline knocked at the downstairs door where

Frankie had her bedroom, it was easy to signal to Beppo to go around the back, and then to help her in quietly through the window, as Frankie had become accustomed to doing with those other friends—especially her white friends—of whom her father so disapproved.

Beulah ('Beppo') Delgado is sixteen, but because she has been to reform school she is in the same grade as the thirteen-year-old Frankie. Her grandparents are Cape Verde Islanders and live in River Junction, where they once worked in the now-closed mills. Beppo's neat nose is constantly threatened by a lock of lank dark hair. When she smiles, which is rare, she half shuts her eyes, as if some dream of delight were sending her to sleep . . . She is a little cruel. She is bothered by younger girls, but she likes to catch them and squeeze them until they cannot breathe and are too choked to cry out. Frankie has felt those hands on her body, and once or twice a strange fear has filled her, a fear of some future death. (Indeed by the time that Frankie runs into Beppo at Henry Street, Beppo has become an object of fear and fascination, not only to Frankie herself but to all the girls who had known her before dropout days, at the Moon Street High School.)

Frankie is jealous of Beppo because of Opaline. Yet, also because of Opaline, she is impelled to love her. How is it possible to love *one* without the *other*? It is as if they formed together the imprint of a two-headed heraldic animal; whichever way the picture turned the image remained the same. Beppo and Opaline—Opaline and Beppo. Two in one and one in two . . .

In the spare bed in Frankie's room the two-headed creature lies, and alone in *her* bed, Frankie tries to sleep . . . William has left the house . . . Alva is far away upstairs in the kitchen . . . The full moon swims in the window above the heavy eaves of the houses—clear, remote, mysterious. Opaline's long and lovely hair hangs over the edge of the mattress and nearly to the floor, and in the dark forest of that hair Frankie seems to lose herself, as if she might bind herself there, smother, and die. "What you doin'?" she whispers.

". . . Nothing . . ." a voice comes at last. Whose voice is it? What combination of movements has produced this voice, so strangely mutual, as if it flowed from two bodies rather than one?

"What you doin'?"

"T.c.b.," murmurs Beppo.

"What's that?" whispers Frankie in discomfort.

"Taking care of business."

Opaline seems to laugh, but is it a laugh or simply a catch in the throat. The two bodies are thrashing about in the bed.

"I want to do what you're doin'."

Frankie's love for Opaline mingles curiously with the hurt of Beppo's power over her, and in the midst of jealousy, it seems to want Opaline's delight, to observe her shuddering lovely head and be grateful for it.

There is a long silence which disregards her, yet is alive and charged with a tension and concentration which shut her out. Beppo's whole muscular frame raises for a moment from the bed —like a creature out of the sea—arched.

After a long time the voice of authority comes again, the voice of no one. "Go to sleep," it says.

Miss Green stopped by at the cell row and told the drowsy Ana that she was to be released sometime after twelve. "Your mother will come to get you," she said briskly. "After breakfast you are to take a bath and get ready . . . Lunch is at eleven o'clock and you can have it in the dining room with the rest of the girls. You will then come back to your cell until your mother calls for you."

"My *mother*," Ana protested, pushing back her hair in amazement, "she mus' be coming in a wheelchair!"

"These are the instructions we have," Miss Green said briskly, "so be ready." She proceeded along the row and looked in on Harriet who was lying fully dressed on her cot and staring at the ceiling. She paused again at Brenda's cell and noticed that she was picking aimlessly at the stuff of her nightgown and not attempting to get dressed. She noticed also that her face was rather flushed and high-colored as if she had been crying and that there was a sheet of paper on the floor with "DEAR DENNIS—" scrawled on it in large unformed letters. Miss Green felt a mild curious pity for Brenda, as if she were of the same human stock but belonged to another kind of tribe than she herself did, and as if the customs to which she was addicted must be responsible for her downfall. *Catholic!* she thought significantly. Then aloud she said: "Brenda, time to get dressed. Get going, dear."

Glancing in at Frankie she saw that the girl had put on her dungarees and her orange shirt and was kneeling by the bed with a book open in her hands, her lips moving, a rapt expression on her face. For a moment Miss Green thought that it must be the Bible she held, and was about to pass on, when she saw that there was a picture of a bearded man engraved on the cover, and that Frankie was murmuring aloud words which seemed foreign and elusive. If it wasn't the Bible, what was the girl doing on her knees!

"Francesca!" she said in a tone of intense irritation. "Will you please stop reading that stuff and make your bed. Take that scarf off your head—and finish up your breakfast as well."

Frankie got to her feet slowly. "In case you're interested, it's not *"stuff"*—it's poetry," she answered, "and I don't want any of your goddamn breakfast."

Miss Green pulled at her uniform and commented icily: "Don't be fresh. Your cell is a mess—"

"Who wants lousy stinking food in a lousy stinking jail . . . ?" questioned Frankie. "It makes my flesh crawl—" She indicated with some exaggerated shudders, the little tray with its oatmeal and milk and bread and margarine. "The oatmeal's got worms in it; an' the milk's powdered; and I can't eat margarine . . ." She abruptly turned her back on Miss Green, who said in a quiet incisive tone: "Perhaps you prefer to go hungry," and walked off without further comment. Frankie was calling after her in a husky drawling insolent voice, which seemed to have in it all the esoteric knowledge of the Negro slums, "I know 'real' food—why should I eat the food *'the man'* send me?"

Miss Green went on upstairs, her emotions tangled, her early-morning mood already ruffled. She checked the cells of the older prisoners, let out those on the list for baths, instructed the laundry girls to finish their breakfast, and led the group downstairs into the basement where they began to operate the large washing machines, and went to work at the ironing boards. "Lolly," she told a tall thin white prisoner, "please start on the Sheriff's laundry at once." Upstairs again, the cells had been opened and the three women assigned to cleaning the area were engaged in sweeping and mopping the floors so that Miss Green, seated on the only chair on the floor and at a single steel table, could hear their brooms and mops moving with the slowness and lack of enthusiasm typical of prisons the world over. The orderliness and cleanliness of the prison supported her, yet kept her also, she thought, from really reaching these human beings in the cells and bringing them into subjection. How dared that little bandy-legged Negro girl Francesca think herself too good for the prison food, the prison environment? What was more, dare to express it in that scornful way? She, Miss Green, would have liked to make out a report exaggerating the scene between them, and painting the girl as a dangerous character—only fourteen years old, but already hardened! . . . Yet she did not do this, although, in theory at least, it was within her power, but only held her emotions in tighter rein, and turned with greater composure to talk with Jeanette Tobey, who had approached the desk and, leaning on her broom a little, was trying to get her attention.

"What is it, Jeanette?"

"I have a problem, Miss Green."

The young Negro woman looked rather embarrassed, and put her hand up to touch the glossy coil of hair she wore on top of her head. "Mary goes downstairs, you know, and she tells me that my young niece is in . . ."

"Your niece?"

"Yes—Francesca Ford, her name is. She seems to be waiting for trial . . . She jumped bail."

"Is Francesca Ford your *niece?*"

"She sure is," Jeanette answered in her quiet musical voice, "my sister Alva's child."

"And very fresh she is too," Miss Green said crisply.

Jeanette looked down at her broom. Her face, like a weary

Polynesian mask, expressed little emotion, but Miss Green seemed to see a faint struggle take place there, as if old conflicts were playing out their drama, and fading again into silence. "She's very apt Francesca," the aunt said at last. Standing there—even in her prison dress—she looked neat-figured and classic-featured. "But she sure is bodacious," she added.

Miss Green, who didn't know what the word bodacious meant, made no answer, only hearing Jeanette murmur gently: "I'd like to have permission to talk to her. She's just a child."

"Very well." The officer was gracious. "On the way to dinner I'll take you there. The superintendent gave orders for her to be kept in isolation as much as possible, since she's still a minor—but if she's your niece, visits will be allowed . . ."

"Yes, she's my niece," Jeanette answered with a sigh. She continued with her listless sweeping.

———————

Already the days had been long, already the idea of doing time had taken on meaning. When she saw Miss Green approaching with her Aunt Jeanette, she could not understand that Aunt Jeanette was a prisoner, too.

"So what you done *now?*" her aunt asked her, catching the impatient fingers which ran restlessly up and down the bars.

"Nothin'," Frankie said grinning, "almost nothin'."

"They told me you was here. What you done, baby?" Frankie looked up, her face a little strained, the whitish mark on her cheek gleaming like a beauty spot in reverse.

"Them nuns, Jeanette," the voice lingered in memory of long hours of bondage at St. Ursula's Home, ". . . it was a dra-a-a-g."

"Your mama told me you were happy there."

"Happy as a sissy in a Boy Scout camp! . . . I tell you I learned a thousand prayers a day!"

"So what—a few prayers won't hurt."

"I learned a *thousand* prayers. You pray before going to the *toilet!* . . ."

"You're not in here for that!" her aunt judged.

"He let me go home after Nana came to call, and I was tied

over to Mama on bail . . . Then I took off again, and Mama got the truant officer after me, and they put me here till the case comes up."

"You're *heading* somewhere," her aunt said testily. "You got no *sense!*"

"Mama put me here," Frankie protested aggressively. "She turned me over to the white folks."

"Listen, Frankie, I don't want you being bodacious here." She glanced over her shoulder to see Miss Green on the ramp in earnest conversation with Miss Walton. "You hear me?" she added severely.

"Mama put me here." Frankie's eyes blazed. "Mama had no business taking me to the white folks . . . Whitey got nothing to do with *me!*" she added with disgust. "They got a board for my ass."

"Well, don't you be bodacious!"

Her niece gave a professional smile.

"I'm not bodacious . . ."

"You were fresh to Miss Green."

"Oh, *her!* But Miss·Walton, now, she's swingin'."

Jeanette shrugged her shoulders. "That shirt," she said, "that all you got?"

"It's all I got."

"Give me the shirt this afternoon," Jeanette commanded, "I'll wash it. And look at your hair! Perhaps I can get permission to process it for you. Mighty hard to keep your self-respect in a place like this."

Her tune suggested the concern for a fashionable appearance which so characterizes an affluent society that it penetrates all classes—high and low, square and hip.

"What *you* here for?" Frankie asked wonderingly. "Didn't he bail you out?" Her eyes were reproachful, as if to say: "I thought *you* had all the angles figured . . ."

"The judge disallowed bail," her aunt said tersely, not expressing anything, not explaining. "I got six months for 'pros.'"

"Where's Wally?" Frankie asked in amazement.

"I don't know," her aunt replied quietly. "On the Avenue I

suppose. He came to get my coat . . ." Behind that quiet voice Frankie felt the uncertainty, the double standard. She herself had ridden in Jeanette's purple car, seen that mink stole, those three wigs . . . Now Jeanette, for all her virtues, paraded in the masquerade of a prison dress.

He was a pimp for a whole stable of women after all. He, Wally Williams, a deadpan study in sepia-toned good looks, the man who had turned out Jeanette Tobey, and who was often to be seen in late afternoon cruising slowly along Moon Street in his cream-colored Cadillac, en route to greener and more expensive parts of the city.

"Why," *an old friend of Jeanette's was to reminisce in later years,* "Wally Williams was the slickest you can imagine. He was known in San Francisco and Chicago and on the Boardwalk as well as he was known in North City. He was a real fine cross-country pimp!"

She added then that it wasn't until he took to dope that he had lost everything he owned, his stable and his car and his silk suits, or that news came from Frisco that he was doing bad, living in a cheap apartment on the earnings of a faded cancerous street-walker.

This, said the friend *(sic transit Gloria)* was delayed payment for putting Jeanette half out of her mind, so that she herself had seen Jeanette propped up in bed, breathing hoarsely, staring ahead of her with sightless eyes *("stone blind, she was, and an empty bottle of Seconal on the table beside her").*

Now Frankie said suddenly and anxiously: "There was a noise."

"Noise . . . ?"

"In the *night*." She twisted her hands together. "An awful *noise* . . . crying and moaning . . . crying to God . . . I tell you, Jeanette, I was scared to death . . ."

"A girl kicking a habit," her aunt soothed her. "Don't mind it, baby. A prison's no place to be in."

"What *was* it?" reiterated Frankie.

"Drugs," her aunt said, seeing Miss Green approaching the cell. "Listen—don't go shooting your mouth off while you're here . . ."

"I won't . . ."

"It was a girl I know," her aunt soothed her. "She came in last night . . ."

"It's not for *me*," Frankie declared, shutting her eyes in urgent memoriam for those cries in the night . . . "No, Lord, it's not for *me* . . ."

The room has five green tables covered with plastic cloths. The thirty women and girls are sitting in their places, eating, as if their lives depend upon it, their Sunday dinner of frankfurters, potatoes, and cabbage. Each little burst of conversation has an enigmatic and temporary quality, and most of the time only the sound of forks and knives breaks the heated silence. The summer, and the sense of being endlessly indoors, is weighing over the tables like a bad dream.

"Franks," someone murmurs in disgust.

"Better'n baloney."

"Sheriff signs for it," sighs an enormous Polish girl whose two arms rest like hams on the table before her.

"If he sign for it, why don't he sign for better?"

"He sign for milk, 'n' we don' get milk," protests a thin redhead who is obviously pregnant.

For a time everyone is quiet again.

Beppo, who is in charge of serving coffee, pads silently around the rooms, making a survey of the terrain and at the same time replenishing cups. Her skills have always counted to her advantage; it has taken the staff exactly four days to find out that she can be depended upon to carry out a task with a minimum of noise and a maximum of efficiency. Slim, with her boylike handsome head held high, she darts to and fro in the dining room. No one would know, from her compliant if cold politeness, exactly how ambitious she is, nor how adept already at using every opportunity to further her ends. Only her walk, which is masculine and somewhat rapacious, gives her the look of a foraging animal, so that when she stoops over Ana Pug Nose Pulaski's plate to give her an unnecessary cup of tea, and rests her hand for one moment on the vulnerable back of the girl's neck, the onlooker might guess that she has already singled out this girl as her prey.

Pug Nose is holding forth to her table companions about her mother, and wondering in a loud voice how she can come to Henry Street to get her. "She been crippled since I was seven," she is saying. "First a cane, and then crutches, and then a walker! . . . And I tell you it make no diff' to me, but I don' know how she gonna get here . . . But she's probably awfully worried about me!" She draws a card out of her pocket and proffers it to her neighbor, holding it in her white shiny-fingered little hand which has a boy's name tattooed on the wrist. There is a religious picture on the outside of the card, and the girl to whom it has been offered reads it aloud to the assembled group:

> Jesus' heart is your true refuge
> To him you can always flee,
> Even when your hopes are sinking
> He will then a TRUE FRIEND be.

"Very nice," comments the girl.

"I'm a true friend also, baby," Beppo murmurs, caressing Ana's neck, "except that I'd cut you up if you fleed from me." She passes on along the table before Ana can answer.

"Why they call you Pug Nose?" one of the other girls asks from across the table.

"I fell off the platform at the Polish Club when I was in a play," says Ana plaintively.

Silence falls on the room again.

. . . At the farthest table over near the door, Jeanette Tobey, without lifting her eyes from her plate eats quietly. From eyes set a little obliquely in her face, long lashes flutter onto matte cheeks, and a calm coil of hair rests above them,

giving her the air of some brown-skinned madonna from the
South Seas. On either side of her, the women look horren-
dously ugly. To the left there is Bertha, awaiting trial for larceny, a great, clumsy redheaded woman with pale, pale eyes
under bushy eyebrows, and a chin which has a male aggression
seemingly at war with the large, loose breasts clasped together
under the cotton prison dress. And to the right sits a small distorted woman whose dead-white face is squeezed together at
the brow and broadens curiously at the chin, making way for a
capacious and almost toothless mouth. This woman sits with
one shoulder higher than the other, so that her bones seem
thrust forward—the bones of her shoulders into which her
neck is sunk, and the bones of her lower jaw, which are protu-
berant like those of a monkey. Her dark eyes, narrowed under
that inadequate forehead, blink rapidly like some light turned
off and on, and so inharmonious is she that her hands seem to
have difficulty in handling her knife and fork. Her name is Flo
and she is in Henry Street for cruelty to minor children . . .
Between these two women, Jeanette blooms like a flower, but
a flower touched by something, as the dark of decay touches
the waxy edges of a camellia. Serving the coffee and leaning
over the shoulders of the women, Beppo leans with exaggerated respect over Jeanette and sees only the shadow of her dis-
dainful eyelashes set slant-wise in her profile. Beppo, who has
once lived in Moon Street and who has been so intimate with
Opaline, Frankie's cousin, knows Jeanette by reputation and
has therefore the utmost respect for her, because here indeed is
a woman with class, the sort of high-class broad who, if you
had her 'up tight,' would not only make you rich but would
make you happy as well. Jeanette is beautiful—beautiful by
any standards, square or otherwise—and Beppo, because the
object of her attentions takes no notice of her, feels free to
allow herself to drift on the full stream of a romantic fantasy.

All by herself, in the sense that she knows none of the
women around her, Brenda O'Reilly chews miserably on a
piece of frankfurter. The food she masticates is like the cud of
her depression, tasteless, endlessly regurgitated. And like a

baby, she wants to cry and spit it out onto her plate, to be assured that someone cares about her, that she will get something better. This dependence is constant in her. It is what is to make her the slave of others, a fit victim in the future for cutting, whipping, abusing. They had had a social worker talk to her in court, and the social worker had tried to find out why Brenda had run away from the state school for girls, where the court had placed her, and gone to a house in Leland where colored and white girls were living together and, according to the police, entertaining men. Had she *wanted* to go there? the social worker asked her. Had it been her own choice, or had someone *persuaded* her? But Brenda, after having insisted first that her name was Baby, not Brenda, had burst into tears, and kept saying, "It was getting next to me, I had to run from Wentworth . . . I couldn't stand it any longer . . . It was getting next to me," until at last the social worker sighed, wrote something down, and gathered up her papers . . . Now Brenda eats because she is young and hungry, and swallows her tears with her food; her broad Irish cheeks are red as if congested, and her shining black hair descends like rain down her broad back, and she shakes it, as if she were a trembling unkempt pony penned into a little yard.

"My auntie rai'ed me," a fat sleepy-eyed Negro girl is saying. "She rai'ed me in South Ca'lina . . . She awfu' good t'me . . . awfu' good . . ." Her dark scarred hands crumble the bread by her plate while she talks of picking cotton on her father's farm, of working in a sawmill gathering lumber, of having a job in a café when she was thirteen, of being the cook in a timber camp at fifteen . . . "They put me on a floater to South Ca'lina, but my man he bro' me back 'gain . . . Wish Ah ha'nt come . . . Men, they's a buh'den . . ." She sighs deeply. "Jus' a buh'den . . ."

"No," Jeanette says dreamily but finally, without looking up at the officious Beppo, "no more coffee."

Beppo takes a napkin and leans over Jeanette again. She loves the struggle of trying to get attention from this full-breasted broad, and she notes with well-controlled curiosity all the good points the woman has: the way she is built, the matte skin, the full yet finely cut mouth beneath the straight nose, and most of all her evident intelligence (for Beppo is drawn by intelligence as others are drawn by charm, and she knows that intelligence is the forerunner, in sexual matters, of an exciting struggle). With the napkin she carefully gathers up every last crumb on the table near Jeanette, lifting the cup and saucer and wiping under them (but not yet taking them away so that she will have an excuse to come back again) and at the same time leaning a little in a suggestive but gentle manner against Jeanette's shoulder . . . The heat and the silence drift around them, but Jeanette does not move . . .

"How she shape her mouth to say that?" someone cries loudly at one of the other tables. "How that goddamned bitch shape up them words?"

"She snooty . . ." is the answer.

"Ef you take the 'c' out of 'class,' that leaves 'ass,' " the other declares.

There is a gust of laughter, and the pall of silence falls again.

The officer in charge of the dining room walks over from the corner and parades once around the room, her face calm, but her eye on the offender who has just spoken, as if this were a routine reminder, as if each woman in the room were held by a fine rein, not seen but there all the same, and as if the officer had given a quiet soft tug to the rein, to remind each one of the potential force of the prison, of the invisible authority.

. . . Outside beyond the thick wall and high barred windows (which here on the dining-room side border a busy city street) the glittering metallic flood of automobiles flows by, rushing silently in an ever-striving and hastening stream . . . Inside in the well-protected, barred dining room, in the hot silence broken only by jerky communications, quick-flaring quarrels, sporadic obscenities—in this little dead-end for the weak, the erring, the confused, and degraded—there is a stagnation, a kind of death.

Desperately Beppo tries to make contact with Jeanette, but

is repulsed. Desperately she tries to say an adequate good-bye to Ana, but manages only to whisper to her to look for her at The Burrow (a Lesbian bar which serves as a clearinghouse for commercial and emotional purposes), and to ask for 'Man' Delgado.

" 'Man'!" whispers back Ana, "that's somepin'."

"You'll find out," promises Beppo from the side of her mouth, as she darts to open the door for the officer. But she knows that she may never see Ana again, and feels, as she has felt before, the unnaturalness of her quest, its iron compulsion . . . So the minutes pass, while the dark fat girl from South Ca'lina laments to a disinterested audience, while the enraged girl at the center table hacks with her blunt dinner knife at the oilcloth before her, while the huge redheaded woman shivers at some old memory, and while the heavy-armed Polish woman gazes hungrily at an empty plate . . .

As Miss Walton came downstairs to go home at last, she was waylaid by the superintendent of the jail, whose thin worn face expressed the anxiety of one whose cares pursue her less because of their numbers, than because of her failure to understand and classify them. Now, however, she was experiencing a moment of triumph as she explained to Miss Walton that the problem of the name of the girl in Cell 20 had been successfully solved.

"It's Suzy Browne," she said proudly.

Miss Walton searched her extensive memory and produced the image of a thin little girl with enormous eyes. "She was in for arson?"

"It's the same girl," the superintendent exclaimed. "I thought she looked familiar. Although now she's two years older and ten times tougher. But when she gave her name as Suzan Enworb I was completely taken in."

"What a name to choose—Enworb!"

"Not at all," the superintendent corrected rather formally. "That's how we tumbled to it. It's Browne spelled backwards.

Don't you remember how someone on the male side called him-self Charles Senoj, and everyone thought he must be Russian—but it turned out he was only old Charlie Jones with his name switched the other way?"

Miss Walton's laughter became lost in pity.

"It's an interesting kind of identification, like the desire so many of them have to reform and become officers in the de-partment of correction. I remember one taking the name of our sheriff, who at that time was Horace David Buchanan . . ."

The superintendent already seemed out of touch. She said: "Thank you for staying, Edith—it was a great help." Her face, fair, slightly nervous and troubled, bent over the forms on the desk.

Miss Walton, remembering something, got to her feet heav-ily and returned to the first floor of the block, where she ap-proached Frankie's cell. "What you reading?" she asked.

"Walt Whitman." Frankie gave her a brilliant but rather forced smile.

"Well, aren't *you* making good use of the time. I came to say I couldn't bring the colors till tomorrow. I had to work late."

"Oh, that's okay . . ." Frankie regarded Miss Walton's moon face with its small, tender mouth. "Will you *really* bring 'em tomorrow?"

"Sure I will."

"Like I'm sitting here at night and it's a drag."

Miss Walton sensed but did not resist the danger of a hu-man relationship. "I know it, honey," she said, as if to herself. "Take it easy." She added: "You appealed didn't you?"

"You expect me to bend down while they kick my ass?" Frankie asked gloomily.

Miss Walton looked puzzled.

"You expect me to take it when he send me to Reform School?" translated Frankie.

"I don't know about your case." Miss Walton sighed, and looked into the girl's expressionless eyes.

"What did I do? I ran . . . that's all."

"I'd want no child of mine in here, nor in Wentworth either. But then if you were a child of mine, you wouldn't be running around at night."

"I'm a child of yours," Frankie said, smiling again. "Okay —jus' so long as I'm no child o' that bitch Miss Green."

"Frankie!"

"Oh, honey," Frankie drawled affectionately, "that word— it been around since Central Park were a flower pot!"

Miss Walton lingered, charmed, half-conquered, but aware of her protégée's changes of mood, of the way in which she constantly peered inward at past scenes of violence and frustration.

"Well I won't stay here long," the girl said. "I'll turn the place out!"

Miss Walton's large capacious figure seemed to melt through the bars—the breasts, the belly, the thighs, in their white matronly garment, absorbing the dangerous dark leanness of the little prisoner. "No such thing . . ."

Like an unspecified caress, the suggestion of physical contact soothed Frankie, and her shrillness ran to ground.

"Okay," she said softly. "Okay, Miss Walton . . . you're swingin'."

Her eyes glowed again, like faint lights flashing in the darkness, her hands unclenched. "Okay . . ."

"Swingin'?" Miss Walton smiled too, her cheeks creasing into archaic patterns, the curves of clay cheeks on long-buried idols. Flesh was momentarily given mythical importance. "Swingin'? I'm gone with the wind," she said.

Literature about juveniles is redolent with poverty, crime, and the horrors of institutions. It is crammed with small figures, always innocent-eyed and often ragged: "half-starved and asking for more" (Oliver Twist), "child labour" (David Copperfield), "beaten by the big boys" (Tom Brown's Schooldays), "frozen in winter" (The Little Match Girl), "made to feel the condescension of charity" (These, these were the joys) and "victims of wicked stepmothers" (Cinderella and Snow White). These earlier heroes and heroines are consistently pure in heart, and not perhaps to be compared to the children of the prisons, who, because they grow so slowly in wisdom, have long child-hoods, during which they lose some of their bloom. Yet such in-carcerated children are like iridescent humming birds, which healthy and alive flash a thousand colors, and even when half dead and shut up in cages (or stuffed and mounted on pins) never quite lose their brilliance. The prism on the feather of a bird cannot die; like the flash of hope on a face, it remains to remind the onlooker of the age of innocence.

So Miss Walton, leaving Frankie in her cell and returning to the ground floor, left a figure as controversial as any immor-talized by angry idealistic writers. She found the superintend-ent laboring—turning over page after page of the week's reports, as if she thus wiped away all the distracting impermanency of the ebb and flow of prisoners, an impermanency which, despite the evident fact that in a county jail like Henry Street one could scarcely expect stability of any kind, worried her orderly and logical mind.

"That's finished—and that—and that—" she said aloud into the midday heat.

She was not a particularly reflective woman and, until the murder two years ago of a matron at an upcounty jail, had never questioned her position as an upholder of tradition. This murder committed by a temporarily housed psychotic had caused a tumult of criticism and a rash of letters to the press. Attention had been drawn to faulty security in the county jails, to overcrowding, understaffing, and lack of recreational and hospital facilities. And she, Mrs. Mary O'Connor, had be-gun to follow with special care and anxiety the vicious circle of which she had been conscious for so long—the bringing in of new prisoners and their subsequent reappearance year by year after that, so that one seemed to see juveniles converted by their very sentences into hardened adult prisoners. Hadn't she read somewhere, she worried, that 63 per cent of the juveniles committed to the county jails ended up in state reformatories?

"They all follow the same cycle," she commented to Miss Walton, who had now come downstairs again. "It's as if we were *educational* establishments. Here's Suzan Browne, or Suzan Enworb as she called herself, who's been through the Catholic St. Ursula's, the Protestant Home for Unmarried Mothers, the State School for Girls at Wentworth, and now is back here at Henry Street . . . If I'm not mistaken, Francesca Ford went through St. Ursula's and she'll probably be sent to Wentworth when her case comes up . . . Then the one they call Baby—Brenda O'Reilly, in the cell next door—she was picked up after she ran from Wentworth, and before that she was at St. Ursula's, *too*."

"Yes," Miss Walton agreed, "that's how it goes."

"Harriet Brun seems to be an exception." The superintendent shuffled the cards. "But she's so silent I doubt anyone knows much about her . . . As for Beulah Delgado, the one nicknamed Beppo, she's also been to Wentworth, though for some reason she was released after six months."

"Perhaps she was too hot for them to handle," Miss Walton suggested.

"If she was too hot for them to handle, she was sent back to parents who couldn't handle her in the first place," the superintendent argued. "The parents pass the buck to the state, and the state passes it back to the parent. They go to St. Ursula's, or to St. Eulalia's over in Tasseldone. If they're pregnant, they go to the Protestant Home or to Belveson. In either case, they generally graduate to a state school like Wentworth where they compare notes as old alumni . . . Everyone says, for instance, that you can always tell an old Wentworth girl . . ."

"Then *we* get them," Miss Walton commented. "And after we've had them, they go to Paragoula." She had seen this pattern of continuity so often, so long ago, that it didn't seem new to her.

"Well, what do they expect of a county institution?" the superintendent said.

"At least we have better records now."

"Yes . . . that's true."

"And remember when there wasn't even a recreation room."

"Yes—remember."

"I'm going to start a hair-dressing class . . . Yes, I think that's coming through very soon."

"A hair-dressing class? That'll be nice."

The superintendent had regained assurance. "Well, I'll be going, Mary," said Miss Walton.

"Okay, Edith—good-bye then. Thank you again."

"Don't mention it. Good-bye now."

"Good-bye. See you tomorrow . . ."

"Yes, indeed. See you tomorrow."

A hair's breadth lies between sentiment and sentimentality (as the superintendent of an enlightened institution commented when asked to give a speech about rehabilitation). She delivered the speech in somewhat the following terms:

I remember Maud, an eighteen-year-old Negro girl from a horribly deprived background, deserted by her father, rejected by her mother; a girl who had been institutionalized since she was eleven years old, who came pregnant to our institution on a six-month charge for drunkenness . . . Her baby was born on February 7. Her legal release date was February 10. She left with $5 release money, with all her worldly goods in a cardboard carton tied up with string . . . In six months we had been expected to 'rehabilitate.' We had been expected to undo seventeen years' damage, to change the attitudes woven over long and difficult years, to reassure her that there was friendliness in the world into which we discharged her; although we sent her, ill equipped as she was, to an impersonal job, a fur-

nished room, a scarcely existent family . . . This is what is called Rehabilitation!

Harriet Brun, lying on her cot and staring up at the ceiling, finds that the prison cell forms a circle of protection, although she still dreams of letting herself out of it by using the spoon which she has slipped into her brassière on the first day she condescends to go to the dining room. It is as if she acknowledges that she *likes* the cell, that it is what she has been seeking out—a hiding place, a place where no action is necessary. At the same time the spoon seems to have significance for her, because it alone lets her out of places from which she can no longer release herself by turning the key of her psyche. She can feel it now, wrapped in toilet paper and pressing against her breast, and she imagines that with its help, she will be able to say: "Fuck you world!," which in her vocabulary, is saying a lot.

She is five years old and her mother is showing her off to the French Canadians who have come to visit all the way from Quebec, a group of people who have the same name as her father but pronounced differently, who talk loudly and incessantly in a strange language, who throw out their hands and jerk their elbows, and who terrify the silent child by picking her up and saying: *"Elle est une Brune . . . une vraie petite Brune! . . ."* Her mother wants her to say "Hello Aunt," and when she won't say a word—standing there on the table surrounded by strange waiting faces, sturdy on her fat legs, her tawny hair tangled, her large blue eyes solemn, and her face red with the effort to keep from crying—her mother gives her an irritated slap on the hand. This is the last straw! She still refuses to speak, but her face turns purple, she screws up her eyes, and lets out a savage and unrestrained howl, which horrifies and discomforts the horde of relatives.

. . . She is always shut up. She is shut up for dirtying her pants and for breaking a cup, and for putting her finger in the cement which her father is mixing. The locked door represents the end of the world, the final barrier against which she must hurl herself in endless rage, until her body is bruised and her head beaten into insensibility. She can be reduced to trembling by the very threat of it, so that even when her little face goes white with anger, they can threaten to shut her up, and she will become docile, and pathetically eager to please.

Because her mother, an anxious brooding woman with a deprecatory smile, is too irritable and too nervous to have her around the house, she is allowed to help her father. And in the nearby shed, where her father makes cement blocks for a living, her readiness to adapt herself to male behavior is great enough to transform her into an asset (even if she is only turning water taps on and off, or, as she gets older, answering the telephone). Always in blue jeans, her tawny hair cropped close, smudges of dirt on her white skin, silent like her mother, and when she does speak, gruff like her father, she moves through her joyless childhood, as a clumsy boat might move on a river, constantly colliding with the banks. Her father is the "man" and she is the "boy" working for him, and they seem bound together by the actual physical factors in the environment—the littered yard, the junked cars, the paddling of the cement, the fresh smell of it in the close air. Yet even as she learns to be adept at helping him with his trade, rushing back from school each afternoon, tirelessly running messages, endlessly patient in cleaning the current automobile, she realizes that he is always critical of her, never pleased, that he is not *proud* of her . . . Isn't she like a boy to him? Isn't she even 'Harry' rather than 'Harriet'? Then how is it he is not proud of her?

Her father has a strong reaction to liquor, an intolerance which seems to be inherited by his children. When he is drunk he passes into a state of morbid gaiety or childish vengeance. (Once he had broken her mother's jaw, and her mother had gone around with frightened eyes peeping above a white bandage.) Harriet sees that it is not just, and slowly, laboriously—

conscious of her mother's nervous placating smile—she tries to explain it to Billy, her younger brother. "It's something terrible because she doesn't fight back."

"We oughter tell somebody," Billy suggests, because of all the family he is closest to his mother.

"Who we gonna tell?"

"Mother Holy Spirit," Billy says. (Mother Holy Spirit is the Mother Superior of the parochial school.)

"You tell her," Harriet suggests sullenly.

"I'm scared," Billy admits. "I'm younger."

"Well, Ma's so miserable," Harriet complains, ignoring him. She sees her mother's weakness, her fatal inability to resist force, and this makes Harriet herself feel powerless. "All she does is cry. That's why he won't give her any money . . . He gives me $5 a week."

"You're strong," Billy says admiringly. "You're awful strong, Harriet. That's why he gives you $5. You do a lot out there."

"I wanta buy a car," Harriet says suddenly. "I wanta buy a car that's not too big, with a hood like this . . . a coupe."

"You're only twelve," Billy doubts.

"I've got $50 saved up now. Sister Agatha says I should get a savings account."

"Tell Sister Agatha to tell Mother Holy Spirit."

"About what?" Harriet has already dismissed the question of her mother.

"About *her*." Billy jerks his thumb back toward the house, and there is panic in his voice. He feels his sister failing him as his parents fail him.

"*You* tell Mother Holy Spirit," Harriet says. "I don't *like* to talk." The habit of silence and endurance settles upon her like an invisible garment, and Billy, still young and uninhibited, restless, violent, begins to dig angrily in the ground with a stick.

"Let's run away," suggests Harriet suddenly.

"Where to?"

"Anywhere," says Harriet briefly.

She suddenly stands up and flexes her arm like a boxer, until the muscle stands erect.

"See that?" she says to Billy. "See that?" Real rage shows in her blue eyes, and she makes imaginary lunges with her arm. "If anyone tries to stop us . . . *that's* what they get . . ." Her volubility runs out, and she sinks to her knees again, and lapses into silence. Billy digs in the unanswering earth. Harriet draws her outlines of cars, symbols of escape. The silent angry father treads his well-worn path back and forth between the shed and the office. And the mother inside the house shuts windows, puts letters away unread, and nurses the reasonless bruise on her cheek, which is only the last one in a long line of blows she does not understand . . .

Harriet turns at the infantile smile of a younger girl.

The blond, frail girl is called Marie Budette (her name is a corruption of Boudet, and her grandparents, like Harriet's, had emigrated from Canada). Marie's welcome is childlike in its completeness, and drives Harriet to strut, whistle, boast, and parade in a ballet of relief at such easy acceptance. Where the other children cannot molest them, in the parking lot next door to the school playground, the simple-minded Marie and the withdrawn Harriet form an *entente cordiale.* Here the cars parked each day—the ordinary cars of a small town—undergo a brilliant metamorphosis. Their paint shines with extraordinary luminosity, their flanks are stroked by all the winds of the road. Marie and Harriet, with a false air of loitering indifference, creep up on them, tracking them through the forest of the lot, glancing sideways at their radiators, their bumpers, their nickel-plated decoration. The idea of entering the cars, one by one, exploring their virgin interiors, possesses Harriet (while Marie, feeling her friend's excitement, trembles in her turn, and turns paler still at the mere idea of touching a steering wheel with her thin claw of a hand). For years Harriet's father has fed this automobile fantasy, handing his daughter tool after tool, urgently reprimanding her for any slowness of mechanical understanding, binding her as his helper to his own narrow routine, and ignoring whatever femininity she possesses. Since she knows, shudderingly, that she doesn't want to be like her mother, it is better, and more practical, to follow *him*. But if in spite of her long devotion, he does not look at her, then she must draw her love from these machines of steel and chrome, and seek upon the spreading senseless roads orgasms of pleasure. Like a pilot without wings—and followed by the jerky-walking assistant pilot— she searches, armed with knives, screw-drivers, and straps of plastic, for the perfect flight vehicle . . .

(*Harriet's one-sided obsession with cars will make her vulnerable in the future, as certain illnesses make their victims unable to stand stress. Although her story will overflow the pages of this book through the course of which she remains silent and withdrawn, the observer would be wrong if he thought her life absolutely disassociated from that great panorama of organized crime which threatens our present world and which, with the sure instinct of a thriving business, seeks to embrace, with voracious octopus-like tentacles, all that lies around it. Harriet is older than that sixteen-year-old boy, who was Mafia-organized, along with his teen-age gang, into a well-supervised systematic stealing operation; and later on like any adult gangster, 'rubbed out' on the pavements of South Brooklyn. She shows no gift for stealing on such a scale, nothing but a childlike tendency to take joy rides. She is, for all that, for all her inoffensiveness and mental weakness—to tie herself ever more firmly to the only world which will receive her, and much later on, her first serious attempt to support herself 'in the life,' will be by selling the parts of the vehicles she steals, to an organized group in Murmaine County. So that Harriet, bewildered car lover, in high school 195 out of 196, is later to form a tiny link in an illegal export chain which stretches through Canada and Cuba and endlessly on behind the Iron Curtain.*)

At this time when she still cannot drive, and is safe inside her silent childhood, she has learned to maneuver her way into many of the cars she encounters, and once inside them, to get the engine started by crossing the wires of the ignition and the cigarette lighter. She has also developed the technique of shifting practical necessities from her immediate family toward less concerned relatives, so that an irresponsible cousin is teaching her to drive and an aged alcoholic uncle on her father's side has promised—when she gets the car—to register it in his name, and even to say nothing to his brother.

This uncle lives on a rutted road in a patch of woods at the far end of the town, and the idea of having a car around pleases him so much that he is already in imagination half-owner, and chuckles with Harriet as he promises to fool the traffic court and get even with the police who have in the past arrested him for drunken driving. "You're a real sport," he says to Harriet, nodding his plaintive but ferociously whiskered head. "Yes, you're a real sporting niece . . . You'll get away with it. I'll wager you do," and shrewdly he cuts the brush farther out at the back of the house, so that the car bought some six months later will not be visible from the road. "We'll take some trips in it," he promises her, while he carefully tapes up the cracked back window of the '48 Chevvy, and Harriet and Marie paint and polish the body, straighten the windshield wiper, and tie up the rear left door.

. . . At first she only takes it out in the early evenings or at night, with the uncle in semi-disguise, sitting beside the driver, his broad-brimmed hat coming down over his eyebrows, his shoulders hunched into his checkered woolen jacket. Behind sits the pale and smiling Marie, sometimes with her eyes shut to hide her fear of a crash, holding tightly onto the back of the front seat. A swift swing to the left, a grinding of gears, an unsuccessful attempt to back up—all these produce emotions in the two girls which are terrifyingly pleasant. Because of having for so long lacked natural outlets, they now experience in this clandestine driving, an intoxicating therapy.

. . . But Harriet's skill can never catch up with her emotions. To escape—to break out of the prison and get somewhere—this has always been her need.

She grows bolder. One afternoon she runs out of the kitchen

door, and calling to Marie dives into the car and guns the motor. In a matter of minutes the girls are on the main highway and heading towards the Northern mountains.

"She's creepin' up, Harry," reports Marie, her fair empty face pinned to the speedometer. "She's creepin' up. Can you go to 90?"

"Sure—120," answers Harriet.

"We could go to the Beanery and get a hamburger," Marie offers.

"No . . ." Harriet realizes that she is in the car without her uncle's protection, and that she is only fourteen and has no license. Abruptly she swerves off onto a dirt road, jolting the car up a steep track of dried mud. "We'll go and explore the old shack up here. Hang on."

Through the thin woods, the ribs of the shack stand out like bones through light clothing and young trees are pushing up past the broken side walls and the sagging steps of the hut, so that the whole leaning building seems to be bowered in spring green.

"Pretty," says Marie holding out her hands.

"You're damn right," replies Harriet gruffly. "Now we got a *home* that we can come to when we want."

By the time that Harriet is nearly fifteen, she and Marie have been, for more than a year, taking short experimental trips in the Chevvy, and making their headquarters in the shack in the woods. Old blankets, a flashlight, matches, a bottle opener (true to the male cult and in imitation of her father, Harriet has begun to drink beer), a saucepan and frying pan, old jelly jars, comic books, hard candy, and cigarettes—these are the necessities for exquisite pleasure.

Harriet is growing into a handsome girl, but she prunes back aggressively those feminine qualities which, like the clinging tendrils of a grapevine, seek to curl tentatively from her psyche. She hates to wear a bathing suit, having some conviction that she both looks, and is, different from other girls, and that she should cover, not only her body but even her long round arms with heavy clothing. Marie, now taller, has the flat chest of a child, and from eyes as clear and empty as water she regards the friend she calls Harry as if she were the epitome of strength and knowledge. "Gonna get up in the hills someday," Harriet says, "way up . . . there's lakes up there."

"Lakes? We can swim, Harry!"

It is nearly summer again. "Sure we can swim." She has developed a voice which grows deeper and gruffer. "We'll be hermits up there." She opens another can of beer, and slowly pours it down her throat, adding unrealistically, "We must get an ax and cut our way through."

The beer is affecting her strangely, turning some joyful confident key in her brain, making her want to sing loudly, to do a clumsy dance. Her father has always said that no one in his family can drink, that his father before him, and his two uncles as well, used to go crazy when they drank liquor. "Back in Montreal old Pa Brun was *paralyzed* after a drinking bout . . ." To this rule Harriet seems no exception. Alcohol in any form turns her into a figure of power. Two cans of beer transform her. Later on, half a glass of whisky is to trigger some violent reaction in her nervous system, to make her famous in the county jails which house her, for keeping the whole block awake with her abandoned singing. But now her habits are still moderate . . .

Marie sees tiny images of a campfire in the woods, surrounded by glistening green foliage. Pure happiness fills her and she embraces her embarrassed partner with frantic adoration.

"You're my *best* friend, Harry."

Outside the jail on North City's River Drive, the cars move bumper to bumper, themselves like small opulent prisons, housing within their mirrored metal sides vulnerable human beings, soft and shell-less. With their subdued power, these machines tame their occupants, schooling them to a bland control, suggesting in the busy murmur of this car culture an enforced idleness, a moving forever without arrival.

Harriet and Marie, young and awkward, too human to be accident-free, house a monster in their chariot, and two weeks later, when they venture into a parking lot near a hardware store, they crash into a telephone pole, and are escorted to the local police station, while the juvenile officer rounds up their parents.

Marie's foster mother is angry and ashamed. She knows that she should look after Marie better but, after all, the child is not quite "all there" and seems safer with Harriet than with other children, who are apt to get impatient when she can't participate in current games. Besides, what is a busy mother to do with the state only paying $11 a child per week, and with three other foster children to manage? If the state would pay a decent sum now, she'd be able to afford a few dollars for a girl to come in occasionally, and she would have more time to consider what Marie might be doing after school . . .

The juvenile officer, who has to make a trip to North City that afternoon, cuts these explanations short by asking her to look after Marie better in the future and telling her to take the child home. Then he turns to Harriet, "*Fifteen and a half years old. Bad record in school. But A in science. Parents together for twenty-five years. Father a hard worker and bringing in a good income. Own business making cement blocks.*"

"How do you account for your daughter's driving this car?" he asks her father.

"I didn't know my brother *had* a car," Harriet's father began, standing there wearing an expression at once belligerent and helpless, an expression very much like Harriet's own. "And I didn't know the girl *could* drive . . . I mean even enough to get to that parking lot . . . She's never driven *my* car."

"I'm not sure she *can*," the officer says, "or only well enough to crash into a telephone pole . . . But how did she get the car in the first place?"

"I'll have to ask my brother about that."

"How did you get the car?" the juvenile officer asks Harriet.

"I just took it," admits Harriet, her eyes on the floor.

She only admits that she has taken her uncle's car without permission, that she has driven it sometimes in the yard when he wasn't around, and that she and Marie have wanted to see how it would go on the main highway. Her puzzled blue eyes suggest to the juvenile officer that there might be more to the story than that; but the fact that the father seems to be a hard-working man with a good reputation, and the fact that he, the juvenile officer, has an appointment for which he is already late, makes it considerably easier not to inquire too deeply. He therefore appoints a date for Harriet and her father to appear before the court and promises himself to make further inquiries before that time . . . It is by accident only that three days before the hearing he is sent to do some special work in another county, and a substitute officer takes his place and sees nothing inadequate about the fact that the child, without any further understanding of Harriet's uncle's role in the episode, or of the place that the car—any car— plays in Harriet's life, is put on probation for one year, and remanded to the care of her father.

Nor is it surprising that almost immediately after the episode, Harriet and Marie sit again in their shack in the woods, making inarticulate plans for a 'free future,' drinking beer again, and sometimes also little shots of bourbon (which Marie has stolen from her foster mother's supply, and brought to the shack in a jam jar). Nor that long before Harriet is sixteen (and after a certain amount of disgusted submission to her uncle's ineffectual but affectionate hands) another '48 Chevvy—substitute for love, and symbol of departure—stands there in the cave of leaves behind her uncle's house.

At three o'clock they come to get Ana 'Pug Nose' Pulaski because her VD test has proved negative and her father has arrived to take her home. She leaves the cell, dressed again in her street clothes, her panda clutched in her arms, her exaggeratedly high heels tapping, her long red rope of hair swinging. She is full of self-importance and oblivious to the farewells of Beppo, the nervous pacing of Harry, the despondency of Baby, and the large, dark, and now melancholy eyes of Frankie. She is going to tell off everyone, for having had her arrested in the first place, and especially she is going to tell off the policeman, the Big Guinea who chews his cigar there in front of Perry's where all the kids go and whose passionate desire to take her in she interprets as a reverse kind of love. In fact, in two minutes she's pouring it all out to her father (who has long left her mother, and who only in this moment of emergency has been re-elevated into a position of family responsibility).

"Why'm I here? You ask that Big Guinea why I'm here? . . . He thinks I'm a ruff-tuff cream puff and that the only way I'm goin' to learn my lesson is by puttin' me away. *That's* why I'm here. Well, he got to think different that's all. He'd say I was a whore, and now my test says I'm negative . . . So I guess he's got another think coming . . ."

In the cellblock the tedium gathers and hangs heavily in the air. Beppo does her hair. Harriet paces to and fro, and dreams of cars. Baby reads a copy of *True Confessions*. Frankie sketches a bowl of flowers and then throws the paper angrily on the floor. The energy of youth curdles, contained and paralyzed by the bars, the silence turns upon itself, becomes static . . .

Continually outside, the stream of cars flows on, surrounding, ignoring, bypassing the prison . . .

Frankie rewinds the white cloth about her head and keeps a watch upon those who pass by. Miss Green, who has just come on duty, has let Beppo out to clean the reception room downstairs, and now has gone to call the girls to bring her up the mops and buckets, leaving Beppo waiting by the corner of the cells, where she carries on a guarded conversation with Frankie. Between them is the barrier of the past, the downstairs bedroom, Frankie alone in her bed, Beppo and Opaline together in the other bed.

"How you doin'?"

"Lousy."

"What a hole!" Beppo casts a swift, intelligent look at this younger comrade. "How'd you get here?"

"My mother turned me in."

"Saw that coming." Beppo smiles her lazy smile. The freckles dance on her nose. "How'd she whip it on you?"

Frankie is evasive.

"I was away in South Mackay Street two days."

" 'Stubborn child'?"

"Yeah—'stubborn child.' I was too much for her, and she had to turn me over to the white folks."

"Aren't *you* swingin'?" Beppo looks reflective.

Frankie feels like boasting about how tough she is, although she sees extended the image of Opaline, lying at her most beautiful on the bed in Frankie's room, her head shuddering, the long dark hair swaying to the floor with the intense vibration of her neck. This image seems to force her into silence.

With a motion of artificial kindness, Beppo puts her hand on the bars and says gently: "Stick it, kid . . . It's not so bad."

"When am I going to get *outa* here?" Frankie asks.

"You're a spade," Beppo says, "you'd better not get *in*."

"Whitey got you, he got you good," Frankie admits obediently, playing the old game. But at the moment she isn't really interested in the white man's injustices. She looks up at Beppo with those dark eyes which, like ponds under evening skies, swim with a subdued light. Beppo responds to that gaze, but her glance is both receptive and cynical, as if she were summing up Frankie's capacity to be a victim, weighing the independence and the energy in that wiry little body, the bowed legs, the elongated fingers, thinking of what pleasure she might get from subduing it.

"What you got there?" she said, pointing to her friend's arm. Frankie stares at the little heart on her inner forearm which, while she was shut up in St. Ursula's, she had tattooed with the help of a pin and a bottle of ink. The heart is carefully shaped, as well done as the artist, Francesca Ford, could do it, and there is the name 'Lacey' pricked out in the center of it.

"I did it at St. Ursula's Home."

"So you did, baby." Beppo casts her a knowing glance, her smile with its touch of cruelty, mocking this infantile effort. (Later, in another and longer-lasting confinement, and when time has further unfolded the male in both their natures, Beppo is to write this way to Frankie: "*Can you meet my stiff and heavy requirements? There will be no bucking each other. I am aware that you can play the hard role also, but you will have with me no mind of your own . . . I captivate your mind as well as your body.*"

. . . But now she only glances with a smile at the immature inked-in heart on the younger girl's arm, and promises: "Someday —*I'll* cut my name on you."

He told his wife that if Frankie ran around the streets like that, she would bring home a baby. His wife, Alva Ford, told William that *he* could start getting rid of *his* extra women and so set a good example. And Frankie escaped from the house and ran through back streets to the *Encantada*, the gathering place of the Blue Notes, an elastic ever-expanding and always-changing group which had served during the last ten years the musical and social needs of the elite of the teen-agers of Moon and Gregory streets.

Here Larry Luigi and his brother, Salvatore, were waiting for her, Larry having promised to pay her in Wild Rose wine the $2.00 he owed her and to take her to the Riviera on his motorbike —during the course of which program, the whole gang might foregather at Ginger's pad for an hour, to practice the numbers they were supposed to contribute in the high school auditorium on the following Saturday night.

"If you don't like my friends I'll leave," Frankie had threatened her father two days before when he had told her to stop fucking around with that integrated group, because some trouble would come of it.

"I don't like you to be out there with the white folks," he told her now. "I don't like that intermixin' girl, that's what I don't like." Coming from Georgia, William had been well trained in the dangers of integration.

"The Blue Notes is not intermixin'," Frankie cried, "and this is no Atlanta, Georgia . . . It's North City, and I'm as good as they are."

"It's not intermixin', I'd like to know what that 'fay Luigi doin' in your room, along with young Loper Robinson and Ginger Norris and the Sánchez girl?"

"We're not *doing* anything, Papa!"

"You're crazy girl! No good'll come of it."

"No good'll come of acting like a dumb Southern nigger either!" she cried. The group was all that she had, and now she thinks he wants to take it away from her. "Don't you shape your mouth on me," her father said as he had said before, advancing on her with his arm raised (Frankie representing his own inadequate past). "Don't shape your mouth, girl. The thing was brought to light when your mother found those friends going out the window. Why don't they go like they come in? Eh?" His mouth was set in the murderous line which Frankie feared, and she shrank back into the corner of the room, saying, "Daddy"—imploring, relieved to see her mother come between them, her face fatigued, her eyes half shut as if she were praying. "You keep outa this, Alva . . ." her husband stuttered. "K-k-k-k-kee-ep out I say." He needed to hit Frankie, as he needed to go on living. "You don't understand the girl . . . She lying to you right and left . . . You a *sucker* for her . . ."

"I try to point you both in the straight and narrow path," Alva said meaningfully. Over the head of their daughter, she told him with her reproachful eyes what the doctor had told her two days ago, what she had suffered because of him, and how *his* tongue also was swollen with lies. "After so many witnesses and so many prophecies," she said, "if the wicked do not see nor heed, I can only rest in the Lord . . ."

"L-l-l-leave the L-l-lord outa this, too," William cried.

"You stumble, William," Alva told him, her arm still holding him back as if she were an avenging angel. "You stumble around doing right and wrong at the same time . . . You'll not live saved that way . . ."

. . . Frankie escaped. She ran down the back alleys to the *Encantada*, delighted with her success, but heavy-hearted because of her mother. When he was in such a mood, he sometimes beat her mother instead of her, and as she ran, she seemed to see her mother's face crumple up under the force of his hand. Guilt filled her like a dark heavy liquid which penetrated into and destroyed her joy, and which yet seemed to drive her further and further into what her mother called sin, and sent her jitterbugging with Salvatore on this particular evening until long after midnight; and then drinking the debt owed her in Wild Rose wine, so that she was perched at last, almost insensible, on the back of Larry's motorbike.

It had begun to happen when she was only twelve years old. In the bathroom where she washes Rosina's face and instructs Bobo to pick up his clothes and hang them in the closet, she sees her father's head reflected in the little spotted mirror which hangs on the equally spotted wall. She knows that his bloodshot gaze has wandered vacantly because he has come from the bar at the corner, where he has been drinking with the white woman with the weary, carroty hair. She knows that each step to the house has been heavy and uncertain, that there is something in his brain, an insistent insect, a worm of disorder . . . The head vanishes . . . the steps blunder in the kitchen . . . "He all beered up," she remarks to Rosina who gazes fearfully, trustfully toward Frankie's twelve-year-old strength. "He gonna beat us up," Rosina murmurs.

"No he's not either. He not gonna beat on *us*." Frankie is filled with a genuine fear, not only for the younger children but for the integrity of her own body, so long threatened. "He not gonna have a chance, because we're goin' over Salvatore's and Larry's, that's why. If he lifts one finger . . ." Frankie threatens dramatically, pulling Rosina's pajama top over her head, "we put on our coats and go on over, pajamas an' all."

"Salvatore's mother hates niggers," announces the precocious Rosina.

Frankie, not yet ready to proclaim herself Spanish as she does later on, accepts the truth of Rosina's remark. "We go up to the top floor by the fire escape," she says, "that how we always do.

Larry and me, we climb up to the top floor where the boys sleep, and she too fat to climb up after. She weigh all of 250 pounds."

In the kitchen William Ford plays with the coal stove until the fire's almost out. Habit alone makes him stop in time. In the chilling room he is fire itself, the energy in his short intense black body turned inward to carve out a smoldering abyss. He looks at his daughter as if she has already grown, understanding his own evil.

"You no good, girl," he warns her, advancing toward her, "You no good."

"Keep back, Daddy," Francesca tells him, "keep back."

"You gonna feel my hand," he threatens as he stumbles forward, "running the streets like that . . . a no-good dog . . . a little bitch . . ."

Francesca waits no longer, feeling her weakness before this onslaught, retreating to the back room, bundling the children into their coats, aware of a strange, sad love for him, as if she could only be happy once she had fallen into those treacherous and strong black arms. "We gotta get out," she is muttering to the children, but the hysterical flight is mixed with desire, the desire for him to chase and catch her, and so end the suspense forever . . .

In the morning when her heavily lidded eyes seem more deeply carved than ever into her coffee-colored face, the teacher, teetering on unsteady heels, leans a motherly bosom over the school desk.

"Now Francesca dear, don't dream like that. It's daytime now, dear. We are going to write a little essay on how to budget our time . . . Are you all ready at the back there? Do you all have your pencils and papers, children? . . . Good . . ." The teacher's well-rested face, with its blond nest of hair rolled in great hairpinned curls, nods above Frankie's desk, and the kind blue eyes shine with enthusiasm as her voice sweeps through the room, gathering the scattered attention of her pupils. "Now I want each of you to write down what you feel to be the best way of budgeting the time allotted for homework. All right LeRoi in the corner there, are you ready? Richard? Susannah? I'll let you have ten minutes to do this in." Her voice slows down, becomes empathic and precise. "How-can-I-budget-my-time-after-school so-that-I-have-enough-time-for-my-homework-and-my-recreation."

Francesca's sleepless head nods. She collects herself and begins to write eagerly: *"It is all very easy to talk about budgeting your time, but in my house you couldn't do this. My mother works and I have to go home and see that the kids are back from school and get their supper; and then get my father his supper. He will come in between six and eight all beered up and in an ugly mood; and then when he begins to beat on us, we have to get out the back door and go up to Larry and Salvatore Luigi's roof."* Having written this she pauses, and some instinct of adult caution warns her not to expatiate about how she is able to budget for 'recreation,' recreation which is provided for by the simple expedient of staying up the greater part of the night. There, in the bare dirty rooms on the Luigi's top floor, while Rosina and Bobo sleep beside her, Frankie helps Larry make his zip guns, and listens to his boasting tales of drinking, stealing, and hanging out. It is important that she should be a little cleverer and tougher than Larry, and that she should cling as long as possible to the edge she has gained by being leader of the Vivaldos. It is as if some premonition of her fate stands over her, urging her fingers to make a better zip gun, her tongue to coin a newer and more obscene word. Larry's long-chinned face, blotched and good-natured, is protective only as long as she clings to this gamin character and holds the whip-hand of the gang. Beyond that, it is to be feared.

. . . Now, two years later, she is telling him incoherently that she is too drunk to go home.

"I can't go, Larry," she shrieked above the night wind that whipped past their ears. "He'd hang me, I tell you . . . I'll go to Ginger's."

"You can't go to Ginger's," Larry shrieked back. "Her boyfriend's there . . . I'll take you to my mother's."

"No, don't take me to your mother's, Larry—she hates me."

"She don't *hate* you, man," Larry muttered. "She's prejudiced, that's all."

"I won't go then," Frankie said, feeling the wind dry the tears on her cheeks, "but I won't go home either." She had for a moment, a vision of the street as actively hostile, as forcibly rejecting her. To protect her face from the wind she buried it in the back of Larry's jacket, and soon she felt the motor-bike turning and heard him say: "I know what, you can stay at Vito's—he got a good pad and he's not home now. He's up to Murmaine County."

"How'll we get in?" she asked in discomfort, seeing that they were heading east.

"I gotta key."

"How you gotta key?"

"I gotta key, man."

Later, Frankie never quite admitted that it had happened. She had brought it upon herself, she realized, and this she was too intelligent to waste time in refuting. At the same time, she felt bitterness and repugnance, a certain bewilderment, as if somewhere along the line she had known grace, but that grace had been denied her. Her mother's belief in the miraculous had become hers, and this event, therefore, had the force of a dream . . . Now, dark room, dark window, the smell of wine and cigarettes, and Larry, her companion, after a brief contact with her body (not so much in union as in betrayal) gone on his motorcycle, leaving the night full of harshness and noise. Afterwards she was always to say that she hated big men 'beating' on her, and that she couldn't bear men to touch her breasts—that anyway her mother had told her that if men touched her breasts they would give her cancer.

But the truth was that she had suffered more from a lack of touching than from touching itself, from a hasty and violent sex act which had been more of a gratuitous insult than an introduction to love, and had indeed no chance of drawing by clever caresses the sleeping woman from her body. Afterwards she lay in a dream of fatigue, only getting up from the bed to guard herself against a hostile world by putting the chain across the door. But an hour later the window opened stealthily and she felt on the bed beside her the clambering clumsy form of another creature of the night, her fingers touching the chill surface of another leather jacket, a voice like Larry's but not quite the same, urging her to be quiet, and when she struggled and protested, another male hand similar but different—Salvatore's hand—upon her mouth. In shadowy terror she felt twin events become one.

On the second day she left the room, begged a nickel from a woman at the subway station, and went back toward home and Moon Street, stopping on the way at the police station, a small Negro girl, thin and forlorn-looking, but extraordinarily verbal, telling as if in solace to her terrified heart an improbable story of being abducted at knife point, and being kept by masked men in a shack at Riviera Beach.

From this time on, the street becomes Frankie's home. She accepts an idea long ago indirectly suggested, the idea that the street is for the tough and the free, that the harm that has been done her has its compensations, that those bonds binding her to her family are, in any case, soiled, frayed, and soon to be broken. She realizes that the figures of Larry and Salvatore—wooden, emotionless, inevitable—had long stood in some niche in her intimate life; and she begins to know the night as she knew it in that tunnel of darkness traversed on the back of Larry's bike, bearing her for the first time from her own turf, and into the territory of the adult enemy. Here her defenses were broken. Here in the land of the outlaw she accepted her characteristic role, became one with those who violated her. The boy's belt, studded with brass buttons which held up her jeans, was unbuckled by hasty hands, and her immature narrow legs parted for Larry's satisfaction, and afterwards—still in darkness and silence—for his brother's. But as if nothing had happened, as if this hasty act in a foreign bedroom had been without meaning, as it had been without direction, Frankie (the tears like brief dew falling on the desert, staining and drying on her cheeks) buckled the belt again and walked the streets as before, once a boy amongst boys, and now studying to be a man amongst men.

—————————

*Between the generations great gulfs open out. One mother knows
so little about what her daughter is doing that she lives for a
whole year under the same roof without realizing that this quiet
girl (who goes to bed at nine o'clock) is hooked on heroin. When
it appears that her daughter is pregnant (from prostituting in the
afternoons to support her habit), she cries defensively, "As long
as I have breath in my body . . . the house is hers. You wouldn't
believe the respect I get from my daughter. I never heard her say
damn in this house."*

*And only when she knows at last that her daughter is an ad-
dict, does her voice despair. "The mother is the last to know . . ."*

*Frankie's mother, too, struggles to believe. She pretends that
her daughter's indifferent marks at school are more important
than her husband's unfaithfulness or Frankie's rebellion. "If the
apathy could be less constant," she murmurs. And then, turning
on the TV set, and watching the international spotlight play upon
the poor quality of the teachers at Moon Street High, she comments quietly: "Even Premier Khrushchev can see how this distresses education!"*

The grilled iron gates embossed with golden crosses open from
the wide busy street into a garden, which in May shows rank
grass and sunless beds of ivy. The heavy wooden door, also protected against nameless evil by the mark of the cross, has a peep-
hole through which the bland eyes of nuns inspect—before the
latch is opened—those who would enter the highly polished hallway and sit where yet another cross is placed, like triple protection, above a solid bench of cedar . . . Inside, the robes of the
nuns rustle along the silent corridors . . . a crucifix looms with
its pale yellow and tortured form bent upon it . . . a pattern of
black-and-white linoleum suggests the marble of foreign refecto-
ries. Somewhere far away little bells tinkle faintly and there
comes, like the reply to an eternal question, the smothered and
reassuring sound of chanting. God has been invoked, and his serv-
ants have received the assurance of this invocation. As the linoleum has been polished in the very early morning, the solid silver

doves beneath the picture of the Madonna, rubbed to dazzling brightness, so have the voices been called forth at this later hour, and the correct replies obtained. For a time at least, until that next moment when a new step of the ritual is required, and must be forthcoming, all is ceremonious and safe, in St. Ursula's Home for Wayward Girls.

Sister Monica leads the little group of three along the passages, stopping to bow her head before the statue of the home's patron saint, beneath whose image is written in letters of gold "SISTER MARGARET ASCENCIA PRAY FOR US." The passage whispers to the tread of the girls' black sneakers, and to the swish of their black pleated skirts. Their faces bob above the blackness like disembodied flowers, and Ginger, who is Italian and superstitious, bends her head and prays to St. Margaret, as Sister Monica has done. Frankie, however, keeps her head high, whispering to Lacey, whose fair profile turns from side to side, "I'm not *their* religion, and *I'm* not gonna bow to the *lady*."

In the dormitory Sister Monica supervises them while they make their beds properly, showing them how to smooth the edges down with exactitude, and how to fold the corners in like an envelope. All the beds now appear as smooth marble gravestones. Here again Frankie is recalcitrant, until Lacey offers to do it for her, and she finds herself motivated to reply belligerently, "I can do it well as you, Lacey—ef I want to," and at once proceeds to demonstrate, while Sister Monica murmurs approvingly, "A clever little Francesca," and looks at her with a glance so completely wedded to love that Francesca turns subdued. As if someone had touched her on the shoulder (an angel perhaps) and had said to her: "Frankie, you are saved!"

Filled with this sense of the world's love, she, too, seeks to express it, but in the only way she knows. She turns to Lacey while they both hang up their pajamas in the communal closet, and says: "Lacey, honey—tonight we'll have a pajama party—okay?" "Okay," Lacey whispers back, nervous and giggling in the haven of the nightclothes and dressing gowns hanging about them, conscious of her youngness in front of Frankie, and respecting Frankie tremendously for her open defiance of the nuns.

"I'm glad you're here with me, Frankie . . . I love you." "I love you, too, honey," Frankie whispers back generously, "I sure do." And under the cloak of the closet door she strokes Lacey's fair thin soft-as-silk hair, the hair of a child-fairy never to be a woman. "Don't you worry, doll, I'll look after you." Lacey over-joyed, whispers back: "April loves you, too—she tole me; and Euphemia she's *mad* about you, Frankie. She knows someone who knows you in Moon Street." "You're kiddin'. She does? . . ." Frankie lapses into her laconic mood again, aware of Sister Monica's quiet advance toward the closet. "Euphemia, a smart cat," she announces stepping boldly out and colliding accidentally-on-purpose with the black serge and the white starched armor of Sister Monica's habit, "a smart cat—Oh, sorry, Sister," she says gaily, her teeth gleaming in her dark face. "I'm just not together this mawnin', jus' not together!"

The nuns, whose disciplines are major ones, hover over their charges with the concentration of animals in cages with their young. Where God is the keeper, his word, even translated through bars, is law. The prayers at mid-morning support Sister Bertha in the schoolroom, but to the diverse group of girls, gath-ered from various city slums, the prayers are, even to the Catho-lics, unnecessary—and to the others, so much gibberish. Frankie, proud of her Evangelism, has eyes for something a little bit racier, but her only square prowess is intellectual, so that she learns the prayers faster than the others, and earns kudos accordingly, be-sides rolling occasional Latin phrases off her tongue with the fer-vor of a musician. When 'Indoctrination' gives place to letter writing, however, emotion takes over, and soon big tears are roll-ing down her dark cheeks as she bends over the single sheet of paper, her hand gripping the pen with a concentration which takes her back to Moon Street, to a freedom which seems clear and intense now that she has lost it. *"Dearest Mama— I'm home-sick. I want to come home and be with you and Daddy. I don't want to sit here day after day and* ROT. *I can't stand it and I will run away . . ."* If the tears welling from her eyes hesitate on her tilted cheekbones, they are collected near her mouth by the tip of her tongue, so that she seems to drink her grief, even while she writes out her doubts and inadequacies. "*I keep getting into trouble . . . because I laugh and talk too much and even when we watch TV Mother Mary Maria makes me sit near her because of my cheap talk . . . Nobody wants me, even* YOU *won't let me come home. You put me in here, Mama, so I'm not sure that you care anyway . . .*"

This letter (like most of those letters in which the internees, big and little, attempt to deal with their real fears and grievances) is censored by the good sisters, and never reaches its destination.

. . . Here in the home, the supper hour is known as the 'Collation'; and this brings more prayers, a general call for a blessing and a practical demand to ignore the quality of the meal itself, and to offer up enjoyment of it to God. "Bless us Father for these thy gifts," leads the Sister, "which we are about to receive from thy bounty, through Jesus Christ Our Lord."

"*Amen*," intone the girls . . . And in the ensuing silence the forks clatter on the plates.

Mother Mary Maria sits on the highest platform in the room, swathed like a mummy in her black and white clothes. She eats sparingly, and with the sparse chewing of her jaws, her little yellow monkey-like face moves in contemplative rhythm. Like—Frankie thinks—someone already in a coffin, and this thought is so in opposition to what she, Frankie, has been brought up to think of as suitable religious conduct, that she whispers to the ever-absorbing Lacey, the fatal words: "Mother Mary Maria, she chew like she tired o' life." Unfortunately, this comment is overheard by Sister Bertha, who first murmurs to the Holy Mother, then leads Francesca by the shoulder, and in front of the whole silent room, forces her to kneel at the foot of the platform, on which stands the table of the sisters of the order.

"You must commit an act of penance," Sister Bertha commands in a stage whisper. "Kneel—put your hands together—and tell the Mother Superior that you are sorry."

"Kneel?" protests Frankie, already kneeling.

"Put your hands together."

"Like she some *queen?*" Frankie cries, now truly amazed. (Crying, singing, proclaiming one's sins—that she understands—

but this kneeling in humility is another thing.) "I can't *tell* the lady," she says defiantly.

The Sister is frowning. "Kneel—until you feel grace."

"I don't feel *nothing*," says Frankie sullenly. But her protest is swallowed in the silence, in the faint tinkle of silver on china, in the subdued quiet of her contemporaries, in the controlled accustomed withdrawal of the nuns . . .

And at three o'clock that afternoon when an unexpected visit from Frankie's grandmother—Mrs. Wilhemina Tobey—broke all precedence in the home, Mother Mary Maria was able to look back on the incident during Collation, and to wonder whether Frankie's presence amongst them was necessarily desirable.

"Greetings in the name of Christ," Frankie's grandmother had said. She was an extremely tall thin woman, with a beaked nose, a light-brown skin, and a great bush of white kinky hair. (Linking herself with the missions in Africa, she liked to wear her hair in its natural state.) She affected the brisk practical clothes of a traveling Evangelist, and she seemed to have arrived only that morning by air from Chicago, since for evidence she was holding her airplane ticket, and was busily explaining that her concern about Francesca had been great enough to bring her home at once.

"Francesca's parents have no sense," she declared, sitting upright on a great refectory chair, "and I've come to claim my child."

"As I understand it, Francesca's mother sought help," Mother Mary Maria replied gently. "And the youth board have committed her to us."

Mrs. Wilhemina Tobey, who had a perpetually angry and haughty air, protested: "The child has always prayed to live with me. Her father has a record before her, and I have written proof of the horrors she has been subjected to. Yes, I am a traveling missionary . . . As a churchwoman yourself, you will appreciate the fact that I am saved, and that the child Francesca will be brought up with Christian training . . . In Chicago, our group is taking over a camp, and until quarters are ready there, I can put her into the YWCA."

Mother Mary Maria leaned forward and Mrs. Wilhemina

Tobey leaned forward, too. For a moment expressing all the pathos of evolution, one small yellow monkey-like face communed with another somewhat darker monkey-like face. And then Mother Mary Maria asked: "Do I understand you to say, Mrs. Tobey, that you have the custody of Francesca?"

"No, I have no custody," the child's grandmother admitted, "but I have heard this morning that she was raped by two Italians and that these men got off with a $50 fine . . . I shall reopen the case . . . I shall claim custody . . . Besides," the slight but wiry woman sat back with a defiant attitude strangely reminiscent of Francesca's own, "I claim her *soul.*"

Mother Mary Maria sighed. She was not accustomed to quarrel with the case records of girls turned over to the home by the youth board, but she knew enough about them to perceive that the real story often looked, as a ghost might, over the shoulder of the one already presented. "Whatever the facts of the case are," she said to Mrs. Tobey, "St. Ursula's Home acts as a refuge only, and we cannot determine custody. On the other hand, if what you say about her father is true . . ."

"It's true," Mrs. Tobey announced briefly, "he's a dog . . ."

Mother Mary Maria was reflecting that it was already evident that Francesca was likely to be a troublesome guest, and that St. Ursula's was far from equipped to deal with open rebels, especially with Evangelistic rebels, whose defiance put in question the whole problem of religious freedom. If Mrs. Tobey could provide a new background—however inadequate by true Catholic standards—it might indeed be better for Frankie than was her own home. And she, Mother Mary Maria, might be able to help to bring this viewpoint before the authorities—thus, with a sense of virtue as well as with a clear conscience, getting rid of a difficult charge.

"So," she inquired sympathetically, leaning forward again, "you are a traveling Evangelist?"

"Since 1930," her visitor said briskly. "It's a good thing I am saved, and can tell Jesus everything, or I'd be sick and famishing for want of food . . . Yes, with me Francesca will not want, but I must get her out of the county as quickly as possible . . ."

"Out of the county?" inquired Mother Mary Maria.

"It's a nasty place," the old lady said, a faraway look in her eyes, as she rocked to and fro in her chair, "a nasty place. The Baptists are nasty and the Methodists are nasty, and I don't trust those dogs one minute . . ." Her attention lapsed and Mother Mary Maria felt nonplussed, realizing that family situations are generally more complicated than one would think, and that Francesca Ford had not only an unstable father, and a somewhat helpless mother, but a decidedly queer grandmother as well.

"I don't know what we can do," she said tactfully, "but I will look into it and in the meantime I am sure you would like to see Francesca." She tinkled the little bell at her side.

"I intend to take the child with me," Mrs. Tobey said rather unrealistically. "I'll telephone the Attorney General if necessary, and I'll get her over the state lines as quickly as possible . . . They're waiting to strike me . . . and they're even breaking open my mail . . . but Jesus has told me that I have this child to save."

"We must talk it over," said Mother Mary Maria soothingly, "and in the meantime I'll have Sister Bertha send Francesca to you . . ."

That night when the lights were out, the defiance of Frankie the "newcomer," and her own accounts of her grandmother's promise to alert the Attorney General's office, had made her an interesting figure in the dormitory, where imitation heads took the place of real ones in the beds and where, under canopies draped with down-hanging sheets, the girls had gathered to draw closer to each other, to wreathe their faces in the smoke of smuggled cigarettes, and to float upon that dream of liberty which intoxicates more surely than liberty itself.

The moonlight flooded the stone walls and penetrated through the high windows, turning the line of washbasins into silver, freezing the folds of the girls' pajamas into the sculptured folds of Roman togas, making upon the walls flowers of shadow more delicate than the flowers of day. The girls under the beds talked of their homes and their loves, their escapades and their defiances, while at the light of the moon, and with the help of pins and a bottle of ink, the more adept of them pricked little tattooes into their soft young flesh . . . It was May, the time when the year turns openly toward summer; and in these female bodies, precocious but for the greater part still virgin, sexual desire took the form of immature intimations, or the more refined forms of hysteria. The two members of the group who were already pregnant and awaiting transfer to Taselldone, were naturally considered experts, though in each case it had been ignorance rather than knowledge which had catapulted them into pregnancy, and their information was still so inaccurate that one of them claimed a Virgin birth to be really possible ("Honest, there was a girl in our street who knew that she was that way, though she'd never done it, or never even been down for a guy") and the other claimed that VD was more easily caught in the summer than in the winter ("Because in summer you're all hot and everything, and my girl friend, Jeannie, she got it in August and said that through that month she felt flushed up"). Frankie took no part in this discussion, deeply ashamed as she was of the episode with Larry and Salvatore, and feeling that because her body had been as tense and resistant after the episode as before it, nothing had really happened to her. She knew herself an uncaptured citadel, successfully repulsing the enemy, and her emotions remained knotted there in the tangle of sheets where Beppo and Opaline had loved and struggled . . . Now she put her cheek against Lacey's (several of the girls were being equally affectionate) and said: "I dig you, honey," while Lacey, even smaller and thinner than Frankie herself, and subject to epileptic fits as well, answered: "I dig you, too, Frankie. I dig you a lot."

"I like to feel your lips next to mine," Frankie, the reader, improvised hastily, and Lacey asked, timidly leaning against Frankie's shoulder: "Wasn't it awful when Sister Monica nearly caught us in the closet today?"

"Don't you worry, honeybunch," Frankie reassured her. "She won't catch us, and when we get outa here, you can come straight to my house."

"Can I, Frankie? I got nowhere, really."

"Sure can. I'm gonna protect you from now on," Frankie replied bravely.

And the next day, when—as a punishment for minor disobedience in the classroom—she was shut up with her schoolbooks in a little room near Sister Agatha's office, she whiled away the time by writing a letter to Lacey in which she promised that she would tattoo Lacey's name on her forearm and that they would be together "in the street."

"*I'm so happy I'm making you happy,*" she wrote. "*To say the least I dig you an awful lot and if you take off without me, and go somewhere where I'll never find you, I think I'll die. I want us to be together, and I've got to protect you . . . because Lacey, you're like the world's sugar lump, and all the world's sweet because of you. You can come right to my house when you get out, and we'll be together all the time. Doll, your troubles are over from this moment . . . I love you and April and Euphemia. But I love you and dig you the most, and send you all of my undivided love.*" After some thought she ended the letter as her mother might have done, "*God bless you and keep you always.*"

In the prison cot at Henry Street, Baby lived in an eternity of her flesh. She examined her toes and poked at her toenails, from which the scarlet nail polish was slowly peeling off. She scratched the soles of her feet, soles once hardy from running barefoot at the Catholic Camp in the summertime but now soft and unattractive. If she felt dissatisfied with her body it was more because it was not up to standard at the moment than because she thought it inadequate. In fact, she had an admiration for her large, full, ruddy, and coarse-skinned body, which like a sack, shaped in the classic female form, and filled with the rosy liquid of her blood, stretched out on the narrow prison cot, and seemed to overpower the cell, to say that bars were weak and temporary, to proclaim that life was everything. With her long, painted, but slightly grubby fingernails, she scratched the back of her neck and as far as she could reach downward—then scratched her shoulders until she had left upon them long, red savage marks. Pushing against the mattress, she saw with vague pride how her round breasts made hills through the thin material of her nightgown, and how the nipples were continually erect, like the spikes of flowers that pushed out of the earth. Lying like this on her back, alone and melancholy for so much of the day, she looked to this body of hers to bear her company, inspected it with anxiety and care for cuts, bruises, and signs of illness—and lived again through times when she had defended it from harm, as another might reconstruct emotional stress, or financial difficulty. Quietly, with a broken comb in her hand, she swept through her long black hair with gentle, passive strokes, and when it hung around her in a coarse shining curtain, she might sit there for a while with her face hidden, as if she were enveloped in a tent, which had sprung from the crown of her own head. And only as her blue eyes grew melancholy and as fresh terrors pierced the cell's quiet would she feel for the sharpened nail file in her mattress and run its edge against her fingers . . .

If it grew hot in the cell, she would throw everything off her but the sheet, and feel up and down the inside of her thighs, and around the bush of dark coarse hair between them, where so much of her life had centered, ever since the time that the boy had seduced her on the sofa at Rachel's, and had told her, in what had seemed a brutal tone, but which had had in it all the same overtones of tenderness, to 'open her legs' . . . Baby would turn on the narrow cot in the cell and lie on her face. Her confused eyes would be closed, her hair would hang as Pug Nose's had, down over the edge of the cot, and almost to the floor. In those five cells there had been three girls with short hair, and two with long. Now Baby was the only one with long hair, the only one who was a broad. Yet, when the blood moved through her veins and began to warm her to a state of familiar sick restlessness, it was of Rachel that she thought, and not of King (not because King had never satisfied her physically, but because more often he had hurt her and had sent her out into those dangerous night streets). But Rachel had never hurt her, or so she thought, and in the untidy bedroom, filled with time-payment furniture and the paraphernalia of her illegitimate children—cribs, diapers, little sweaters, plastic bottles, and woolly dogs, as well as brassières and deodorants, hair rollers and lipsticks, discarded aprons, sexy novels, and stockings with runs in them—Rachel had sometimes made love to her, until it seemed to Baby that the physical world tightened around her, built up to a pitch of tingling and tense expectancy, and then at last exploded in a confusion of spreading molten light.

Relaxed and unafraid afterward, like a coarse wide-open and ravished flower, Baby, when asked if she had liked it, was able to say to Rachel, gravely, seriously, as she had never been able to say to King: "It seems wonderful to me, Rachel. It makes the world . . . everything around you . . . it all seems changed."

Miss Green, who is on duty again, avoids Frankie's cell and gives scant attention to Beppo's (this last, as she tells her colleagues, because she hates to see "that girl, strutting around"). She is sympathetic, however, to Baby and to Harry, especially to the latter, whom she has seen sitting at meals in absolute silence, and lying on her back on the cot in her cell, staring for hours on end at the ceiling. With her usual conscientiousness, Miss Green feels that something should be done about this, but she herself can think of nothing else to do but to force the girl to join in the recreation session held downstairs in the dining room each day.

"Harriet," she says, therefore, as Harriet struggles slowly to a sitting position and turns drugged blue eyes toward the bars, "you mustn't just lie like that dear. It won't get you out of here, you know . . . Come, I'm going to take you down to Recreation."

Harriet looks at her, seeing only the form of a woman in a white nylon uniform, and answering automatically: "I don't want to go to Recreation."

"I think you should, Harriet."

"I can't."

"Why?"

"I'm sick."

"You're sick?" Miss Green feels all the alarm of the hygiene-centered.

"Yes." Harriet's voice is soft but resistant.

"Well, we must take you down to the nurse," Miss Green counters.

"Leave me alone," Harriet says more aggressively.

Experiencing a moment's insight into that alien fortress world so familiar to Harriet, Miss Green unlocks the cell and enters it to sit for a moment on the bed.

"What is it then?" she asks.

"I don't like them to watch me."

"The girls, or the staff?"

"All of them."

"They'll watch more if you stay in *here* all the time."

Harriet doesn't answer. She is not resentful of Miss Green's presence, but it makes her feel uncomfortable.

"Would you like some magazines?"

"No."

"No kind at all?"

Grudgingly Harriet admits: "I only like *Popular Mechanics*."

"*Popular Mechanics!* Well—perhaps they've got some over on the male side."

A faint warmth lights Harriet's eyes, and she looks guardedly at the woman beside her. "I like to read about cars."

Miss Green, who has not yet seen Harriet's record, asks her. "Have you got a car?"

"Not now."

"What happened to it?"

"We were arrested for speeding, and the cops took it because they said it was in bad condition. I tried to find out what they did with it but the screws wouldn't tell me."

Miss Green winces at the word 'screw,' and hears Harriet's sad voice going on: "Marie and I worked on it all summer . . ."

"I see . . . but you're not here for speeding?"

"No . . . Marie and I spent two nights in the jail in Killian while they contacted our parents, and when they let us out we picked up another one."

"Another car?"

"Yes. Out of a parking lot."

These replies are given with more willingness than is apparent, but unfortunately Miss Green returns to the moralistic approach, saying with evident surprise: "Well now . . . what do you *expect?* Stealing cars! You can't go round doing that, you know," at which Harriet returns to her old quiet, and refuses to talk further or, in spite of Miss Green's reiterated pleas, to go down to the recreation room.

"We'll have to consult the superintendent," Miss Green says finally. "It's not a bit good for you," and she adds in a tone of faint irritation that she will send over to the male side and try to get her a few copies of *Popular Mechanics.* "Though they don't seem very interesting to me."

Harriet looks up hopefully and her lips part as if to express gratitude, but the habit of years predominates and she remains silent.

"Wouldn't you rather have the *Ladies' Home Journal?*"

"No." Harriet shoots her a swift and almost pitying look. *How to explain to a woman who puts green plastic earrings in her ears, and wears a bunch of imitation lilies of the valley pinned at the throat of her uniform, that* Popular Mechanics *is a beautiful magazine?* "I don't like the *Ladies' Home Journal*—I don't like all that crap!"

Unskillfully, the officer contributes: "There are some lovely stories in the *Ladies' Home Journal.*"

———————

Baby watches Miss Green as she passes her cell, and waits impatiently for her to go upstairs so that she can continue the catalog of her sorrows.

"I sure wish she'd go," she complains to Frankie.

In a laconic voice Frankie agrees: "Too bad she don't let the wind hit her in the ass!"

"Them jive rollers!" Brenda turns on a sad smile and leans against the cell bars.

"Oh Frankie, they juggin' with me . . ."

"Juggin' with you?'

"Sure . . . they put my bond too high."

"That your mother, Baby," Frankie suggests, "she see the judge."

"Maybe it's Pa. He'd of croaked me if he'd knew what I did when I wuz younger."

"Didn't he ever get hip to it?"

"Are you kiddin'? It was go to Mass, go to Confession. Live right . . ." Brenda's voice takes on a mocking half-angry tone. "Ma's got her little smarts, but never any *information*—she let me find it out in the street, that's what she did. An' Pa'd always say he'd scar me. He called me everything but a child of God." A ponderous sigh shakes her. "I wish they'd hurry up and give me my day in court. It gets next to me being in here."

"Maybe your mother thinks you got a lesson coming to you . . . Maybe that's why she's not here to see you? That's why my mother's not here I know. My grandmother got me outa St. Ursula's Home by calling the Attorney General's office" (although Frankie knows better, she still pretends that the Attorney General himself has interceded for her). "I jumped bail, and that's why my mother won't come to see me. She'll pray for me . . . and she'll write to me . . . but she won't come to see me. She says the Lord has a reason for my being here."

Brenda's rather slow mind grapples with this philosophy, and fears that her own sins, too, are preordained. "I'm going to write Ma a letter," she suddenly threatens. "I'm going to say: '*Dear Ma— Just a few lines to say I'm lousy, and I hope you are the same.*' "

Frankie lolls against the wall of the cell, producing one of her contraband cigarette butts. "Did she turn you in this time?"

"No—but I ran from Wentworth and my mother told them about King."

"Who's King?"

"I told you about King," Brenda said. "He's colored."

"Oh sure you did. You like the colored?"

"Yes I do, Frankie," Baby says in her soft earnest voice. "I don't see nothing wrong with them, that's it. I mean I'm Irish and the Irish are prejudiced . . . But somehow I don't go for prejudice . . ." She stumbles over her words a little, afraid to hurt Frankie. "They say I'm retarded," she adds. "I don't know, I never did like school too good, and my brother Dennis, he calls me 'Tardy.' "

"You're all right, Baby," Frankie soothes her. "You're all right."

"D'you think I'm crazy, Frankie?"

"No, honey, you're swell."

"King says I'm all right . . . You see, King turned me out. I never knew what he did for a job, and he'd always say he was in the Blue Notes . . ."

"The *Blue Notes?*" Frankie is excited. "Why, Baby—that's *my* gang. I was in the Blue Notes."

"You *was?* Since when?"

"Last two years . . . all over . . . singin' with the group and everything. Was King Whitfield turned you out?"

"Sure—you know him?"

"Since he was *ten!*" Frankie's voice has the emphasis of one who has at last found a level for communication. It's clear now that Brenda is linked up to her by the closest of ties. "King—why he's my *heart*," she says without much attention to truth. "King Whitfield, why he was a senior when I was a freshman and tops in the high jump. He'd sing in all the performances." (That he'd 'turned Baby out'—which Frankie understood was an immoral performance—scarcely mattered in view of the fact that he was such a competent member in the gang.) "So your mother knows he turned you out?"

"No . . ." Baby hesitates. As Frankie is not proud of the episode with Larry and Salvatore, Baby is not proud of the period when King put her on the street. "No . . . she never knew *that* or she'd of killed him . . . My mother's prejudiced. She doesn't like me having colored friends . . . She calls them half-breeds. And when I ran from Wentworth and I'd just got outa Secure, one of the officers found a note from King, telling me an address in Leland."

"So the police go *there?*" Frankie always makes an effort to understand the facts of a situation.

"Yes . . . They go there all right . . . and King is with us and Calligan . . . and Rachel and Angel . . . and they book us all for L and L."

"What's L and L?"

Brenda looks uncomfortable. "Well, it's booking you . . . like for disorderly."

"Well, what were you at?"

"Nothing . . . Some of the girls were in pajamas. We was all drinking beer."

"The police got no right to do *that,*" protests Frankie. Like most children from families touched with various kinds of deviation and lawlessness, she has heard constant attacks made upon the police, the fuzz, the screws, the nabs. "You got rights, you know," she warns Baby.

"I know—but I ran," Baby reiterates. "I was just outa Secure and I couldn't stand it, and so I ran."

Frankie has been told by Jeanette that when her case comes up the judge might send *her* to Wentworth, and now she asks: "Was it *awful* there?"

"No—it's better than here . . . No cells or nothing . . . But the superintendent calls us up all the time. I was friends with Sugar there." As she mentions this friendship in the reform school, Baby's voice tails off vaguely. Again she is not sure how much Frankie knows, and her sense of loneliness and dependence increases. "I wish my mother'd come."

"She'll come, Baby."

"I don't think she'll come." Brenda moves about restlessly and sitting down again on her bed, she begins to chew at her fingernails. "She says I want to put her in her grave. She says I choose niggers over her."

"That's natural," Frankie soothes her, "the whites always think of us like dogs. . . But she'll come all the same."

"Sometimes I wish she'd *die* . . ." Baby explodes. "Sometimes I get all disturbed and wish she'd croak."

"You better occupy your mind, honey," Frankie warns her, "or you'll be ready for the Funny Factory . . . Your mother's your mother and you shouldn't put that wish on her . . . My mother had me up to the youth board, and when they put me in St. Ursula's she John Hancocked it—but I don't say I wish she'd croak . . ." For a moment her voice is as earnest as that of the many traveling preachers she has listened to. "I hope my mother hasn't got to die for me to do better," she murmurs.

Baby tries for the truth that Frankie is trying for, and says in a faltering voice: "I'm not scared of my father except when he's mad and says he'll scar me . . . But sometimes I'm scared to *death* of my mother . . . Yet she's the one I miss the most . . ."

At this point the superintendent and Miss Green descend the distant stairway and stand in conference at the top of the ramp.

"Let her out this afternoon, then," the superintendent is saying. "Let her out on every alternate afternoon . . . It's quite true that the child can't be kept shut up permanently . . . If only they wouldn't *send* us these minors . . ." She is referring to Frankie, who, with the departure of Ana, is the only younger girl left in the jail and whose presence, therefore, acts as a special irritant.

Miss Green, despite her failure with Harriet, is comforted by the fact that Frankie is to get out of her cell and join the rest of the prison inmates in the recreation room. Optimistically, she believes that wholesome recreational activities (such as checkers, solitaire, and sewing) cannot fail to have their effect upon young lawbreakers like Frankie, Harriet, and Baby. She plans also (possessing as much faith in sunshine and fresh air as she does in hygiene) to get the girls out into the prison yard for the last half hour of the recreation period, where they can sit on the benches in the narrow yard and even play ball for a while, or some other circumscribed game. Yet when she unlocks the cells and leads the girls (except Harriet) into the downstairs dining room, where Beppo is again put in charge of pouring out tea for the afternoon snack, she has a momentary question in her mind as she realizes that Frankie—tiny and neat in her blue jeans, her orange shirt freshly laundered by Jeanette, her huge eyes glowing—now that she is in the recreation room with the older prisoners, appears not to be at all ashamed of her presence in Henry Street, but only anxious to create a good impression. She sees that Frankie seems to swagger a little, to grow talkative and to laugh too loudly, that she is fluid as quicksilver, curious and imitative as a monkey, eager to conquer this new world where she is identified as Jeanette's niece and where she is introduced around in the guise of the princess who will sooner or later mount the queen, her aunt's, throne.

Within minutes, as a small lizard's coloring might deepen on a volcanic plain, Frankie has blended in with those others in the room. Instantaneously, it seems, she has taken on the disguise of the prison.

Jeanette Tobey parts her niece's hair and, taking one strand, presses it gently with the processing iron. She wears her usual expression of weary attention, and stands there, behind the chair in which Frankie is seated, a smock over her prison wrapper, accepting graciously the combs, curlers, and bowls of liquid which are handed up to her by her several helpers. She is a High Priestess absorbed in a rite of Beauty; and Beautification is indeed one of her skills, but since she can scarcely boast of the situation in which she finds her sister's child, she has little real zest for her task.

Frankie, however, is fascinated. Not only is she the center of attention, and gaining kudos as the favored niece of one of the most successful girls on the street—but she is also the 'baby' of Henry Street Jail, and as such a subject for protection and education. Everyone has pronounced her cute. And almost everyone wants to give her something, or tell her something . . . What is more, while she is the focus of attention in one way, in another she is the forgotten listener—a child who stands at the threshold of life and watches the movements of life itself.

Like a weary mountain, the great dark prostitute in the red

dress lisps of her experiences on the streets, and Frankie, sitting beneath the spell of Jeanette's agile hands, follows the inarticulate drama with the intentness of a rural girl at the theatre for the first time.

"Ah come home . . . Ah can tell yuh, Ah come home with 70 dolluhs . . . 'n' ma man he ask me: 'What yo' doin' alla time . . . all yo' got is 70 dolluhs?' " Her face creases into an expression of anger as she imitates her man's rage. " 'All yo' *got*, you bitch? . . . Don' you tell me is no trick out there,' 'n' Ah say: 'Is *rainin*' out there, man, and Ah not goin' out any moah'—'n' he lif' his hand to me, and he say: 'Go back on out, 'n' don' come back till you bring me a decent piece o' money' . . ."

Her listeners are nodding, punctuating the familiar recital with murmurs of recognition, as the members of a chorus might confirm an announced theme. "An' wha' *you* do?" a young woman from the West Indies asks crisply, her fingers busy with wool and a crochet needle. "You get more money fo' he? You let he lavish he mouth?"

"Wha' Ah *do*?" The dark mountainous woman sighs, her body quaking in self-pity and resentment, but a certain faded cunning showing in her eyes. "Ah go ri' out and catch me a cab, 'n' go ri' ovah t' ma girl frien' . . . Thas wha' Ah do."

"Good fo' *you*," one of the listening women murmurs, "good fo' *you*."

The approval seems unanimous, but many of the women listening don't speak at all. Their eyes seem blank and show neither indignation nor excitement. They are only aroused when Beppo, passing the tea with her usual efficiency, comes by and announces that Bo-Bo Teasdale is in the front office.

"Who *busted* her?" a thin white-skinned girl asks quickly.

"Who you think?" Beppo drawls. "McCarty, that's who."

"She comin' in?"

"She waitin' on the bondsman." Beppo gathers up empty cups and takes the opportunity to murmur a compliment to Jeanette. "She says Manny got busted, too, but Happy come and took her from headquarters . . . Your hair goin' to be nice, little feller," she adds to Frankie. "Look who's doin' it."

"Sure will be," agrees Frankie.

"I wanta see Bo-Bo," the thin anemic-looking white girl says. "I wanta see what my man's doin'. He sent me no money, the bastard . . ."

"You know what you do next time you get out?" the aggressive-jawed Bertha asks. "You got *that* figured, I hope?" Her tone sets her apart from the prostitutes seated around her, and it is logical to them all that what *she* is in for is larceny and will never allow a man to push *her* around, just as it is logical to the women who work for men that, with *that* kind of face and nature, she is half man anyway and so will never be in *their* position. Because of this the thin girl looks at her briefly, but her glance seems to say simply: "*You* haven't got *my* problems." Then she complains: "He just said to me, 'Baby, you know I can't go down to no jail,' and I say: 'Nothing wrong with the mail, far as *I* know . . .'" Her voice tails off.

Frankie is listening with growing indignation. She has always known that women work for men in the street, that the pimp gets money and cars in this lucrative business, and that women 'do it' for the proper rewards. She has always had before her the golden image of her aunt—an inscrutable idol, swathed in furs and encradled in the purple Cadillac—an image touched by sadness perhaps, yet a sadness which is the more romantic because it is never explained. Now, however, she is forced to become aware that these women 'take it' from their men, more regularly and with less reward than her mother 'takes it' from her father, that they go out into the street and 'do it,' and then they come to jail, while both of the men who benefit—the trick and the pimp—remain free.

"Why don't you work for *yourselves?*" she suddenly demands of the women gathered around. "Why do you take all that crap? You give the *money* to them . . . and you get *nothing* . . . ? They don't even bail you out! Or send money . . . or *nothing!*" Her tone grows more and more urgent and scandalized. She sits up abruptly, so that Jeanette has to stop doing her hair. "You *fools?*" she asks. "You just *fools* . . . ?"

Jeanette presses her gently on the shoulder and she relaxes again, but the women around her laugh, some of them with pity, some of them with delight. Her remark is like the remark of a child—bright and penetrating but utterly impractical.

"Yo' wait," the big mountainous Negro woman in red prophesies. "Yo' wait, baby . . . Someday you have a man o' you own."

"Never," Frankie explodes, sitting up again. "Never . . . Never! . . . No man do *that* to me . . ."

In a tired indulgent voice, one of the women says: "You be out there, too." Jeanette, who has contributed nothing to the conversation to this point, turns suddenly to pick up scattered bobby pins from the floor.

———————

"*In on the good, in on the bad*," is what they say in the street. Loyalty is as necessary as it is in wartime: just as death faces a spy or a deserter, so there can be no 'burning,' or the humblest pickpocket might be found dead in the morning. At this moment in Henry Street Jail, Jeanette can pause with the bobby pins in her hand and her faraway eyes can encompass the whole city, a busy and preoccupied scene, its citizens unaware of the termites of the life, of those stable unstables who bore through the pockets of honest men, who 'prat' and 'fan' and 'shade the stick' in crowds and subways and buses, who 'heel' and 'boost' in stores, who extract bundles of notes from banks by means of skillful 'fishing,' who defraud jewelers, who prowl hotels, who throw their hats over keys left on hotel desks, who carry out the 'lemon,' the 'tap,' the 'wire,' who 'hang paper,' who set up mock banks and carry out real estate frauds, who practice the 'short con' on strangers, weak women, and would-be gamblers, and the 'long con' on hustling businessmen and rich suckers. Jeanette can survey the scene without allowing changes to appear on her handsome and well-schooled face. Just as she can open up a Pandora's box of pain and tears without fluttering her eyelashes, she can remember Wally, who argues with her about turning out Opaline for him—Opaline, her own sister's child. She is conscious of a long-delayed sickness, which breaks like a dew over her face and breasts. "I'm leaving you," she says to him at the bar. He pulls out a gun and says: "You're what? . . ." And she repeats it: "I'm leaving you . . ." Brownie, the owner of the bar, begs them both: "Take that stuff outside in the street. I don't want it in my joint." She turns to Brownie and cries out: "I'm not going out with him . . ." And she adds, with curious attention to logic and politeness: "If I get killed in front of your place, Brownie, the joint's *still* going to be closed."

Someone takes the gun from Wally, and afterwards in the back of the bar he puts his fist in her eye. Out in the street, when she hastens blindly uptown, she hears him following her, and then he tells her that he loves her . . . He *loves* her? . . . Yes, he says that he *loves* her; this phrase which has always worked with women, 'I *love* you.' In the end she is wearied by argument, and sends Opaline to meet a trick.

––––––––––

As Jeanette does Frankie's hair, she touches her life.

"Jeanette," Frankie murmurs.

"Yes, baby."

"Won't Wally get you out?"

"He can't, baby."

"He can't?"

"The judge disallowed bail."

"Oh—it's not Wally then? It's not that he don't *want* you out? You don't take *that* crap? Like the others?" There is relief in Frankie's voice.

"Not quite like the others," Jeanette answers with an enigmatic expression. She stands like a robot woman, placid, quiet, ladylike, and her fingers continue with the task of subduing the vigorous kink in her niece's hair.

––––––––––

In the far corner Beppo is arguing with a young, thin, brown-haired woman who wears high-heeled shoes and silk stockings, but whose cadaverous figure looks oddly sunken under the loose prison wraparound.

"I don't care how I *look*," the young brown-haired woman

says with a clear shrill intonation. "I'm what I am, and if you don't like it, you can go jump in the fucking lake . . . Who're you to criticize my clothes I'd like to know?"

No one can hear Beppo's taunting reply, but its effectiveness is evident, because the girl rushes from that side of the room and joins the group gathered around Jeanette, calling loudly over her shoulder, "I can walk in silk stockings if I want—it don't make me any less a feller!"

"Don't pay her no mind," the redheaded Bertha comforts the girl. "She think she got *all* the turf."

"Sure does," one of the other women murmurs. "I'd take a powder I couldn't get a better man than that."

Ignorant of all the ramifications of this exchange, Frankie feels that they are jealous of Beppo (perhaps as she had been jealous of Beppo) because of her capacity to gain ascendancy over others. Ashamed to admit ignorance, Frankie asks no more questions but feels it necessary all the same to tear apart the veils which separate her from life. It is not enough to look at the flower of life, one must tear it to pieces, examine its form, test its texture, put it in one's mouth and devour it—petal, calyx, stem . . .

She is alone again. Jeanette has gone to help Miss Green. The thin anemic-looking white girl is talking to Bo-Bo Teasdale who has just been brought into the room. The redheaded Bertha—'Big Bertha' as she is called—is trying to bully a friend into giving her an extra cigarette . . . The other women have drifted away . . .

Frankie, her hair tied up in a handkerchief, hunches over a pad and tries to write poetry. But the pencil pauses, not reaching that reservoir of words, unable to fish like a hook in the dark waters. Another language intrudes, the oblique and penetrating language of the life. "I said to her: 'Broad, give me some sky . . .' 'Nothing doing, I'll go freak off with another Jasper. Both of us go for what we know . . .' 'Listen Baby he's only tryin' to cop. He satisfies her, he'll sock it to her, but later on she'll get him when she can.' "

. . . Over the room, in the middle of the hot August afternoon, there is spread a haze of goodness, of camaraderie. Women borrow clothes from each other, and promise to lend them. Cigarettes are cut in two. Comfort is extended. In a distant corner of the room, tears are wiped away by one who has cause to shed them. And slowly, as if in freedom from the punishment of society, the distorted human forms relax and return momentarily to more natural shapes. The sad gossip of the underworld ("He got twenty years, man—a long twenty"—"She fell out . . . Yes, she had Harry's bag, it were too strong"—"You hear of Innocencia—she went right down the South with Gutiérrez and she hung herself up") is spread out in the prison air, and the population reacts with a tender generalized pity, an acceptance close to Christian resignation.

Only Frankie is set apart, hunched alone on her stool in individualistic rebellion, gripping her pencil, heroically engaged in her long fight with fate.

———————

In the morning, Baby is taken to court. She dresses in the lemon-colored slacks she has worn into the prison, and the cheap pale-blue too-tight sweater. This is the outfit she had worn when she ran from Wentworth, and in which she had been arrested at the house in Leland, and now, although it is dirty and stained, she refuses to change it for the plain dark dress offered her by Miss McVee. She spends the extra half hour's wait in her cell, in doing up her long black hair in a great teased mass above her forehead.

Frankie has been stimulated by the apparent weak-mindedness of the women she listened to yesterday, women who are, she sees, only half human beings, their autonomy given over to others. Now she wishes to protect Baby, to convince her that she mustn't allow King to take her money.

"You don't let those pimps hit on you," she insists.

"I won't, Frankie." Baby's clouded blue eyes have some of the proverbial Irish beauty, but her face (very like her mother's) spreads broadly with the solidity of a German *Hausfrau's*. She wears an expression now of naïve adoration.

"I just wish you wuz coming with me."

"I'm not sure I want to go where you're going, Baby. I'm lookin' to go back to school. I tell you I can't wait to get at those books!"

"Where do you think *I'm* going?"

"Baby, you're going back to Wentworth jus' as soon as that judge can John Hancock the papers. It's no good telling you different."

Brenda sighs, and shifts her mature yet somehow childishly clumsy body. "I wish I'd get a break; I been hurt so much."

Frankie wants to appear all-knowing, and she also wants to prepare her friend.

"Hurts nothing," she says. "Don't you know you old enough for the man to sign you off? That youth board not got you now, Baby—not unless they want to. You come of age!"

Brenda trembles.

"What's that mean?"

"It means they can send you up to the big woman's house if they want, up to 'the joint'—to Paragoula."

"That where I'm going?" Brenda asks fearfully.

Frankie shakes her head wisely. She knows no more about Brenda's fate than does Brenda herself, but she at least knows the place names, names which might be printed in capitals, or recited in a rosary with a prayer for each one, stations in a Delinquent's Pilgrim's Progress: St. Ursula's—Tasseldone—The Belveson— The Protestant Home—Henry Street—Wentworth—Bancroft— Townsend—Paragoula.

"You might as well face it. If you're not going to Wentworth, then it's Paragoula, or it's one of those nuthouses where they examine you. Where you think you going?"

"I don't know, but they say up to Townsend isn't too bad. Dennis was there once and he liked it. Not like a prison. Just a nuthouse. Just had to wander around the wards and everything." Her eyes fill with tears and the citadel of her hair trembles.

"I'll see you, Baby," Frankie promises. "I'll see you." She presses a piece of paper into Brenda's hand. "I'll write you from school."

Brenda looks at the paper and sees a short poem, entitled "To a Friend":

> You go back
> To the world which has denounced us—
> My white friend, who through the bars
> Touched my dark hand.
> We're doing time friend—
> In jail, or out of it.

"It's beautiful," Brenda says tearfully. "I'll always keep it, whatever happens." Miss McVee is signaling to her, and she presses Frankie's hand.

"Keep cool, Baby," Frankie calls after her.

. . . And from Cell 5, Beppo joins in the farewell: "Yes, keep cool, princess. And tell the judge hello from me. Tell him to shuv' it."

––––––––––––

The bars draw closer when Baby goes, the flame of excitement dies within Frankie, as a lighted newspaper flares up and disappears, leaving nothing but ash. Her face becomes melancholy. Her eyes take on a dullness like coal.

Yet her depression is less real than that of Harriet in Cell 3. Harriet draws no pictures, writes no words, moves out to no one. She lies stretched on her bed watching the ceiling, the bars striping her body—or occasionally paces to and fro, her pale round face eternally puzzled, her short tawny hair dark with a week's fatigue, her right arm flexing to box at shadows on the wall.

One day they had come to the house with her cousin Alfred—Uncle Gaspar's boy—saying that he had been found lying by the side of the road, as far south as Coletown. Harriet is fifteen and has just got home with a report card which places her 195 in a class of 196. It is her first, and it is to be her last, year in high school.

She is glad of the confusion created by Alfred's rigid body and clenched teeth, because it puts off the necessity of showing the card to her father, who is being forced to fill in a long blue form and to answer questions about Alfred.

How long has he been sick? . . . Why has he no one to look after him? . . . Had he had any treatment in Canada before emigrating to the United States? . . . And similar questions, all of which her father answers unwillingly, his fists clenched at his sides, his replies as brief as possible. Is there illness, the ambulance man is asking, is there any special illness in the family?

Harriet sees that her father doesn't want to speak, that it is an effort for him. In sympathy she watches him, staring tight-lipped at the ambulance man. She suspects that it is from her father that she has inherited this inability with words, just as it is from her mother that she has absorbed this paralyzing feeling of impotence.

. . . Now the world closes about her. Earnestly, blindly, she wants to escape from the cell; she wants to break out somewhere, anywhere. She longs, she yearns for *power*. Out of a blackness around her it seems that any action, any action at all will bring light . . .

The scream cuts across the air in the hot heavy mid-afternoon . . . just before the 'Rec' hour, while the prisoners doze on their narrow iron-rusted cots.

Frankie and Beppo are at once at the bars, for they have heard not only the scream but the clash on the floor of the tin tray with the tin cup . . . The screams go on and on and mount in intensity. The superintendent comes running from the front office, as does the officer on duty, while with the automation of experience the girl at the switchboard telephones to the male side and asks for help. "Right away, please—a male officer to stand by."

A voice is saying: "Now Harriet, quiet down please—just quiet down now." But Harriet doesn't hear. She has torn the mattress off her bed, and lifted up the side of the iron cot. With the strength of that unused right arm, so constantly flexed to lunge at the wall, she is beating the iron bed on the floor, and at the same time she is screaming as if she would flail from her throat a lifetime of protest, filling in each interval with choking sobs.

As the iron bed bangs and scrapes on the floor, and as the

officers converge upon the door of the cell, a single childish threat
rises above the din—"Keep away from me, screws!"

But the door is unlocked and the officers enter. With the help
of the man from the other wing of the prison, they lead her away.
Down the ramp, and along the passage. The noise recedes . . .
There is silence again.

II

Wentworth—The State School for Girls

. . . the problem in an institution for [adolescents] is far more complex than the public or the administration or scientific students have realized. It is obvious that lifetime patterns of sexual behavior are greatly affected by the experiences of adolescence, not only because they are the initial experiences, but because they occur during the age of greatest activity . . .

KINSEY, POMEROY, AND MARTIN, in
Sexual Behavior in the Human Male

Ana 'Pug Nose' Pulaski arrived at Wentworth State School for Girls on August 15. It was a warm day and the heavy flood of summer leaves made green tunnels of the country road, tunnels through which bored—at a steady speed of fifty miles an hour—the little dark wagon carrying Ana, Miss Mary Brownley (Wentworth's physical-education officer), and the driver, Mr. DeMarcio.

This little dark wagon, distinguished only by a departmental insignia, yet had a certain dignity, as have those vehicles which bear kings, queens, sheiks, and heads of state. It seemed set apart from the automobiles which carry ordinary mortals as the tumbrel which bore Marie Antoinette to the guillotine might have been set apart from a country cart. And so, too, little Ana's face, vacuous and bold, yet open as a white poppy, pressing against the conservative window of the wagon, suggested contrasts as sad as those which must have been suggested by the face of one of Marie Antoinette's children, pale beside her mother's skirt.

Ana had been picked up for shoplifting almost immediately after her release from Henry Street, and her commitment to Wentworth followed a review of her record, and consultation with the Youth Board (which had her in custody), the Society for the Prevention of Cruelty to Children (which had followed the family through ten years of emergencies), the North City General Hospital (which had treated her crippled mother for muscular dystrophy), and the Department of Welfare (which supported the family with Aid to Dependent Children checks).

"If you don't want to be an outlaw from society, Ana," the judge told her gravely, "you must try to settle down at this school, and see that you don't come before me again."

"No, your Honor," Ana had promised glibly, tossing back her long rope of red hair, "I won't!" And then, teetering on her spiked heels and bouncing the small hips in her tight pegged skirt, she had turned with elated promptitude to go out of the court-room.

Still somewhat elated but with ever-increasing anxiety, she sat on the edge of the seat in the wagon and waited for her arrival at the new school. There she hoped to find Margie, her best friend in the street, who was sentenced to Wentworth for starting a fire in her aunt's basement. She also hoped to meet Rita who had been to trade school with her in Beltondell, a girl who was at least a step ahead of Ana in the hierarchy of the promiscuous and the unstable. She hoped to find status, excitement, unheard-of glories —but, like the fisherman who goes fishing all his life without real-izing that it is not fish he is looking for, Ana searched for some-thing which still had not been clearly identified. She bounced on the edge of the seat, nervously smoothed back her long reddish hair, fluttered the dark, thick lashes around her large pale-green eyes, and every now and then asked the patient Miss Brownley for another cigarette. When she received it, she held it as if it had immense importance, in her dead-white shining-fingered little hand, on the wrist of which the name 'Alec' had been tattooed.

A study in her 'name-color,' Miss Brownley stretched out sen-sible lisle-stockinged legs, took out her lighter, flipped it, and ex-tended the flame to her charge, thus illuminating her own earnest brown eyes, and a calm brow encircled by an amber-colored plas-tic band.

"Got it?" she asked cheerfully, and shifted a little to cross those sensible legs. "That's the last cigarette, Ana. Okay?"

"I'm nervous," Ana explained. Then she added: "Gee, look!" as the wagon turned in through the outside gates of the institution and passed by fields where black-and-white cows grazed on emer-ald daisy-starred grass.

"Yes, we have cows and pigs and chickens," Miss Brownley answered, "and we grow vegetables."

Ana began to move joyously on her seat. "Oh, I'm going to *love* this school," she declared. "I'm just going to *love* it . . . It's beautiful . . . Look at all those cottages 'n' everything. It's like a *park* . . . 'n' the *animals!* I love animals. Now I miss my cat . . ."

Miss Brownley said to the driver: "To the front office, please."

"I miss my kitty," Ana said. "He misses me, too. When I was in Henry Street, he wouldn't even eat. See this cat got slammed in the door once by my niece—that's Daisy—and I put it in a basket and got hot cloths for its leg, until it healed . . ."

Miss Brownley was looking at her with a patient smile.

"I'm crazy about animals . . ." Ana moved excitedly on the seat. "Even little *rats*, I'm crazy about . . ."

"We get out here," Miss Brownley said.

The cottages were named after famous women, and at Florence Nightingale Cottage, 'Auntie Casey,' as she was called by the girls, noted on her daybook that a new girl, Ana Pulaski, was expected to sign in at four o'clock. She found herself hoping that this girl would get in promptly so that her arrival wouldn't conflict with the pre-supper crush, and at this moment she heard a plaintive voice saying at her elbow:

"Auntie Casey . . . Kin I get in my locker?"

"Now one moment, Midget," she replied, "just you stand by a moment," and she went on filling out the daybook with an air of absorption.

Midget, an extremely thin and stunted thirteen-year-old, edged up to her as she wrote, and poked her precocious, almost wizened face over her shoulder.

"You do it real nice, Auntie Casey," she said, looking at the neat figures in the ruled columns. "You got it down to a T . . . Now, kin I get in my locker?"

Mrs. Casey rose, closed the daybook, put one arm around the girl's shoulders, and produced an enormous bunch of keys. She opened the locker and stood by while a pair of sneakers was extracted, then she watched as Midget sat on the chair near the office, and put them on carefully, tying the laces in neat knots.

"*That's* the way!" she applauded cheerfully, and the smallest and most dependent of the cottage population slid off the chair with a proud smile, and rushed off down the hallway toward the sports field.

> *A neglected child, Mary Huntington (Midget), found beaten and abused and almost starved to death in a basement at the age of six. Five years in an unsuitable foster home. One year in another foster home where the foster mother turned out to be an alcoholic. The last year with an aunt who thought she 'wasn't all there' and tried beating her to 'make her wake up.' Picked up by the police in a park at nine o'clock one night because a man complained that she tried to steal his wallet. Thirteen years old. Remanded to the Wentworth State School for Girls.*

Mrs. Casey returned to her desk, and began to make out the hospital sheet. Just as she put down her pen, Miss Brownley entered the door with Ana Pulaski in tow.

. . . The showers poured, and the steam rose from the tiled floors of the cubicles. Feet ran bare—in slippers, in sneakers—along the shining waxed linoleum corridors. Voices rose—in question, in laughter, in irritation—as forty young women between the ages of twelve and eighteen struggled with the problem of getting to the dining room in time for supper. Ana, too, struggled, firing occasional remarks to the other three girls to whose room she had been assigned, her natural excitability increased by the hubbub around her.

"Where's my brush? . . . Oh I would lose it just now . . . Thanks a million! . . . What you in for?"

" 'Stubborn child' "

"Oh, gee . . . My girl friend Margie was a 'stubborn' . . . but now she's in for arson."

"You a friend of Margie's . . . ? Margie King?"

"Sure, she's my best friend on the street."

"Hey kids—here's a friend of Margie's."

Someone appeared in the doorway.

"You a friend of Margie's?"

"Sure thing . . ." Ana reveled in her importance. "Say, how's that Ma Casey?"

"Oh, *she's* all right. Auntie Casey's all right. She's strict but she's good people."

"Well, I gotta have my shower now, or she'll be mad."

In moments she was under the shower, even her eyelashes dropping, a pink shower cap casting a glow over her rather coarse little face, her small body seeming robust and feminine, yet disproportionate, seeming somehow like that of a clean little porker, stripped and ready for the table.

"Hey, new girl, get out of that shower," someone warned her. And a moment later Mrs. Casey appeared in the doorway and said in her authoritative voice: "Okay, Ana, you're clean enough now. You don't want to be late, do you?"

"Oh, I'll be ready." Ana tossed her head as she wrapped herself in a towel. "That's no sweat!" she shouted above the noise.

"When you're out, put on clean underwear. Give me all that you wore down here, and I'll have it washed. Your locker is number 29. Can you remember that?"

"Sure I can remember, Mrs. Casey."

Ana swathed in a towel smiled invitingly. "My nickname's Pug Nose," she offered.

"Well, Pug Nose, you run along and get ready," Mrs. Casey paused, feeling that Ana's pint size gave her the same rights as those given to Midget. "Try to keep out of trouble," she said, "but if you can't, then come to me! If you feel disturbed . . ."

"Okay, Mrs. Casey," Ana said shyly. "Auntie . . ." she added.

"Another one looking for a mother," Miss Bailey (the social worker) said later that evening, as she briefed Mrs. Casey about Ana.

"I guessed that already." Mrs. Casey moved her mending closer to the light.

"Did you see the mother?"

"No, the mother's crippled with muscular dystrophy." Miss

Bailey consulted the sheaf of papers in her hand and began to tap her pencil against the rim of her glasses, a reflective habit she had adopted since dealing with case histories. "Let's see . . . Parents are Polish. The mother is a *very* devoted Catholic, and says nine or ten rosaries a day, an understandable habit since she is so weak that she is almost completely confined to a wheelchair. Ana is the sixth child in a family of six and was born in 1945. She is now nearly fifteen and a half. The child closest in age is Daisy, sixteen and a half, and Ana's constant companion. This girl is actually not a sibling, but the illegitimate daughter of Ana's older sister, Rosie. Partly because of the mother's helplessness and the father's desertion, partly because of the delinquent attitude of the parents themselves—their habit of scoffing at teachers, concerned neighbors, and law-enforcement officers—these children, but especially Ana and Daisy, have been able to live a completely undisciplined life for the last five years."

Mrs. Casey leaned back with a sigh, her sewing in her lap. Her strained blue eyes looked off into the distance. Although her talents seemed purely practical, she had a visionary side to her nature, which gave her the creativity of the mother and made her more optimistic in her work than many of the other officers at Wentworth.

"The girl's rather appealing. If only I'd had her earlier . . ."

Miss Bailey, a young graduate of Olsen College, shot her a quick curious glance and tapped the rim of her glasses again. She couldn't imagine how anyone could think Ana 'appealing.'

"Let's see," she said. "Before the father left the family he bought a truck, and one midnight he loaded everyone in (as well as the toilet fixtures which he detached from the bathroom of their rented apartment) and drove off to Oregon . . . Well, this didn't work out . . . Back in Massachusetts, Mrs. Pulaski consults her priest . . . an older boy is sent to a reformatory for threatening a policeman with a gun . . . one of the younger boys is picked up for stealing money from drunks in the park . . . the two girls, now aged twelve and thirteen and a half, respectively, repeatedly are returned to the apartment by the police . . . Mrs. Pulaski says she 'can't manage them' . . . Daisy dyes her hair black and Ana tries to bleach hers. Mother scoffs when the police return them one night at 10:00 P.M., informing her that they were with a group of boys and girls trying to rob parking meters . . . Mother says police are always picking *her* kids up, and that the police have no *proof* they intended to rob the parking meters . . . Let's see now. Here's a social worker's report, September 19, 1959:

> *Mother has no control over children and no sense. At one time mother was hospitalized for amnesia. Allows children out at all hours and gives good reports to Youth Board just to keep them from bothering her . . . Mother's difficulties evident, because of extreme disability. Has considerable ambivalence toward authority figures herself. When social worker came to home she found Mrs. Pulaski had attempted to get out of her chair to reach her crutches and had fallen, pulling down her small breakfast table. On arrival of social worker, Mrs. Pulaski was still lying on floor amongst the broken crockery, and unable to get up again. The accident had happened at 8:40 a.m. and it was now 10:00 a.m. . . . In spite of Mrs. Pulaski's evident need for help and companionship, social worker thinks that girls should be removed from home environment."*

There was a silence.

"What action was taken?" Mrs. Casey inquired.

"The girls were given Big Sisters, who were very involved with them for about six months and then lost interest." Miss Bailey crossed her legs and reshuffled her papers. She knew that Mrs. Casey would be more familiar with Ana by the week's end than she was herself. "Ana, absent from school forty-eight times in six months . . . Would you like to hear the psychiatrist's report?"

"Yes." Mrs. Casey leaned forward attentively. "Let's hear it."

" *'This girl is very immature and demanding. Shows poor self-image and no social controls. Extreme fear of bodily harm suggests early violence on part of father, brothers, other male figures. Ambivalent about mother who alternately threatens and cries. Hides desire for affection under tough façade'* . . . etc., etc. . . . That's about all."

"Well, there's one thing they left out," Mrs. Casey said. "They don't say that the child loves life!"

"No," Miss Bailey agreed, "they didn't say that." To herself she thought: *What's that got to do with it?*

"And she's in for shoplifting?" Mrs. Casey inquired.

"Yes, but before that she was in Henry Street for three days, because she'd been picked up by the police as a vagrant and a VD contact . . . The tests were negative and she was released."

"And before that?"

"Well, truancy, etc. She was with the youth board."

Mrs. Casey stared up the waxed floors of the corridors. "What do you think?"

"She's a tough little cookie." Miss Bailey crossed her legs again and beat at the rim of her glasses with her pencil. "Very manipulative." In her search for 'professionalism,' Miss Bailey had at least learned to be cautious. Now she looked at Mrs. Casey pityingly. "Better watch her, and not expect too much."

"I would watch *anyway*." Mrs. Casey gazed up the passages and got stiffly to her feet. "And I *never* expect much . . . After all, there are forty girls, and most of them with inadequate parents."

"Well, we can't be mothers, that's for sure, so we'd better not get them to expect it." Miss Bailey snapped the rubber band on her notebook. "Good-night now, Mrs. Casey. And good luck with her." Her heels tapped away down the shining corridor.

———————

At nine o'clock, just before lights-out, the common room is crowded with girls of all shapes, sizes, ages. The undercurrent of a radio fills in the pauses in the general conversation, and from time to time a thin, starved-looking redhead switches to another station, as if some unbearable tension made it impossible for her to listen to the same program for any length of time. That she has had St. Vitus's dance in her youth, and that here in Wentworth her illness is kept under control by medication, is but one part of her history; the rest is interwoven with the fact that she has been committed to reform school because there is, literally, nowhere else to send her. She seems to know this. She seems to know that she has no certain place, and when her restlessness drives her into collision with the group, she goes off, with her rather uneven jerky walk, toward the back of the cottage, and takes refuge close to the officers' study, and to the comforting presence of Auntie Casey.

On this particular evening, the girls have gathered around Brenda 'Baby' O'Reilly, who had 'run' from Wentworth in June and is now, after her brief stay in Henry Street, recommitted—a fate which has filled her with disgust at first, but which she begins to find vaguely comforting. She is safe now, after all, safe from the street and from the exigencies of King's needs, and most of all from herself. "I was real bad," she is saying in her soft monotonous voice, while an interested audience crowds around her. "I was that hurt because of my mother signing me over. She says to me: 'Wake up girl, you're a woman now,' but I says: 'Ma, don't be like that, because I'm your daughter after all,' and she says: 'You're not my daughter while you like these half-breeds. Why don't you ask *them* to get you outa trouble.' "

Sugar, a tall and very black Negro girl, laughs. "We'll get you *inta* trouble, Baby," she promises, her intonation making the more sophisticated members of her audience smile. She lounges on the arm of Baby's chair, her glossy sculptured black face crowned by a heavy smooth processed bob, the bones of her arms and legs, her wrists, her cheekbones, her gleaming white teeth, showing a certain classic heaviness which sets her apart from those around her —even those with some Negro blood—as if, in her particular case, that skeleton, terminal, so to speak, in glistening ivories, was more enduring and more ancient.

"Yes, *Bab-ee*," she mocks, her voice ringing as in the beginning of a blues. "Yes, *Bab-ee*." She gets up, does two or three quick steps to the beat of the radio, and then sits down again, flinging her arm around Brenda's shoulders. "Missed you," she adds.

"Gee," says Brenda earnestly. "I missed *you*, Sugar, honest I did. I tell you I'd run if I'd stayed in that hospital . . . I'da run till no cop coulda picked me up . . . Dennis, he tole me how to get out. You jus' don't eat 'n' pine away, and the doctor thinks you're in need of more life, and they let you go."

"Where you been at?" one of the girls asks now.

"At? First I was at Leland where Rachel and Angel was at, then I was at *Henry Street*, then I was at *Townsend*. Down at Leland, Angel's working as a cheesemaker, and Rachel's wrapping cigars. But the cops came in on our apartment saying a lot of colored and white were there together . . . I tell *you*, someday I'm gonna run far enough so no one's gonna put their hands on me . . ."

Her broad face flushes at the prospect, and she sounds angry, although in reality she is filled with the pleasure of homecoming. The strong frame of the dark Sugar reassures her, and Sugar's preference for *her* gives her status, makes her feel part of the group. Whereas color brings with it a traditional stigma outside, this world of the reform school reverses these values, and here inmates like Sugar rule, not only they themselves but their color, their clothes, their music, their tastes, their language.

"You playing?" Sugar asks now, laughing and tightening her hold on Baby's shoulders.

Baby blushes, or at least her cheeks become moister and ruddier. The word 'playing,' with its sexual connotation, suggests also the innocence of those who 'play,' and the boredom which makes 'playing' necessary.

"What an instigator!" another girl mocks. "Better watch her, Baby. Spend a night with *her* and what a state you'd be in in the morning!"

Pepper, a tall thin Italian girl with narrow red lips and a swarthy skin announces: "Sugar'd be in no state. *She's* giving up the work!"

At this further and more daring innuendo the circle draws closer, shutting the younger girls out, making it clear that these are the elders of the cottage, the ones who know what's what, the ones who make things happen.

"If Sugar is giving up the work, it's only so she can get the edge," someone suggests cynically, and all laugh loudly, including

Sugar herself, who throws back her shoulders and stretches out her long legs with an assumption of male power.

"I'm the untouchable!" she suggests, pointing to her breast and shrinking back with exaggerated horror.

"I'll believe it when I see it," someone murmurs.

"You won't see it," Sugar offers. "Me and Baby's going to steal Miss Casey's keys and shack up in the officers' room."

There are shrieks of delighted laughter. Pepper asks if they've seen the new broad, the 'little one,' and someone on the edge of the group searches out Ana and pushes her into the circle so that all can inspect her charms.

"You a virgin?" Pepper asks Ana.

"Sure—" Ana asserts boldly.

"She's *built*," Sugar suggests lazily, so obvious an untruth that the group resounds with laughter.

"Come off it, honey," Pepper pleads to Ana. "Don't tell me you've never been *had*. Nice as *you* look? Mean to say hasn't anyone been inside *there* yet?"

Ana doesn't know how to answer this, and is so undecided as to whether to tell the truth, that she simply opens wider and wider her light-green eyes, until one of the girls questions her bluntly. "Don't you know that girls go for girls?"

"In *school*?" Ana asks in amazement. "I didn't think we could *love funny* in *school*."

Losing interest in baiting Ana, the girls turn their attention elsewhere, and Pepper attempts to curry favor with Sugar by looking admiringly at Baby's coarse black hair (which, before the hospital signed her out, had been freshly waved and lacquered, and piled up on top of her head). "Baby's got class," she announces, at which Sugar murmurs in a low voice the inevitable reply, "And *ass!*"—raising another hysterical scream from the initiated.

"We keep this up," Sugar adds, "and the rollers will hear us."

Several girls look uneasily over their shoulders, and Pepper warns, "and all of us be in Paragoula," a reminder of the State Reformatory for Women, which has a sobering and slightly disruptive effect, and sends Candy, one of the younger girls into a fit of shivering.

Candy has been named a 'stubborn child' at the age of eleven, and at fourteen she already shows signs of allying herself with such leaders as Sugar. In spite of this, she feels extremely nervous whenever uncomfortable subjects are mentioned, and now, as if it soothed her to feel they were all safely in the schoolroom, she begins to talk about the redwood trees of California.

"I wanta go there," she insists wistfully, "honest I do." Tossing her head of golden curls, she speaks in the dulcet tones which remind the girls of how she sings in the choir on Sunday. "All the time I'm thinking about them big red trees . . ."

"What big red trees?"

"You know them big red trees."

"You mean in California—that's too far for me to know."

"Could hitchhike." Candy is gently and wistfully insistent.

"Might be they're oak trees," someone suggests.

"No . . ." Candy is impatient. "Them big *red* trees . . . Miss Willis told us about them in school . . ."

"Like over *there*, where all those *rocks* are?" someone else asks.

Midget declares with an air of authority: "That's Switzerland, with all the rocks."

"People camp there, and carry blankets on their backs."

"Oh yeah . . . That's boss."

Sugar and Baby have retreated into a corner, and a nostalgic shadow has fallen over the rest of the group, as if those who feel no peace dream of a world in which peace is paramount. They recline on hillsides, touch brilliant flowers, borrow wings of strange birds. And there are no laws in that country which they, in their weakness, will be bound to break, but an interlude in a no-man's land where they can rid themselves of their imperfections and approach a realizable heaven.

Ana Pulaski stands listening to Candy's story of how she had crept into a milk-chute on one of her early flights from home. "I was so skinny," Candy says, "and I went right in . . . right in."

Her hysterical laughter shakes her head of short fair curls, and she stretches out her thin legs beneath the full, frilly gingham skirt which Mrs. Casey has given her.

"Oh my mother and dad were always having fights, not just nagging. I mean he would beat her up something terrible. I mean she was a nervous wreck. I mean even Father knew about it. Father Arturo Dilitelli . . . just by looking at her he knew it. Dad'd beat her up and nag her, and not buy her anything, like he had no respec' for her at all. That's what a man should have for a woman Father says, respec' . . ."

"Ugh, like *my* dad," Ana says, shrugging the shoulders of her short compact body, and waving her little white hand with 'Alec' tattoed on the wrist. "He used to beat my mother up terrible, but now she's crippled, he just left, you know." Ana, who is in a state of exaltation about Wentworth (no one had told her how pretty this place was, with the little buildings and the trees and the flowers and the animals; no one had hinted at the fact that all the girls took turns to wait on the table and to wear lavender uniforms with white aprons; nor about the way you walked from building to building like in a real school, and took turns at everything, the kitchen, the laundry, the gardening—not to mention sports like swimming and ice skating), can only seem to balance that excitement by boasting of her lurid past, of the violence of her father, of the extent of her own sexual knowledge. ". . . Yes, but now he lives in a room up by the bridge, and he doesn't come to see us, only like when I was in Henry Street and the police brought him to get me out . . ."

"Was you in Henry Street, little one?" Sugar calls now from the corner. "You must be pretty tough, man!"

"Cell next to mine," affirms Baby.

Ana is flattered to be noticed by Sugar. "Yes—'n' what a lousy stinking place that is! *Nothing*—not even a wastepaper basket in your room. 'N' they always fresh outa milk and meat. Worms in your oatmeal 'n' everything." Ana sways her body with the intensity of her description. "I'm saying the bad about it," she adds, "because there *ain't* no good."

"What's your name, honey?" drawls Sugar from the corner.

"Ana, but they call me Pug Nose," she answers, at which everybody laughs again.

"You like it here?" Candy asks, feeling that Ana is closer to her in size and age than are the others.

"Oh I *love* it," Ana cries enthusiastically. "I knew the minute I saw it . . . I'm gonna *love* it."

" 'S not bad," admits Candy, feeling enthused herself. "It's nice at Christmas—you get presents, and chocolates. And cigarettes if you're sixteen . . ." She looks back and finds that Wentworth is the only home she knows. "I been here so long . . ." Her face grows melancholy and she sits slumped with her legs stuck out in front of her. "I been put away so *much*. Sometimes I'm even scared to run . . ."

"I'm *tired* of running," Ana says frankly. "If the police see me, they bust me. It's the cruiser on one side, and the wagon on the other. I'm gonna stick here as tight as Dick's hatband. Unless Margie runs . . ."

"Who's Margie?" Candy asks.

"Margie's my best friend. She's an *arsonist*."

"Oh." Candy feels inferior.

"If Margie stays, I stay," announces Ana.

. . . Sugar turns up the radio and begins to jitterbug with Baby. She wears an orange dress, and her tall loose figure moves with a minimum of effort, her narrow hips swinging neatly to and fro. Baby, on the other hand, has a heavy maturity, which is thrust backward from her pegged skirt onto her spiked heels. Her head bobs back and forth, rhythmically, as if her great dark headdress would fall. Baby, like a plump quail with a dark incurving feather on its head—Sugar, like a tall, loose-stepping orange crane . . . Then Pug Nose catches Candy's hand and swings her onto the floor, and she, too, is a bird—quick-footed and chunky, compact-tailed and flirting. "I love to dance," she says energetically. "I'd *die* dancing . . . Oh I'm gonna *love* this school!" Her eyes half shut, she flips Candy around, until Candy's curls are flying, and she also becomes a bird—a small, blond, endlessly floating dove.

Afterwards, when Mrs. Casey turns off the radio, Ana goes submissively to her room, where, still in her clothes, flushed and excited, she flings herself onto the bed, stretches in an ecstasy and cries out to whoever will listen: "Oh, I don't want *ever* to grow old!"

The Frankies, the Anas, the Babys of our time stand in the reception rooms of various institutions, and are considered old enough to distinguish between right and wrong, to accept that differentiation agreed to by Latin jurists who spoke of *malum prohibitum* and *malum in se.* Yet what other wrongs, these young prisoners might ask, were they astute enough or had they enough insight to argue their own cases? How cold indeed a law (at once precise in its terms and vague in its intentions) which fails to truly examine the situation of its difficult children, and so sentences them to tread a narrow and limited circuit between streets hungry for their talents, families which have failed them, and custodial institutions.

After her stay in Henry Street, Frankie appeared in court and due to her superior record in school, had been given three years' probation. But the school had then refused to take her back, the Headmaster commenting that she was not of the proper 'caliber' —"It would endanger the other pupils . . . we cannot receive her back after a summer in jail . . ."

Frankie only remembered trembling with rage and screaming loudly: "You can keep your fucking school . . ." The next day she appeared in court with her mother, and was sentenced to a year in Wentworth.

Now she stood in front of the Wentworth superintendent, Miss Helen Turner—a plump and rather dumpy little woman in a beige-colored jersey dress—and fought, in the only way she knew, to make Miss Turner respect her. She could not have explained that she seemed to hear voices as visionaries do, and that since these voices came out of books, she resented being rejected from the rather shabby high school on Moon Street.

For her part, Miss Turner was surprised by the comparatively high marks on the school record which lay before her, but in all else the outlines were only too familiar. A fourteen-year-old Negro with a father who himself had been committed for minor offenses, and a mother who appeared to be a religious fanatic; a girl who had already, it seemed, been promiscuous and who had an aunt who was a prostitute; a girl who had been described as a truant, truculent, rebellious, insolent, and demanding.

"You have some very good marks on this school report," she said, putting the file down onto the polished desk. Her eyes, magnified by her glasses, gave her an owlish look which Frankie noted with displeasure. She also noted that the total physical effect of Miss Turner was solid and lumpish—from, so to speak, her slightly bulbous nose to her heavily clad feet.

"That figures." Frankie's tone was laconic.

"The marks aren't very consistent," Miss Turner added with slight acidity, ". . . which is a pity. You probably found your schoolwork easy, and made no real effort to excel."

This was so close to the truth that Frankie was conscious of a flicker of respect, but she felt also a corresponding pain, as if some illness had been diagnosed of which she alone knew the cause.

"I could do it *all* if I wanted," she said rapidly. "I could do it if I *liked*. Sometimes I wanted to, and sometimes I didn't. If I was going to do something, I was going to do it best." Her voice was lofty. "In a subject I liked I would never accept less than an A!"

Miss Turner smiled slightly. "Well, Francesca, you will do well if you never accept less than an A."

In spite of her naïveté, Frankie realized that Miss Turner was amused, and her mood hardened.

"I didn't come *here* to study. *Here* I'll just do my time and I'll go."

"Oh . . . ?" Again that slightly acid inflection. "You are required to study, as you are required to obey the rules. I am only pointing out what will be to your advantage."

"I'm all right if someone don't beat on me," Frankie said, lapsing into the language of the street. "Whitey's got us."

"What did you say?" Miss Turner looked through the thick

distorted lens of her bifocals, and a distance spread between them.

"I said that white folks have prejudice. All us kids know it . . ."

"We are all the same here." Again the superintendent set her right without effort, held up some kind of truth. "At Wentworth everyone has been in trouble, and we try to help each other."

Frankie stood unyielding, her heavy lashes closed on her beautiful eyes, the little white mark on her cheek emphasizing the warm brown of her skin, her small tense strutting body drawn back as if fearful of contact.

"That why they wouldn't let me back in school? Because they wanted to help me?"

"What school?" Miss Turner began to consult the record, which naturally did not explain such details.

"Moon Street High." Frankie felt that rage again, the rage that blackened her face, tensed her nostrils, stretched thin the skin across her brow. Miss Turner was conscious of it radiating from her, and was afraid of it, knowing that it meant trouble in the institution—aggression—punishment—violent language—rebellion —intrigue.

"This is surely no way to start your time at Wentworth . . . ?" she questioned.

Frankie said nothing, and Miss Turner, who was already weary, soon gave up the effort at communication. The girl before her appeared to be just one more of those bitter, aggressive little prisoners whose energy seemed focused upon destruction. This one just happened to have a dark skin.

"I'm going to send you to Florence Nightingale Cottage. I think you'll find Mrs. Casey is a most understanding person, and remember that in the long run finishing high school will be of more advantage to you than anything else."

Frankie looked soberly, finally, out of the window. She was aware, for one moment, of a whole world she had lost, the world of knowledge which once she had so passionately longed to enter. But she only said bitterly: "I'll do my time, and *go*."

The Wentworth campus stretched over thirty acres and was defined by a pleasant, nonpunitive paling fence. Now in mid-fall, the attractive cottages had their own brilliant flowerbeds blazing, as did the leaves of the trees, with orange and yellow, with burnt sienna and crimson. And the main buildings, though retaining some late-century institution-like solidity, had also the late-century protectiveness, and formed a harmonious background for groups of girls hurrying to classes, to cottages, or to work assignments—and in the afternoons to basketball games, to gardening assignments, or on hiking trips. There seemed on the surface little to distinguish this establishment from a well-endowed private school, where it was customary to ask the students to take part in "cooperative work," such as dishwashing, table-setting, and ground maintenance, but under this surface fundamental differences were apparent, differences in that stream of consciousness which is the motivating energy of any group, differences in knowledge, emotion, fantasy, concept.

So Frankie, on her way to the schoolrooms, met little Ana 'Pug Nose' Pulaski as she hurtled in the opposite direction to her table-setting detail, and learned not, as she might have in a more natural environment, that a movie was to be shown that night, or that there was to be a rehearsal of a school play, but information of a very different kind.

"Baby's here as well," Ana told her. "Gee—her hair's done up and everything. She looks fly!"

"Yes," Frankie said with relief. "I hear *she's* around."

"And Harriet," Ana recounted glibly, "the one that was nuts, she went to the Funny Factory."

"That figures." Frankie's tone was wise. "She sure screamed that day in Henry Street . . . I never did find out what the broad had done."

Ana, who had already absorbed all of those institution expressions with which she had been unfamiliar before, now said knowingly: "Perhaps she was one of them checkwriters. They give them tests and things to see if they're okay in the head . . . They say she's over in *Townsend*."

"Well," Frankie said, "she'll probably end up here with the rest of us."

"And Baby O'Reilly—" Ana went on in a tone of self-importance, enjoying bringing this way-out news to one of the hip Negro girls. "You're just in time for the *wedding*. She's up tight with Sugar Brown, and tonight they're going to *get married*."

"You're kidding," mocked Frankie in her flat surprised-at-nothing voice.

"I'm not kidding either, Frankie . . . They're going to have a ceremony before they lock the cubicles. Baby says she's been turning queer for a long time, and Sugar says this is for real, and Baby's going to be with her on the street . . ."

"Is tha-at so?" Frankie shifted her schoolbooks, and thought philosophically that, whatever happened, Baby would always contrive to be under someone's influence.

"Well, maybe it's better for her than King."

Eagerly Ana asked: "Who's King?"

"King? He's her man."

"She got a *man?*"

"Sure she has. Member of the Blue Notes. Don't know what those broads are at, to give every cent they can earn to those men they have."

Pug Nose looked as reflective as she was able. "I never turned queer yet," she confided with a kind of anxious innocence. "Did you turn queer, Frankie?"

"No, baby—" Frankie let her challenging gaze rest on the wide face of the little white girl. "But maybe I should try it though, with all these dames hitting on me!" A faint smile lit her face, giving it an air of mystery which intrigued Ana as much as did the languorous seductive tones of her voice.

"Gee—" Ana's light-greenish eyes widened with an expression of delighted terror. "Alec'd kill me if I turned queer. An' Margie would too. Margie's my best friend and she's in for arson."

"Hot work that . . ." Frankie said. "Well, see you."

"Sure . . . see you."

At once Ana was aware of waiting on the table, as she had been aware of all the other pleasures of the campus, her undiscriminating and active nature moving as happily toward normal activities as it did toward abnormal.

"I gotta wait on the top table today," she said with great self-importance. "Auntie Casey'll hang me if I'm late."

Frankie swung her books. "I'll see you."

"Don't forget tonight." Ana looked at her invitingly. "I'll keep you a seat."

"Okay, Baby." Frankie responded to the seductive glance with a similar one of her own. "Don't *you* forget now."

"I won't." Ana's plump shoulders shrugged. "I'll be scared to death, so I'll want you *near* me."

"You sure need *someone*, doll," Frankie said gallantly.

In the building which serves Wentworth as a school, there is an atmosphere of permissive tolerance. Mr. Papandou, the Greek-American schoolteacher, believes in 'creativity,' and after the first hours of the schoolday have been given over to the 'three R's,' the time remaining is devoted to the 'arts.'

"I don't suppose I'll write in a place like this," Frankie announces during a discussion of "Inspiration," flinging a rude provocative glance toward the long-suffering teacher, "but if I do, it'll only be when I feel like it."

Mr. Papandou (already nicknamed by Sugar and her friends 'Papa Do-Do') is a small, dark, well-meaning man who yearns for some significance in his life, and tries to believe his friends when they tell him that he has "such a chance to do good in a reform school for juveniles." In private, he feels as if he were offering his students this 'good,' this 'enlightenment,' only to find them rejecting it. Today he has put up some clippings from the *Christian Science Monitor* on the bulletin board (in particular, a piece which is entitled 'Glorious Possibilities' and begins "In every individual there is an ability, which when utilized gives him a richer and more purposeful sense of living"), and after he has drawn this to the attention of his pupils he experiences the disillusionment of seeing them all crowding out of the room, without bothering to read it. Fortunately for his ego, and for the combination of faith and ignorance which keep him tied to his job, he does not hear Sugar drawling in the passage outside, "Papa Do-Do sure gets his kicks out of those liddle clippings," nor Ana 'Pug Nose' Pulaski, anxious to gain status with the others, chiming in with, "Papa Do-Do might do-do it in his drawers."

Yet it seems that this kind of obscenity, heard or not, penetrates his consciousness and makes him watchful and timid, so that when Francesca Ford tells him that what she likes best in the world is 'poetry,' it is a relief for him to think that he has at last come upon something of value in his unsatisfactory classroom.

He inquires, with something close to servility: "What poetry do you like, Francesca?"

"I like *The Prophet*," she declares. "In Henry Street one of the girls told me, 'I got a *bad* book for you, Baby,' and she whipped this *Prophet* on me." (Mr. Papandou doesn't know that for the last forty years tattered volumes of *The Prophet* have circulated behind prison bars, that soft leather-bound copies of it have been found in the glove compartments of gangsters' Cadillacs.)

Frankie is reciting:

> *All these things have you said of beauty,*
> *Yet in truth you spoke not of her but of needs unsatisfied,*
> *And beauty is not a need but an ecstasy . . .*
> *It is not the image you would see nor the song you would*
>   *hear,*
> *But rather an image you see though you close your eyes*
>   *and a song you hear*
> *Though you shut your ears . . . a flock of angels for-*
>   *ever in flight . . .*

Their eyes lock for a moment in unsatisfied contact.

"Splendid," Mr. Papandou says enthusiastically.

"I used to like Walt Whitman," Frankie says. "That was at school. And I still dig him because he knocks me out, but this Gibran, he's an enigma . . ." Completely at ease, she leans back in her seat. "I dig Walt . . . don't get me wrong . . . I dig Walt because he digs life and describes every little thing as if it were all new . . . But that Gibran—you wonder where that stud is *at? He* could of walked the road with Jesus."

Mr. Papandou has to admit that he hasn't read *The Prophet,* but he hastens to add that he will do so at once, at which Frankie nods approval and turns her dark enthusiastic eyes toward him.

"You'll dig him," she promises. "You know where Walt is at, but you never know where Gibran is at. He shoots off and takes you with him. He drops it on you, and you got to pick it up and dig it again . . . He's mysterious . . . You wonder what influence he's under, what sign? . . . Oh that *Prophet* is so *mellow!"*

As Miss Walton had smiled at her in Henry Street, Mr. Papandou smiles at her now. *Why, she's charming,* he thinks to himself, as he hurries up to the front of the class.

Brenda is typing words in Spanish, because she has been persuaded by the vocational counselor that a secretary understanding Spanish can earn as much as $100 a week. To Frankie, whose desk is near hers, she complains in her low, depressed-sounding voice, "ten Hamiltons a *week*, why with King I'd be bringing in a yard and a half a night."

The conviction that she is stupid intensifies. Ever since that long-ago seduction the calm world of childhood had receded and become unreal, and she had been left sitting in school stupidly, impatiently . . . The figures dance before her eyes. The shorthand symbols seem unreadable. The little yellow-covered book, *First Steps in Spanish*, lies there like some ancient tablet dug up from an antique grave. Brenda's serious neat face, shadowed by its tower of hair, bends blindly over paper, pen, book, hieroglyphics . . . She is inside Rachel's apartment and she and Rachel are entertaining Mr. Hutton, the man from the drugstore on Highfield Street. Brenda doesn't know much about Mr. Hutton, but she instinctively distrusts him, partly because he is cold, cold as a fish— his face, his dress, his limp, damp hand. She doesn't know why Rachel always receives him so affably, nor why he brings her small parcels, nor why he disappears with her sometimes into the bedroom. She knows that it may be something to do with business, and that Rachel has declared herself always ready for a 'nice piece of money.' But it is impossible to associate the tall, thin, out-of-proportion loose-jointed Mr. Hutton with the sex act. He is cloth, *papier-mâché*, but he is not flesh. He has power of some sort, but it is the power of an inhuman will . . . Rachel's child bangs on the door outside and cries plaintively, "Mama . . . let me in. I wanta go to the bathroom . . . Let me in . . ." Rachel ignores him, her eyes dreaming, conversing in low tones with Mr. Hutton. Brenda wants to open the door, to embrace the child, feed him, clothe him in clean clothes, love him; but Rachel forbids her with a quick frown. Brenda kneels by the keyhole and whispers to Bobbie: "Bobbie, go down the hall to my house, and Ma'll let you use the toilet. Your mummy's busy now . . . go along Bobbie. Go along to my house." She hears Bobbie's whimpering breath, and somehow associates it with her own, drawing it into her own thirsty lungs. She still has in her the natural maternal instinct, the peasant instinct of her mother, not yet stifled. For a moment, indignation struggles with her sense of friendship for Rachel.

But Rachel—uncaring—is in conference with Mr. Hutton on the sofa, her body in strange humble juxtaposition to his, as if bound to him by bonds of business stronger than love. The moment is transfixed. Brenda sees money conquer, sees Rachel's hand move out for the small carefully wrapped package, but her thoughts follow a long dark corridor at the end of which a child knocks uselessly on a door, his cries exhausting themselves against the wood . . .

Now Frankie pushes her desk closer to Brenda's desk.

"What you doing?"

"Spanish," whispers back Brenda. "They speak it in Spain."

"I know," Frankie murmurs testily, "I more or less studied Spanish under my mother."

"Under your *mother?* She Spanish?"

"Half and half," lies Frankie.

Then she catches herself, and adds hastily, "I'm a Negro."

She is just beginning to find out that it is all right to be a Negro, that the latest idea on the street is that it's 'something' to be black, that the white man had brain-washed all the Negroes into believing that they were inferior when they weren't inferior at all. Only now does she understand that there is a *reason* why so many Negroes feel bad about their color, a *reason* for her grand-mother's snobbery and her urging Frankie, "Don't marry beneath you—don't marry *black*. That father of yours, he's too black to be good!" She is immensely relieved that she need no longer pre-tend that she is Spanish as she once did, and at this moment she feels pride, although a jealous pride, because Baby has chosen a black girl instead of a white girl.

"You like 'em dark?" she whispers to Baby.

"Dark?" Baby shifts uneasily as if her mother were attacking her again. "Yes, I like 'em dark, but Sugar ain't *dark*. She's kinda taffy."

"She's stone dark," Frankie says proudly. Then she evaluates Brenda's confusion.

"What's for tonight? Is it for real?"

Brenda's eyes film over. "Oh yes, Frankie—I take it *very* serious."

"I believe you, doll. I'm just asking you to run it down for me."

"It's for real—and we're gonna be together in the street."

Frankie hears Sugar's laughter, stronger and more vibrant than her own.

In the corridor outside the classroom, Baby, as if drawn by a mag-net, has gravitated toward Sugar, while Ana, forever seeking status, expatiates about the great event which is to take place that night. "They sure love funny," she says, indicating the way in which Sugar inclines her body toward Brenda's and sweeps her with a possessive gaze. "It's a kick." Frankie ignores her because she has been seeking for a suitable love-object for herself, and has fixed upon Pepper, the swarthy-skinned Italian girl whose black eyes smolder above a neat nose and red lips. Those red lips are accented with a faint dark down, which fascinates Frankie, who considers it a sign of passion. It will be all right for Sugar to have Baby, Frankie thinks, if she, Frankie, can have Spice. Though what she means by 'have' she is not quite sure.

That 'love,' 'sex,' and 'belonging' are here in Wentworth welded into a whole, and worn like a symbol on one's sleeve, is clear to her, and that this symbol makes one part of the ingroup is also clear. But she is confused by the general innocence of the proceedings and, advanced as she is (having been an observer of Beppo's domination of Opaline), she still has no very clear idea of what might be expected of her, if she were to work her way into the crowd. "Why," she hears someone say in a bored and rather pretentious voice, as Sugar and Baby saunter down the passage toward the far windows which look over the chilly fields, "if we'd taken all those girls who hit on us, we'd of been half dead with sex . . . You know, all of them cutting themselves and jumping out of windows"—a remark which echoes in Frankie's ears with no more weight than does another one made by Candy, who stands in the middle of the passage, advancing toward those far windows, against which the snow has suddenly begun to fall, holding her skirts away from her thin body in a gesture of surprise, and lifting up her fair head, as she says in the hushed voice of a child: "Look . . . Look . . . It's snowing!"

Still the snow falls. Without a whisper it sifts through air mildly cold and saturated with the scent of damp dead leaves. The branches etch upon the fading sky, but the pattern is broken and loses its definition. Old trees are bound to the whitening earth. On foreshortened and spiny bushes, prickles are softened by the white snow, and red berries are suddenly filled with light. This same mysterious light, half violet, half orange, seems drawn from a sun not seen in its descent, but spread briefly upon the landscape, upon the buildings of the institution and upon the cottages which give no hint of their troubled occupants. Outside the light is like a mysterious evocation, but inside it reaches no one—unless it creeps somehow into the words so often repeated, words which

Frankie (because of her literary and oratorical talents) has been chosen to read: "*Whom God has joined, let no man put asunder* . . ."

At the central desk of Florence Nightingale Cottage, Mrs. Casey is writing up the daybook, noting that the doors are locked, noting that everyone is present, that Candy has complained of a headache and has been given an aspirin. In another book given over to 'special' reports, she writes that Emilia Martinez, the newly arrived Puerto Rican girl, has been crying herself to sleep each night because of 'loneliness for her mama' . . . and that Sugar has been found twice attempting to be alone with Brenda O'Reilly, once in the shower room and once, more audaciously, in the little room where the officers keep their coats and drink their coffee, and which by accident had been left unlocked. Now as Mrs. Casey writes, she is not aware that as soon as the passage lights are dimmed, and in that last half hour before complete silence falls upon the cottage, Emilia Martinez, her face buried in her pillow, her long hair spread out on the sheets, will begin to cry again, or that Midget, already the willing slave of Sugar, will complain of a toothache, so that Mrs. Casey's attention will be diverted to the south side of the cottage, even while stealthy bare-footed girls will be gathering for the 'wedding' in the room shared by Francesca Ford and Mary Kelly.

At this moment, Frankie wears scuffed navy-blue slippers and, over her pajamas, her long navy mannish dressing gown. Her hair is a little greasy from the pomade which she uses on her process, and is tied around with a white scarf, over the top of which projects a parrot-like crest. To add to the 'Male Preacher' effect, she has put on a large pair of dark sunglasses.

"*Whom God hath joined,*" she intones again, "*let no man put asunder.*"

Mary Kelly, an adenoidal beanstalk of a girl, too nervous to do anything else, has been given the task of holding the flashlight so that Frankie can see to read the prayerbook. And Candy, drawn by Frankie's charisma, and now curled up on her adored one's bed, her toes tucked under her pink flannel nightgown, holds the dime-store ring. In the meantime, Brenda 'Baby' O'Reilly, the *bride*, is in her own room three doors away, perched on her bed and supported by pillows. She is writing a last letter to her mother, as if indeed this wedding were a final step in her life. "*Dear Ma*," she has written, "*I'm almost going out of my mind. It seems like a spell comes over me. Can you write me once in a while? I know it's a strain for you to write me and I've only given you gray hairs in my life but please write, it helps. Love Brenda.*" Having got this far she sits staring at the wall before her, a big mature girl of Irish-German parentage, her wide cheeks polished from the heat of the bath, her coarse blue-black mane of hair spread over the shoulders of her best nightgown with the lace on it. Underneath her nightgown she wears, for modesty, a brassière and a pair of panties, and she intends to tiptoe up the passage to Frankie's room carrying a pair of patent-leather heels, which she has borrowed from Sugar, the *groom*. As the image of the groom should indeed dominate the life of the bride, so Sugar dominates her, and King, with his rough masculine coercion, is forgotten as is forgotten also the innumerable times she has stood in misery under the light and waited for a customer to appear out of the darkness. Closer to her now is the sheltered stuffy apartment where Rachel, the tolerant, not-to-be-feared, caress-perfect female, had educated her. "*Ma*," she writes in a postscript. "*Ma, I know you are sincere when you talk about my friends, but I have friends here and they are for real. For example, when I need cigarettes and toilet articles they give them to me and any little thing I want—if that's not real friendship I don't know what is, Ma. I know it sounds stupid but what does it matter what color someone is, as long as someone loves you? I'll close now. B.*" As if all had been explained to the home front, she folds up the letter, puts it under the pillow, glances once at the watch on her plump freckled wrist, and then stares calmly at the wall, waiting for the hour to strike . . . Three doors up the passage Candy turns her pathetic fair gaze upon Frankie, her immature love like a halo around her, and then sucks in her breath once or twice, and smiles self-consciously. Mary Kelly puts the flashlight down upon the bureau and tiptoes up the passage to give the signal—running one fingernail across the radiator. Immediately Midget on the south side of the cottage is affected by her false toothache pains and sets up a wail, which draws Mrs. Casey away from the central desk. Ana 'Pug Nose' Pulaski bounds off her bed and pulls a sweater over her head. Sugar, in grasshopper green crepe de Chine pajamas, feels her way hurriedly along the wall to Frankie and Mary's room, and taking a pair of loafers from under one arm slips them onto her long narrow dark feet. With hands as graceful, as black, as elongated as her feet, she smooths her slick pompadour and, planting herself in front of Preacher Frankie, flashes a brilliant smile around the room, muttering rapidly, "Where's ma 'bride'? Where's ma 'bride'?"

Now Pug Nose, Candy, Trixie, Polly, and a West Indian girl called, because of her English accent, 'Haughty Helena,' all crouch on the beds. Now a latecomer slides rapidly along the passage outside, and Frankie stands solemnly holding the Bible, with Mary Kelly behind her, flashlight at the ready. Now Midget, playing Chickie at the other end of the building, intensifies her toothache pains, and her need for Mrs. Casey's ministrations. Pepper, the elegant girl from 'Little Italy,' comes stealthily into Frankie's room, biting her red lips nervously, her great mass of black hair almost obscuring her tiny, swarthy, dark-mustached face. She has her arm around Baby, who hesitates in the doorway to put on the over-large black shoes, and then advances to stand soberly, even tearfully, her bosom heaving, beside the imperturbable Sugar.

"Hurry," someone whispers, while Spice pushes a wreath made of artificial flowers down upon Baby's head.

"*Will you, Sugar,*" begins Frankie rapidly but clearly, "*take Brenda O'Reilly—here present—for your lawful wedded wife, according to the rites of our Holy Mother the Church? . . .*"

"*I, Sugar,*" Sugar says firmly, "*take you, Brenda O'Reilly, for my lawful wife, to have and to hold, from this day forward, for better for worse, for richer for poorer, in sickness and in health, till death us do part . . .*"

"*Will you, Brenda,*" Frankie is saying now, "*take Sugar Roberts—here present—for your lawful husband, according to the rites of our Holy Mother the Church? . . .*"

In the fringes of the flashlight's hooded eye, the girls' attentive faces swim in the dim light, their features molded by that ceremony dear to women, into rapt and eternal forms.

"*I join you together,*" comes Frankie's voice, "*in the name of the Father, and of the Son, AND of the Holy Ghost . . .*"

Mary Kelly has taken the ring from Candy, and Sugar's dark nervous hand is pushing it onto one of Brenda's plump fingers.

"*Bless O Lord this ring,*" Frankie says with sonorous enjoyment, "*that she who is to wear it, keeping true faith to her husband, may abide in your peace and obedience . . .*" Sugar's ebony features take on a rapacious and birdlike possessiveness, and she turns and kisses her bride with lingering intent. The scene focuses on the kiss, seems to surround it with wonder and doubt, and is then scattered like broken pieces of water thrown into the air. The silent audience disperses.

Only Candy lingers, crouched like a fair and bewildered angel among the rumpled blankets of Frankie's bed.

"You not goin' home, honey?" Frankie asks as she perches beside her, bathed by her adoration, pale and warm like the flame of a candle. "You sure goin' to get the wrath of Auntie Casey. She'll be locking soon."

"Let me stay," whispers Candy, clinging to the blanket like a child to the blanket in its crib. "I'm lonesome Frankie."

Frankie is reminded of the brilliant eyes of Lacey at St. Ursula's Home for Delinquent Girls. "You'll get in trouble, lonesome."

"I just want to be with *you* Frankie," Candy pleads in a whisper as they huddle together under the blankets. She reaches up and touches the little white spot on her friend's cheek. "I just want to stay for a while." Her mouth exhales the fragrance of a small child, but her arms grip like a woman. "What'll they *do* Frankie?"

"What'll *who* do?"

"Sugar and Baby? Now they're married?"

"I guess they'll take care of business."

"What's that?"

"Taking care of business? . . ." Frankie feels Candy's arms around her so tight that they almost strangle her. "They'll love each other, honey."

"I love *you*, Frankie," Candy says.

"Sure . . . I know you do, doll."

She disengages Candy's strangling arms, which clutch like pliant white vines around her brown neck. "Sure you do . . . How about slippin' into your own bed now, sweet?"

"No." Candy snuggles and stretches voluptuously against her. "No! I like it here."

"You do. It's sleepy time."

"Don't feel like sleeping. Once I usta slip out at night when I didn't feel like sleepin'. My mother'd beat me."

"Then what?"

"It wasn't nothin'. She always beat me. Just because she was a nervous wreck I think."

"Always someone beatin' on someone," philosophizes Frankie.

"Oncet I ran," Candy whispers. "I wanted to see my art teacher because she usta give me some good ideas. Then my art teacher took me home . . . My mother cried. She sent me to St. Ursula's Home as a 'stubborn.' "

"You was in *that* joint?" Frankie asks in amazement.

"Yes, before I came here, but only for six months. They sent me away because the big girls were beating on me."

. . . Candy sees herself in the laundry at St. Ursula's Home. She is not quite twelve and fairer and slighter than she is now. She climbs onto one of the soap boxes in the laundry, and stares out of the window into the snowbound yard. A tall seventeen-year-old girl comes up behind her and puts her arm around her. She has a pretty face with dark intent eyes, and Candy feels secure as she holds her there, pressing one cheek into her shoulder. Candy is chewing gum.

"Give me some gum, baby," whispers the girl.

"I don't *have* no more gum," Candy answers truthfully.

"Well give me some of what you've got in your mouth," teases the girl.

Without thinking Candy pulls the gum out of her mouth and is about to offer it to her new friend.

"No, baby—put it back." The girl laughs.

Candy puts it back.

The big girl lifts one hand, gently turns Candy's head downward, and puts her lips against Candy's lips.

"Give me your gum *this* way, baby," she murmurs, her lips opening slightly to enclose Candy's pursed red mouth. "Give it to me, baby."

The long-ago scene materializes again as Candy snuggles close to Frankie's body. She feels her lips open, and the girl's tongue pushing between them. She feels the long unending exploration of her mouth. She remembers, as so many scenes telescoped together, the kisses and caresses of the girl, the unforgettable light upon the laundry walls. She remembers her sorrow when they are discovered by the nuns and separated forever . . .

"Kiss me, Frankie," she whispers.

"Aunt Casey'll be mad if she finds you," Frankie whispers back, touching her lips.

"I don' care. Stroke me." Candy commands.

Frankie begins to stroke her. The white skin of the child seems dead to her fingers, and she wants to bring it to life. This is a baby she touches with her hands, a small white baby, precious and sickly.

"Stroke me, Frankie," Candy commands. "Go on . . . don't stop."

Under the long fingers she draws closer, lies still, is at last content. And her dependence draws upon the older girl's still undeveloped strength until Frankie's sinewy frame is twisted in the bed to concentrate upon this weak pale female child.

"How's that, baby? How's that?"

"Oh I *like* it," sighs Candy, "I *like* it."

"Why you like it, baby?"

"I don' know . . . I jus' *like* it."

Frankie spurred to further efforts strokes Candy's legs.

"You like this?"

"I like everything *you* do," Candy affirms wholeheartedly.

At this moment Frankie loves Candy passionately, unselfishly, beyond reason. She has forgotten Mrs. Casey and Mary Kelly in the bed across the room. She strokes Candy's hair and back, she buries her face in her neck, and showers eager kisses upon her narrow white shoulders, enclosing her tenderly so that the two bodies—black and white—are entwined in a fluid pattern. She is intensely anxious to give Candy pleasure, and as if she were strumming on a guitar, she draws her long fingers up the inside of her thighs, until the younger girl is trembling with gratitude, until, with a little moan, she lets her legs fall open and Frankie feels moisture touch her fingers.

But at that moment something happens. The older girl becomes uncertain, does not know what to do next. She hesitates as if she stood at the border of a strange country, the knowledge of which has been supplied to her in imperfectly glimpsed scenes. An instinct of will urges her to act in some way however inadequate, to penetrate, to conquer. But she is afraid to make a fool of herself so that the mantle of masculinity slips from her shoulders. Candy's bright eyes seem to implore her in the darkness; and a hot hand stretches out and grasps hers, pressing it to parted lips, as if it wishes her to read there, the desire in an exhaling breath . . .

But it is too late—Frankie has become powerless.

———————

Beyond the flower beds—in summer neat and flowering—now showing only the long thorned whips of barberry thrust out of the hardened snow, the big windows of the sitting room in the administration building glow with light. It is a late January afternoon, and five members of the staff are discussing the disciplinary problems of the week.

In a low chair, Miss Turner receives her coffee from the fairhaired Adrienne, one of the institution's model girls. Adrienne, in her little violet uniform with its white apron, thinks she is on a TV screen and turns carefully to show her profile, bowing tenderly toward Miss Turner. No relationship is possible between these two, since Adrienne has already set up her life and has not included Miss Turner in it. But of paramount importance is the fact that the superintendent, sitting in a much-admired chair of rich purple plush, and stretching her short legs before her onto the carpet, *does* sit there, and that she, Adrienne, erect and courteous, her pink cheeks polished with triumph, holds a glittering tray from which she bestows upon all a highly correct cup of coffee.

"Mrs. Casey," Miss Turner begins, as soon as Adrienne has withdrawn, "since this week's difficulties seem to center somewhat upon your cottage, we may as well begin there. How much of a problem is Sugar Roberts?"

"I can't truthfully say she *is* much of a problem," Mrs. Casey answers. "She doesn't often break rules, and when she does, she apologizes at once and without apparent resentment." Mrs. Casey's face with its many fine wrinkles is a little sad, and her blue eyes with their expression of strain and fatigue, look off through the window. "As you know I reported having found Sugar and Baby together in the officers' room at the cottage. But this seems to me of less importance than the question of what to do about it. Can I have any influence on Sugar? And should Sugar herself be here?"

Miss Turner deals with this question briskly.

"She still has a few months to go before she is seventeen; and therefore it is legally correct for her to be under our custody."

"Perhaps Mrs. Casey could clarify Sugar's behavior," suggests Miss Bailey, the young social worker, who smartly dressed, sits knees crossed, swinging her horned-rimmed glasses on one finger. "How does she act?"

"She has a lot of energy," Mrs. Casey replies rather helplessly. "Isn't that true, Mary?"

Miss Brownley nods. "She's excellent at basketball and volley-ball. I've never tried her on a high jump or broad jump."

Although the 'babblings' of the staff aren't important to her, Adrienne who has entered with fresh coffee, hears the last two sentences, and changes in her mind the final term to 'Butch jump.' "What a fellow HE is," she adds silently without moving her neat pink lips. She then retreats to the girls' serving room where she expatiates to her friend 'Baba' on the relative innocence of the staff. "They don't swing nohow," she says, "not up, not down."

In the administration sitting room Mrs. Casey feels herself in a dilemma. "There are about forty girls in my cottage, and most of them need kindness. There is scarcely one girl among them who has not lacked in her own home companionship, love, and elementary decencies . . . I don't feel that I can know what they are all doing at once—nor do I feel it creative to suspect them. As far as Brenda O'Reilly is concerned, she is much under Sugar's influence, but it is only just to say that she would be under someone else's influence if not under Sugar's. As for Sugar herself, she is . . ." Again Mrs. Casey pauses. Filled with the acceptance engendered by years of working with this particular problem, she finishes with a certain modesty. "It is her whole nature . . . She is a young *man*—let loose amongst young women . . ."

There is a silence in the room. Miss Bailey goes on swinging her horned-rimmed glasses. Miss Turner glances briefly across at Miss Brownley, her lucid-eyed physical-education instructor. Mrs. Holly, the gray-haired nurse, rustles in her white uniform, as a bird sinks into its nest. The skeleton of Sugar, white as ash, strong as ivory, dangles indestructibly before the company—and then is clothed suddenly with dark and polished flesh, given life by Mrs. Casey's apt description, a description which has put the entire problem upon a different footing.

"We can't allow overt behavior," Miss Turner protests, recovering herself. "We must always in this case use disciplinary measures. Parents' complaints. Official disapproval . . . The fact that we are a public institution and therefore answerable to the public. Hard as it may be to control homosexuality, we have to try to do so, or at least—if this is too difficult—to *appear* to do so . . ."

"Perhaps Mrs. Casey can clarify," Miss Bailey suggests again. "Is Sugar aggressive? Does she act out?"

"She is very aggressive," Mrs. Casey says, "but it is not in what she does. It is in *her*. It is something I don't see. When I found her in the officers' room with Brenda, they were not touching each other . . ." She sighs seeing the multiplicity of roads which lead to Wentworth. "But that doesn't say Brenda is not under her influence."

"We can't do anything about her until we have some overt behavior," Miss Turner rules. "Let me see now." She is consulting the list in her hand. "Naomi Rosenstein . . . Maggie O'Connery . . . Francesca Ford. Francesca is your other problem in Florence Nightingale Cottage. We seem to have numerous reports about *her* . . . Will you begin, Mrs. Holly?"

Mrs. Holly is shuffling her notes. "*Francesca Ford was very fresh at the hospital on Tuesday the fourteenth,*" she reads. "*She was sent from class because she had a sore elbow, and I soaked it in Epsom salts. She said this gave her no relief, and that Epsom salts was an old wives' remedy. So I told her to go back to class, and she said—I quote—'All right you old bitch, I'm glad to go.'*"

"Miss Brownley?" prompted Miss Turner.

"*Francesca doesn't like sports,*" Miss Brownley reads. "*I have some difficulty in getting her to cooperate. Yesterday she did not come to volleyball practice, and when I sent Rose for her, it turned out that she had been to the hairdresser's without permission, and had her hair cut quite short.*"

"Did you give Francesca permission to have her hair cut short, Mrs. Casey?" (Short hair, since it can be associated with homosexual leanings, is a sensitive question in the institution.)

Mrs. Casey shakes her head.

"This girl is obviously very disruptive." Miss Turner consults her own notes. "Smoking in front of the office—being rude to Miss Lacoutte—accusations from Reina Williams that she is urinating in the bathtub. Do you know anything about *that*, Mrs. Casey . . . ?"

"Reina didn't mention it to me." Again Mrs. Casey feels helpless. "Gossip and tale-bearing is constant, and I try not to encourage it in Florence Nightingale. If Francesca *was* guilty of this, then I should put it down to a deliberate act . . . Perhaps some kind of perverse desire to get publicity."

"Do you have that note, Miss Bailey?"

The social worker produces a note and hands it to the superintendent.

"This was found in Alice Admonson's locker," Miss Turner explains. "It is in Francesca's handwriting and you all know the kind of trouble we've had with Alice Admonson." She reads aloud: " 'Listen, bitch—you call yourself my friend. What you told Sugar is pretty low and where did you get the idea that I was using Candy for a sucker? I'm gonna get you and I'm gonna kick your ass and no one's going to be on your side. When the boot turns, everyone turns.' "

There is a silence.

Then Miss Turner speaks with a hint of alarm in her voice. "It's hard to know how corrupted the girl is, but I feel that she should be put into isolation for a few weeks, until we can see how to deal with her . . . Mrs. Casey, perhaps you have something to add to this?"

"Francesca seems to be a complicated little person," Mrs. Casey begins guardedly. "She has undoubtedly a tough and aggressive side, but she has also a certain fineness and intelligence. I'm not at all sure that she is homosexual . . . She probably doesn't know yet what she is. After all she is still under fifteen! . . . But we have to realize that, like Sugar, she is a leader . . ."

Mrs. Casey is groping toward the expression of a need for other alternatives in the treatment of 'her' girls. Like some frustrated mother, she wants them to have better chances. A slight red stains her cheeks as she leans forward for a moment as if to snatch a grain of comfort from the others.

"Does she have any particular friendship with Candy?" Miss Bailey wants to know. "Candy told me that Frankie was her best friend."

"Candy tags along after her." Mrs. Casey remembers Francesca curled up with a book in her cubicle, and Candy waiting patiently outside, blond and immovable, her pale eyes staring into the distance. "Candy is obviously under her influence—but Francesca seems more interested in books . . ."

"Well there *is* a report from Mr. Papandou," Miss Turner

concedes. She sorts amongst her papers and reads aloud: " '*Francesca Ford shows a mastery of general ideas, and considerable intelligence. She writes and reads poetry. With so many students who are indifferent and unprepared, I cannot give her the attention she needs, and it is a pity she cannot go to a challenging private boarding school. She is at the crossroads, and I feel that she can become either an out-and-out failure or a highly respected professional woman.*' "

"What challenging boarding school would *have* her?" Miss Bailey asks with a shrug.

"I don't think we should keep her with the general population," Miss Turner concludes. "Mrs. Holly, do you have a room for her at the hospital?"

Mrs. Holly consults her daybook. "Number 4 is free."

"We'll transfer her then, Mrs. Casey." Miss Turner shuffles her notes. "Now let's go on to Naomi Rosenstein . . ."

The next afternoon Mrs. Wilhemina Tobey, Francesca Ford's grandmother, appears at Wentworth State School for Girls (as once she had appeared at St. Ursula's Home), although this time she is carrying a string bag into which she has slipped not only her Bible and a package of tracts but also those clothes which she has thought necessary for her 'journey for the Lord.'

As tall and stately as ever, but more impressive than before by reason of her fiercer eyes and more resounding preacher's voice, Mrs. Tobey is received guardedly by Wentworth's superintendent.

"Greetings in the name of the Saviour," she hears Mrs. Tobey saying. "At least I got here safely."

"Were you in some danger?" Miss Turner asks.

"The dogs were following me," her guest announces. "They've hired detectives, and they're breaking into my mail and my phone calls. The people in Murmaine County are the lowest of all." Her eyes become terrible and Miss Turner shifts uneasily.

"I suppose you want to visit with your granddaughter?" she says with forced cordiality. "Visiting hours are generally on Sundays, and after school on Wednesdays, but seeing that you have come so far . . ."

Mrs. Tobey quiets her with an impressive wave of her hand.

"It's quite all right. I have come for my baby. I have come to protect her from that dirty old dog of a judge who called her a prostitute! It grieves me that I can't just lift her up on my back, and carry her right out of here . . . In New Mexico where I have carved out a territory for the Lord, they have put up some model homes. Ninety-nine dollars down and about seventy-five a month . . . I can get Francesca into a permanent room at the YWCA until everything is arranged—they ask about seventeen dollars a week for that. Then I can find her a baby-sitting job . . ."

"I'm not sure what can be done . . ." Miss Turner's voice trails away as she wonders how to rid herself of this unbalanced guest (about whom she has been warned by Frankie's mother).

"Francesca has been railroaded in here." The old lady leans forward and taps authoritatively on the desk. "I can put it all down to the cheap church . . ."

"The church?"

"The cheap church. 568 Evans Avenue."

Miss Turner thinks it wiser not to comment upon rival churches. But she listens to a long harangue about detectives, poisoned food, stealing of mail, and visions in which Francesca appears under the special signs of the Lord's favor.

"I am working for a speedy release." Mrs. Tobey rummages in her sturdy bag, and seems nonplussed not to find an official letter granting her permission to carry off her granddaughter. She rationalizes by telling Miss Turner that she had had the letter, but had hidden it "because Negroes on Evans Avenue are so nosy . . ."

When her granddaughter at last stands before her—even while she is still telling her of model homes and baby-sitting jobs in far away New Mexico—she allows a few tears to fall down her wrinkled brown cheeks.

That night Frankie writes to her mother: *"Dearest Mama. Nana came to see me and she's been to see Mr. Waters on the* board, and the Governor—and they said they didn't see what I'm doing here . . . They read my record and it was perfect! Mr. Waters said that the State School is no place to be used for convenience. That just because I truanted I don't have to be in prison! That someone had put me here just to suit themselves. Nana's hair is nice, and she is as sane as me . . .*"

But as she writes her belief fails her, and she wonders whether it is all her own fault or whether the Lord has singled her out for trouble. She ardently wishes to believe in her own goodness and innocence, but in spite of her stated confidence in her grandmother's sanity some secret doubt remains. *I'm no angel,* she admits to herself, *but they don't give me a chance . . . I'm always hearing I'm not wanted. I'm not wanted at home and I'm not wanted at school.* And because she is ashamed of the depth of her desire to be loved, she puts it down to injustice and prejudice. "*No one's fair to me,*" she writes. "*I thought that Miss Brownley believed in me, but she turned me out of volleyball when I was late, and that really hurt. Everybody's down on me and they take any excuse to dog me. They won't let me into 'Rec' now because of my cheap talk, and here I am in the hospital like a leper . . .*"

Although it is against the rules she has turned on the bedside lamp long after lights-out, and now she dims it by throwing her skirt over the shade. She lies on the bed smoking a cigarette which has been slipped to her by the girl who brought in her supper tray, and the consciousness of being alone—as she is to be alone, isolated, segregated, so often in the future—gives her a feeling of desperation. *Why are they after me about my talk? I don't do anything! I may talk different from older people, but all us kids talk that language.* As if these appeals for justice had already been considered and found wanting, she now thinks belligerently, *It seems like the people who act crazy, or threaten to kick up, are the ones who get anywhere.*

But later, when she has put out the light, and the cold and brilliant expanse of the sky swings again into her vision, bravado disappears. Uneasiness blends with sadness. She remembers the tall straight figure of her grandmother standing in the door of the visitors' room as they are about to part. She hears her grandmother (forgetful, wandering, like some prophet in the wilderness) cry out in a ringing voice, as if bemoaning a symbolic past: "How dare they take my Jeanette from me!"

Frankie begins to cry.

The mail is given out by Sugar just as the supper line forms in the hallway of the girls' dining room, and Baby has a letter from her mother in answer to the farewell note she had dispatched on the eve of her 'wedding.' Like a favored courtier, she receives the envelope from Sugar who stands erect and commanding in the dining-room doorway, and bends sweet smiles upon her special protégée.

"Nothing for you, doll," Sugar then says to Pepper, who eyes the letter reflectively. "*Someone* don' know what they're missing." Her significant gaze sweeps the girl's figure and melts into an expression of forced and mocking rapture as she makes a vulgar gesture with her forefingers and thumbs. Pepper pushes by her with self-conscious pride, and Sugar turns her attention toward Pug Nose, whose body has rounded under the influence of good food and regular hours.

"You waitin' on something, Pug Nose?"

"Don't kid me, Sugar. Any letter for me?"

"No—nothin' for you Pug. But," her voice lowers, "I give you somethin' you come later."

Ana shrugs with a pleased smile. *Sugar sure is in my corner*, she is thinking. Aloud, over her plump shoulder, she warns: "Watch out I don't give you something back!" And she murmurs to Midget archly, running her hand through the red hair which she now wears short in a 'bubble bob': "Sugar got power on me, more than anyone, more than Beppo."

"Who's Beppo?" Midget asks with a certain hunger, yearning upwards toward the dumpy Ana, touching the edge of her snazzy orange sweater.

"Oh she bigtime when I wuz in Henry Street."

Midget, whose mind is not able to cross that geographical gulf, only murmurs: "You got a *bad* sweater, Ana," and holds onto the edge of it as the line moves slowly into the dining room.

. . . Reading her letter, Baby is being drawn relentlessly into that anxious home vortex, where her broad-faced mother, her hair well streaked with gray, sits at the kitchen table and stretches out admonitions on lined paper. *"Brenda,"* she reads, *"what's the good of talking about the colored? I tell you I have good colored friends like Mrs. Hailey in the PTA. But each time you defied me by running away with those Negroes who are your so-called friends, you put one more nail in your coffin. Yes, those black Africans were frightened that I'd make a mess for them, and if once they were white now they are really getting black again. Don't you know they are the cause of all of your trouble?"*

Baby sighs. The perfume of the dark mates she has had is in her nostrils, and she just can't 'see white,' as she puts it to Frankie.

"Don't you know, Brenda," the letter continues, *"that there'll always be someone in authority, someone who tells you what to do. You keep saying that this wouldn't have happened if Daddy hadn't hit you, but I tell you, Brenda, I was at a point where I was ready to beat you into insensibility, you riled me so."* The despair, the frustration of her mother saturates the thin pages, and Brenda holds them in her hand as if she held the family burden. *Ma doesn't understand,* she thinks vaguely. At the same time she gets a certain comfort from the letter, from the mere sound of her mother's exasperated scolding, from the reiterated, worn-out phrases which bring back to her sight the broad, strong forearms bent upon the kitchen table, her mother's large bosom enclosed in the pale silk of her best dress. A kind of love shelters her for a moment, but a love which can give her no support and only reminds her of her own alienation. She wishes that her hand could slowly turn black as she reads the letter, that she could sink down into that world inhabited by King, Frankie, Sugar. *"When you come out, Brenda,"* she reads now, *"you must give up the colored forever. They have been the cause of everything. It wouldn't be fair to Dennis to wonder while he was working, if you were out with niggers!"*

. . . Now that the last of the letters has been distributed, Sugar lounges by the door with a card in her hands. She crosses the room and drops into the seat which Pug Nose has been keep-

ing for her, saying "That's for you, hon. I didn't notice it before."
She twirls the card in her fingers and reads the address aloud.
"Miss Ana Pulaski, State Correctional School for Girls, Went-
worth, Murmaine County."

She then drops it onto Ana's plate and says mockingly: "It's
from your ma, since when did your *ma* go to the Burrow?"

Ana flushes. The card shows Spring Street in North City, and
a black arrow has been marked between two buildings, and 'the
Burrow' printed above it. On the other side of the card is written
"Waiting for you," and this is signed MA. After the MA there is a
tiny 'N,' making the word into MAN. Ana's admiration shines in
her pale-greenish eyes and her self-importance swells, expanding
and coarsening the very pores of her skin. Through her lashes she
looks at Sugar who regards her with intent interest.

"An' who's 'Man'?" inquires Sugar at last.

"Man Delgado—that's Beppo. I met her in Henry Street."

Sugar whistles.

"That Indian type! Better watch out, flat nose. Gran'mother
gobbled up Li'l Red Riding Hood."

"Oh I got my boyfriend Alec," Ana says and shrugs her
plump shoulders (she neglects to say that it is months since he has
written, and that he has never 'made it up to see her'), "but if I
don't get outa here I'm going to go queer, I tell you. I got a kite
from a girl in Louisa May Alcott Cottage yesterday."

"That so?" inquires Sugar, flashing her white teeth. "You
should be glad!"

"I'd like to have the po-lice like me," Ana chatters on.

"The po-lice," Sugar mocks. "Them jive rollers!"

"Well . . ." Ana is embarrassed. "The po-lice have plenty of
money. Like Joanna gets all sorts of things from Miss Brownley.
She bought her the cutest little fluffy dog for her birthday." A
shadow crosses her face as she thinks of Mrs. Casey in the cottage,
and she adds: "I don't mean Auntie Casey . . . I wouldn't love
her funny."

Sugar is only smiling and munching at the celery on her salad
plate.

"It's a dra-ag," Ana says to no one in particular.

Her mind is on freedom—on running the streets and escaping from the cops, hanging on the corner, drinking beer with the sailors, riding to the beach, getting presents of candy and fruit.

These pleasures invade her vision and dull the simple life she has been learning to appreciate at Wentworth. Further memories materialize, unpleasant, pungent, but exciting—memories of that rape when her thighs were black and blue with bruises—swaggering advances of young men—being forced to 'go down' for a guy —waiting on the corner for the stern and rigorous Alec—being manhandled by the police, while she encourages them with violent language and precipitate flight.

"It's a dra-ag, being here," she complains again.

Two weeks later, Sugar, who is just touching her seventeenth birthday, is taken away to Henry Street. She has been discovered in a compromising situation in the vegetable storehouse with Baby. Baby herself, as the nonaggressive one, is considered more sinned against than sinning, and is only sent to Secure. As Sugar, accompanied by Mrs. Casey, saunters along the path from the cottage, dressed in her street clothes, carrying a small suitcase, Baby catches sight of her from the locked room in the hospital.

She begins to scream. Through the frozen air, the screams crack like whips, and Baby's great dark mop of hair sways in the upper part of the barred window, like some small and agitated flag. Sugar, wearing her black coat and high heels, pauses for a moment, propping her long thin legs like a smart long-legged bird about to fly the dull domestic coop. She is full of gaiety and bravado.

"Cool it," she calls vigorously, even contemptuously, across the snowy waste. "*Cool* it, Baby."

"Come, Sugar," Mrs. Casey suggests.

They walk on. The morning is silent except for the click of Sugar's heels.

Brenda lowers her tousled head onto the bars. Sometimes a warmth has seemed to wrap her around like a blanket, to soothe her great womanly limbs until she has felt herself transformed and softened. She doesn't really know whether it is Sugar of whom she is enamored, or whether those long supple pink-lined fingers have only caressed her flesh enough to reaffirm former choices. She is unable, like the energetic Sugar, to feel a bitter pleasure in parting, and now she is filled with sullen despair. Her forehead and cheeks press against the iron of the bars and her hair is loosened from its pins and streams around her face like the veil of a widow.

In Florence Nightingale Cottage, Mrs. Casey, who is about to go off duty, is reading a letter which she had found neatly folded and placed beside her spectacle case. It is from a newly arrived girl called Hilda, whose pale face is the more noticeable because of a red scar which stretches from ear to chin ("My stepfather cut me," she told Miss Bailey).

"*Dear Auntie Casey,*" the letter begins. "*I would like to know if you could listen to me for what I have to say to you Auntie—I have never had any friends on the outside and I always wanted to have friends. I don't mean no good for nothing friends . . . I mean real good friends . . . Auntie I love you just like my own mother . . . I only wish you would have met me. The reason why I am saying this is because I really and truly don't think I'm good. Please help me. Hilda.*"

As Mrs. Casey folds up the piece of paper, she feels the girl's loneliness like a sickness; as if she stared across a desert and saw that solitary figure, advancing steadily, desiccated by fever and thirst. But even as she is touched by Hilda's inarticulate appeal, the problems of the one are merged with the problems of the many, and she finds in herself a familiar reluctance to go off duty, conscious of the unnatural calm which extends throughout her cottage.

Pallid winter faces reflect the strain of Sugar's expulsion, Baby's imprisonment. Cheeks flush. Heads turn. In an atmosphere which had seemed silent, murmured information is passed on, recorded only by quickened pulses, deeper breathing. Insecurity

shifts from girl to girl, like feather-weight pollen. Mrs. Casey
knows that in the warm and orderly dormitory, those who remain
are aware of the two empty beds, and feel themselves threatened
by that emptiness and by the stale material comfort which surrounds them. She wonders whether she should leave them to the
unpopular Miss Lacoutte, but can think of no real reason to
change her plans.

. . . And as soon as her car has pulled out of the driveway, it
seems that her reluctance is justified, since there is at once a herd-
ing together of the group into a heroic solidarity, a restless anger
and sense of boredom, and the hysterical retelling of folk tales
from the past (larded in the telling with obscene expressions and
rousing denunciations of the establishment). The '*Exploits of
Beppo*,' for instance, are recited by the *Fair Troubadour Adrienne*—a long saga which recounts the seduction of a nurse in the
hospital ('*That was before Mrs. Holly of course . . . no one
would want that one . . . It was Miss Allison, a pretty cute babe
. . . but you shoulda seen her . . . she weighed all of 250 pounds
. . . Beppo was put in Secure and she sure made good use of the
time. When she went on Probation, she somehow got together
with Miss Allison, and the probation officer found them together
in a motel, way, way up in Murmaine County . . .*').

Adrienne, telling this story, is neither condemnatory nor ap-
plauding, but her listeners drink it in eagerly, hypnotized like listeners at a fair when presented with some miracle medicine. The
story pours into their veins, exciting some, strengthening others,
sending Adrienne herself, the teller, into a hypnotic state in which
she intensifies her prim pink-mouthed calm while at the same time
whispering contemptuously that Beppo is a 'bull-dagger,' a 'low
dyke,' a 'lady-lover,' a 'Les-wolf,' and a 'double-barreled broad.'
These terms are not understood by all, but the general feeling
becomes one of pride, pride that Sugar, who dwelt amongst them,
has been part of a continuous history, of which Beppo had par-
taken before her. All react differently. Ana exhibits a generalized
sexual excitement which makes her rush around the cottage, gos-
siping and shrugging, swinging her ardent dumpy hips from side

to side; Midget is filled with frail open-mouthed admiration, ignoring the seduction and expulsion, but still gasping at this flouting of authority. Candy, through an identification with Baby who 'liked a Negro as she likes Frankie,' allows big tears to roll down her translucent cheeks as she sits on the edge of her bed and hugs her hands between her knees. Pepper laughs. She listens and laughs, opening her red lips and screwing up her swarthy little face in delight. As for Frankie, she is stimulated by the vacuum in the cottage leadership which has been provided by Sugar's withdrawal, and by the story of the past success of Beppo, her old rival. She sees herself as a little girl at the Gospel Meeting, pouring forth song as a river pours forth sound, and feels a bitter reassurance because she has ended up here with souls as lost as herself.

. . . She is in the Moon Street Park with her mother and her grandmother. Her grandmother is complaining because Alva's husband, tiring of her preaching, has pushed her down the stairs after a quarrel and told her never to 'show her nose' in his house again.

"Black and evil," her grandmother announces to the small gathering crowd which drifts toward her at the sound of her magnetic voice. "Too black to be good!"

A tall and commanding figure, she climbs now onto one of the park benches and stretches out her arms toward the listeners—the stupefied red-faced winos, the little Negro girls who had been skipping rope, the shambling men in pale, sagging, slept-in suits, the sharply dressed young men and women who loiter tentatively, to see the 'old bag making a fool of herself.'

"*If you do not follow my words,*" her grandmother proclaims loudly, "*I will turn you over to a retrobate mind, and you will become all manner of lascivious woman. You will lay with man, woman, and beast.*"

Alva kneels down in the grass and pulls Frankie down beside her . . . Later in the subway, the family kneels again, while Evangelist Wilhemina Tobey prays for the sins of mankind, and while Frankie experiences a sense of shame and an awakening of pride . . .

Now in the dormitory she senses that there had been a reason for this pride, a profound need to give oneself to God. Perhaps, at this very moment, the roof of the cottage may open and pour down light upon her. Perhaps, with God's help, she can be stronger than Sugar, more able to bend the wills of those around her. The girls could be drawn to her to listen to her voice, to beg her to save them, as she considers herself saved. She might develop the gift of tongues, every word she spoke having strength and meaning. The thought comes to her like a revelation: *Where find better souls? Where other than here at Wentworth?* But soon this messianic impulse undergoes a radical change. She becomes conscious of past humiliations, which drive her now to cut the last ties which bind her to social acceptance. She lies on her bed, staring calmly at the ceiling, but she is listening to a voice which suggests that she 'lead these girls.' *If she cannot lead them to God, she can lead them out of Wentworth State School for Girls!* She remembers that it is Mrs. Casey's night off and that Miss Lacoutte, the officer who has earned her enmity by countless small acts of malevolence, is on duty.

"I can lead 'em," she says aloud. "I'm no tackhead."

"What you gonna do?" Mary's nose is pointed upwards as if scenting trouble.

"Not what *I'm* gonna do," Frankie says darkly, "is what *we* gonna do."

"All of us?"

Frankie doesn't answer. With one hand she carefully hitches up the worn brass-studded belt, and with the other she extracts a cigarette from her pocket. Placing Mary's slip over the opening in the door so that the smoke won't seep into the passage, she rummages among the letters in her bureau and takes out one of the matches she keeps in an envelope. Then she begins to outline the situation to Mary, as if she were trying it on for size.

"They took Sugar, didn't they?" she asks, puffing at the cigarette. "An' they shut Brenda up in Secure. That kid's been in 'n' out o' Secure all the time she's been back from the street. They had me shut up there for the longest time, and that *really* got next

to me. I told Miss Turner: 'I don't pretend to be Satan, nor yet
the Virgin Mary' . . . But she can only see me as evil." The
smoke curls around Frankie's head and her eyes stare aggressively
from their dark hollows, as they have after so many of her other
bouts with authority. She feels that she must show her power
now or it will be too late and she will become like the humiliated
girls around her.

Mary has brought in the others—Ana, Adrienne, Pepper,
Candy, even Midget. As she lights a new stub given her by
the devoted Candy, Frankie is asking them all: "You wanta
kick up?"

She looks at their faces and begins to count the episodes on her
supple dark fingers. "Florence Nightingale couldn't go to the
softball game last week. Remember? That ole Lacoutte bitched
on me smoking in the john, and then she had Pepper kept in
school because she found her copying from my history assignment. We don't need Lacoutte, not like a hole in the head. She
gets that mumbling Betty Wilson to tell her everything, and ten
to one she told about Sugar. How they know else?"

After waiting for this to sink in, she goes on: "Tonight we
can't dance, just because of disciplinary action for more than two
members in one week. The knife they found wasn't on one of US
either. They can't pin it on US! . . . *Well, I say—we can't
dance, we can't go to bed either . . . that's what!*"

"Hey—that's an idea," Ana said eagerly. "Let's not go to
bed!"

The idea is considered.

"A kick-up?"

"That ole Lacoutte on tonight—she don't faze me a bit."

"Lacoutte on? No kidding."

Pepper begins to laugh loudly and her rich red lips open wide
like the tearing apart of a pomegranate.

"Shut up, Pepper." Adrienne puts a warning hand over the
girl's mouth. "You want to rouse the building?"

"No, we play it cool." Frankie gets to her feet and extracts
from the inside of Mary Kelly's trumpet case the knife she,

Frankie, had stolen from the hospital kitchen during her time there. "See *that?*" She wraps it in a handkerchief, and pushes it into her knee sock. "Useful when you're running."

"Goin' ter *run?*" inquires Midget in amazement.

"Not you, baby."

"Yes, Frankie, I *want* to . . . I don't like it here . . . I *want* to Frankie . . ."

"You're too little, baby. No one's gonna run except' the ones with heart."

"What we tryin' to do?" Adrienne's face remains blond and carved like that of a Norse maiden on the prow of a ship. "I'm a straight fighter. But who wants to serve another year?"

"Who wants to sit around neither?" Pepper gives her wild laugh. "I had that fucking Lacoutte's hands on me before. I dig myself that Lacoutte don't cross my mind!"

"Kin I run *too*, Frankie?" Midget is pleading. "Kin I?"

Frankie smiles but ignores her. She looks at Ana who is hugging herself with delight—at Candy who waits calmly, smiling, ready to do whatever Frankie does—at the stolid but obedient Mary Kelly—and the laughing red-mouthed Pepper who has set more fires than anyone knows about. Even Adrienne's calm profile doesn't daunt her, although it is upon her that she turns her most dazzling smile.

"If we kick up—you on our side?"

Adrienne gives a qualified nod, but at the same time, like a prudent housewife, draws her pink dressing gown closer around her figure.

"I'd sure enjoy a little excitement, but I got a month to the board. I'm not running."

"Push comes the shove, you won't squeal?" interrogates Frankie.

"I won't squeal," promises Adrienne. "I just won't know what hit the house."

Pepper suggests quickly: "Oh fuck it—let's get going."

"Okay. We're not going to bed," Frankie directs.

"None of us?"

"None of us."

"What about Billy Lee and Ramona, and those cold squares on the east side?"

"Ramona's okay. Don't know about Billy Lee . . . but let's see what sort of guts the others have."

Frankie's smile shines again. She gets to her feet intent on showing up those who oppose her.

"Get your weapons, girls," she warns, "and put on your running shoes."

Five minutes later, when the heavy-footed and corseted Miss Lacoutte gives, with stolid authority, the signal for bed, she is surprised to hear insulting voices coming from all corners of the TV room, a chorus of revenge and rebellion.

"Bed—*we're* not going to bed!"

"No bed for us tonight, Miss Lacoutte . . ."

"We're not *going* to bed . . ."

"Not tonight, thank you, Miss Lacoutte . . . We don't *dance*, we don't *sleep!*"

And from Pepper, who has suddenly become Frankie's lieutenant, and who is standing at the far end of the room with her fist clenched ready in a ball, a loud laugh, which is the more frightening to the uncertain officer who hears it because she has heard such laughs before and can imagine what may follow them. But even as Miss Lacoutte turns her head, Frankie cries loudly behind her: "Have a ball, girls!" and there is the sound of smashing glass as Pepper plunges her fist into the window and there is darkness as Midget turns the lights out, and Mary Kelly saying "No you don't" in a low guttural, as she drags the phone away even as Miss Lacoutte plunges for the receiver.

Someone has tripped Miss Lacoutte (this is the most satisfactory part of the evening, and one long remembered and recounted) and Mary Kelly has snatched her bunch of keys and opened the outside door. The radio which had been forbidden them is thrown to the floor; the tables and chairs are turned over. Candy runs shrieking here and there, wielding the fire extinguisher and spraying the strong-smelling liquid onto the floor.

One of the quieter girls, emerging from her cubicle at the first sound of the breaking glass, has heard Miss Lacoutte's begging her to go for help, and now she runs up the passage and out of the door, her hair flying, but Frankie goes after her and fells her to the ground with the kind of punch she had learned long ago in the racy days of the Vivaldos. In fact, childhood returns to Frankie now as she rushes back into the cottage filled with wild shouts and laughter, and rallies her group around her. She is a leader again, and the wind is with her—the wind which is pouring through the jagged holes in the windows.

——————

. . . They run through the woods, Frankie in front, the lumbering Mary Kelly bringing up the rear, and the faithful Candy jogging up and down and trying to throw the pale rays of the flashlight on the path ahead. The trees, just budding, wave against the pale sky. Dark shadows hide familiarity, throw up black barricades, and camouflage wire fences. The sudden loneliness checks hilarity, makes them sober, suggests loneliness, danger, revenge. Children of the city, they know little of nature, and they long at once for the highways, the shapes of houses and lights. But by now the police will have been alerted, and Frankie and Pepper have been hunted by the police before, and the thought humbles them. Yet they are driven on, as scared animals are driven, straight toward the guns of the hunters. When the woods thin, the five girls come at last to what looks like a road. They have been too excited to watch their direction, and it is not until they have stumbled against the fence and crawled panting through the wire, that they are aware of this, and find themselves straining to see each other's faces and asking, "Where are we? Which way do we go?"

Frankie, as bewildered as anyone, is reluctant to express doubts, and can only search her limited experience for practical ways of covering distance.

"We're out of the grounds that's what."

"What do we do now?"

"We get us a taxi," she answers confidently, remembering city emergencies and city extravagances.

"*Here*—out in the sticks!"

"We find the nearest house." Frankie begins to pat at her hair, already doubting that a group of disheveled girls, dressed in hastily chosen garments and arriving at a strange house in the middle of the night will be received without question.

"We tell a story," she improvised, "about how we took a lift with some boys . . . We knock on some door and we tell the lady that we was out riding, and the boys said: 'Put out, or get out,' and so we got out . . ." She is embroidering upon the age-old theme of sexual oppression. "We tell the lady the story and ask her to call a cab," she finishes. "Come on."

The little procession starts once again through the night. Ana has stubbed her toe and is complaining bitterly, anxious at the same time because she has abandoned her stuffed animals. Mary Kelly is sniffing through her inadequate nose. Pepper whistles and makes inappropriate remarks. Candy keeps close to Frankie, and Frankie, who is aware of the knife in her sock and wonders what she will do with it, fills the emptiness of her mind with fantasies. Through cellars and bars, across open windy lots, up the fire escape to the Luigis, through the subway to Four Corners; these are the excursions which her spirit makes. She searches for guidance through reams of advice from the ill-adjusted of her race and her neighborhood, through the exhortations of the gospel, through tag-ends of prose and poetry, and through the obscenities and extremities of her contemporaries. Somewhere she must find the perfect pathway, with the help of which she can lead the Children of Israel out of Egypt. But as she takes her little band along the dark road, she can only think of strange schemes and devices, none of which her intelligence approves (disguises—lies—night treks—hitchhiking at knife-point), so that she finds her heart faltering as she imagines a victorious escape followed by an inglorious capture.

When the great eyes of a car spin out of the darkness, catching the girls in its rays like flies in a flood of amber light, Frankie is least surprised of all. "Drop," she commands, "get off the road 'n' fall flat!" But only Candy obeys her, plummeting to earth like a bird shot in the heart. Pepper, Ana, Mary hesitate, then begin to run, and as the car slows and swerves and someone swings a spotlight to the left, Frankie and Candy, shivering amongst the grasses at the edge of the fence, hear victorious male voices calling, "We've got 'em—we've got three of 'em!" even while Pepper's shrill cries echo in a kind of ecstasy, "Keep off—keep those fucking hands off of me!"

Half an hour later at a little frame cottage by the road, Frankie sends a shivering and woebegone Candy to knock on the door. Candy has been carefully coached to tell the story of her virtuous struggles to the lady of the house. She is to describe a green Buick, driven by some anonymous boys (while a hundred feet further along the road in the direction of the village, Frankie lies waiting behind a log).

"You get the lady to call a cab, honey," Frankie directs. "She'll have more heart for you, because I'm colored—and when the cab comes, you get in and have him drive along, and I'll get in after. If that cabbie starts anything, I've got my knife . . ." Her voice is more confident than she herself feels. She is aware that the alarm is out, that the car which picked up Ana, Pepper, and Mary has been cruising the roads looking for them, that all the villages within a radius of ten miles of the institution will know about their escape. She sees herself now as the desperate leader of a gang—an outlaw, the toughest and the last captured—with Candy's frailty pinned, like a flower, to her shoulder.

Candy is knocking on the door . . . A light goes on at last, and the door opens . . . Voices murmur. A man steps out into the darkness. There is a silence.

On the grass beside the log, swinging in the night and with the sky above her, Frankie re-creates her world. It is as if she has chosen it, made it the more valuable because she wears its disguise so proudly—just as she wears the knife in her sock, the studded belt around her narrow waist. She is not surprised when a flashlight shines cruelly into her eyes, and glints from the barrel of a gun. "Don't move," a voice says.

She keeps her eyes wide in the startling white light and knows that he is wise, that he has been told that she is armed.

"Roll over," the man's voice directs. "Get on your hands and knees, and rise up slowly . . . Don't move fast . . ."

The cautious slow commands fill her with pride. She fantasies that she is 'dangerous,' and she does all that he asks, complacently, and with infinite respect.

— III —

The Street

. . . *if the boys do not grow to be men, where shall the women find men?* . . .

From *Growing Up Absurd,* by PAUL GOODMAN

If this book is written in dull colors, it is because such colors are those known to the street. The colors are soiled. They are darks. Dun of pavements; dirty white of city snow; gray of cement; smothered and grimed red of old brick; sickly varnish, iron, scabrous plaster. The biliousness of certain paints—curiously heavy and against nature. Upon the impersonal sky the fire escapes are maroon and dusty chocolate. From the lips of the street, life escapes with a great sigh, and this exhalation feeds the passers-by with a quiet unrest. Then, when night gathers, sudden spots of color penetrate the street's fabric. Hung in the atmosphere, there are roses of light blushing oddly in the skin of the city—hectic red or dull bronze. They touch the faces which drift out of the darkness and bathe them momentarily in a glow so deep as to be unnatural, yet bound to those faces as the lights are to the pavements.

When the girls come home from their time in the reformatories, the streets seem exciting to them, not because they are beautiful indeed, but because a life takes place there with which they are now more familiar. All is as it was before, but it is as if they were understanding it for the first time. In the streets of her own ghetto, Frankie looks at the landmarks with a fresh interest: cellar doors, fire escape, downstairs window, school, shops, fences, empty lots—all these are part of her personal history, and they now live more vividly in the life-maps of others. At Wentworth a world of girls had made zip guns, sharpened files, and carried knives in their knee socks;—as a whole world had run in the streets, and climbed out of windows at night, and dropped out of school for truancy or pregnancy or inability to concentrate. At Wentworth knowledge had been pooled, shameful memories exorcised, tears lost in the tears shed by others. In the camaraderie of the reform school, students had graduated into esoteric knowledge —knowledge of rituals, drugs, words, values—into what was smartest, 'hippest,' most modern. As 'returnees,' they were secure in their new enjoyments, and effectively separated from their inept and old-fashioned parents.

But knowledge does not stop here. As the 'street' receives, so does it test out, setting up a seminary suitable for its purposes. *The street wills.* At the same time that it accepts back the girls discharged from Wentworth, it nurtures those boys and young men who are the girls' counterparts, and into whose hands they will eventually be committed . . .

One such fifteen-year-old is Ronald 'Loper' Robinson, who—on Frankie's first day back from Wentworth—stands outside the movie theater as Frankie and her cousin Opaline parade down Moon Street. He is lolling in T shirt and jeans, lethargic in the heat. His smooth brown face with the long nose and the wide-spaced, long-lashed eyes, is further darkened by the sun, and his arms hug his slender body as if to make himself feel how close his body is, how important and how precious. Frankie sees him as part of the re-creation of her childhood, as part of the scenery in that long-ago theater set up by the Vivaldos, and Opaline reminisces about the many times when they had brought him in off the street and taken him home to feed him.

"He always say he gonna be my pimp," Frankie remembers as they approach the theater . . . "Why, I even processed his hair."

As they draw closer she calls out: "Say Loper—what's up, man?"

Loper smiles. Young as he is, he has already an extraordinary sense of self-preservation, a sense which sympathizers, urged on by unconscious symbiotic impulses, observe in him and encourage. He remembers how Frankie and Opaline had long ago made him their special object of care, often sparing him a dollar from their ill-gotten gains, taking him home, stripping him of his single grubby T shirt, and cooking him hamburgers while they washed the shirt and dried it on the radiator.

"Where *you* been?" he now mocks Frankie. "You been put away?"

"I do good as you." She smiles.

"How it up at that joint?"

"Like a *college*," she drawls.

"Let me have a half," he urges now. "You girls let me have a half, so's I can go down the poolroom and run it up to some money."

"I got no half, baby." Frankie smiles. "You got me that quarter three years ago."

"Let me have a quarter then," he begs, hugging himself and moving from foot to foot. "I'll run it up, and I'm gonna see some broads . . ."

"Broads!" interjected Opaline amused at his impudence. "*You* should be lucky!"

Loper pleads, making movements with his hands. "Baby, let me hold the quid!"

"Okay." Opaline searches in her musky pocketbook, flipping out a dollar bill with a careless air, and waving it before him. "Don't go to Atlantic City."

"Put your money where your mouth is," warns Loper, laughing and jumping for the note. "Come with me, baby," he urges Frankie, "come play some pool."

"I can't shoot no pool," Frankie says regretfully, but Loper is already speeding away down Moon Street, the dollar in his hand, with Opaline calling after him like an indulgent mother, warning of the fierce animals in the woods. "Take care now—Slattery's around." And Frankie, watching the flip-flop on the pavement of his almost soleless sneakers, and sighing, "I love that boy to death."

Justifying his nickname, Loper tears through the streets like a young wolf, his graceful elongated body swaying with his long arms, at the end of which the hands seem masculine and overlarge.

He is on his own 'tar beach,' and the shops, the buildings, make up the ocean of ghetto life into which he is so anxious to plunge. Sometimes as he lopes along, disquieting thoughts, vague anxieties attack him, but on the whole he feels a general aggressive hopefulness, an eagerness to run up Opaline's 'hot buck' into 'real scratch.' Slowing down at the corner of Ohio, he sees before him the long length of Evans Avenue, bisected by the shadow of the Realty Assurance Building, beyond which lies North City proper, the white world into which he generally moves cautiously. It is the wrong hour for him to go into the city, too late, for instance, to attempt to 'boost' in one of the basements of the better stores. Too late, or not late enough, to try to lift something from a parked car.

Yet, as if there were some enemy waiting for him in the basement poolroom, he finds himself reluctant to descend those steps —not only because his growing body wants to idle, and because he feels like loitering under the sparse trees in the street, but because he is desirous of forgetting that business which, by reason of its speed, its anxiety, and its sleight of hand, is so well described by the word 'hustle' . . . Yet something urges him on, something close to a compulsive ambition, to the kind of respectable desire which makes his friend Chub, son of the Moon Street butcher, long after the lights are out on the Hill, toil at his books in the room above the shop . . . Loper wants to make good. He disappears into the doorway of the poolroom.

And the 'enemy' searches him out. When he has been playing for half an hour, and the dollar has grown to seven—a sickness has started in him, which begins in his stomach, travels up the back of his spine, makes perspiration bead his long narrow forehead. He leans back. His eyes become expressionless behind the screen of thick lashes. He feels acute self-loathing.

A tall rather well-dressed man has entered the poolroom, a melancholy, reflective-looking Negro with a small furred hat set on close-cropped receding hair. The man moves before him, giving him a slow glance as he passes the pool table. Like a dropping of dark oily water, the glance spreads, all-pervasive, summing up the boys who play pool, who laugh, spread their fingers, stretch their long legs around the table. The man's trousers fit tightly about his rounded hips. He is not fat so much as well-covered with flesh. And he seems to yearn, to desire with his tall-covered fleshy body, with his tentative disarming slightly sad smile.

Loper is transfixed. The man has never spoken to him, but something in him knows him well.

. . . It is night in the house where his grandmother is house-keeper and he is alone in the bed which she will eventually share with him. She is washing dishes in the room next door, and the house is full of the people who have been invited to dinner by her employer, and who now, well fed and a little drunk, mill through the rooms and up and down the stairs. The night is full of music, voices, stridency, but Loper is half asleep, his head buried under the pillow, his legs spread out wearily . . . Shouts . . . laughter . . . the clatter of glasses . . . the beat of feet dancing over-head. His body is like earth, across which march the armies of pleasure.

Yet somehow weight is added to the bed, and through his half-dreams he hears murmurs which merge with what he dreams, be-neath the loud message of the music, swelling and receding in a teasing rallentando. These human murmurs, unimportant as they seem, are more insistent than the music stamping out an emphatic beat above him, or his body sleepily responding, or the noise of the cars in the street—until a sharp whisper awakes him, ominous and separated, included in no pattern.

"How we gonna work this?" it hisses into the night.

He knows that it is Jerry's voice, although for a while it is caught and flung by the music, moving up and down in the laby-rinth of his deadened brain . . . Another voice answers, and he hears it clearly: "What's wrong with here?"

It is the heavy voice of Mr. Harrison, his grandmother's em-ployer, and the words stretch out and out, to the accompaniment of some shifts of weight upon the bed, some rhythm in which Loper feels mysteriously included.

"The boy?"

"Asleep."

"Sure?"

"So what?"

Jerry is the big white boy from next door who drives a truck, who is always laughing, and often drunk. And Loper hears it in sudden sharp awakening, the lilt of sardonic laughter in the voice. "So what?" the voice says.

There is silence . . . The black-velvet night encloses him. A car starts . . .

Nothing is going to happen. But the bed sighs. The weight shifts again . . . "Come over here." The whisper is Jerry's, and somehow Loper knows that Mr. Harrison is on the bed, the quiet dignified elderly white man who employs his grandmother, and who is now a close, inert weight breathing beside him.

The music has gone. No noise is closer now than the noises in the bed—the creaks, the shifts. Loper finds himself part of it. The moans are *his* moans, the sighs *his* sighs. He shrinks. He makes himself small, but as the movement mounts in the bed, it seems natural that hands slide over his back, search dumbly like animals through the flannel of his pajamas, fasten onto that core of him, which is already—and this in spite of his loathing—hard and erect.

In a minute he springs from the bed crying and stamping in his rage, whispering fiercely: "You're dirty . . . you're a dirty old man," and Mr. Harrison's hands are on his shoulders, soothing him, begging him: "Hush—don't—I tell you, kid, I'm going to get you what you want . . . anything . . . Quiet now . . . What do you want? A bicycle . . . ? A twenty-two? Wasn't it a twenty-two you wanted . . . ?"

And Jerry is laughing, pulling together his belt and laughing.

"Shut up," he whispers to Loper and laughs again.

This quiet mocking laughter merges with the break-up of a world, seems to emphasize the plucking of a guitar upstairs. Someone is singing the blues.

"Get into bed." The older man's kind hand pushes him downward.

"Tomorrow . . . Anything you want . . . Want a gun? A bicycle? Anything . . . You tell me tomorrow . . . ? Okay . . . ? Anything . . ."

He has them both at home now—the gun and the bicycle. But still he is aware of the sickness. He turns and leaves the poolroom.

"Stop thinking about it," he tells himself.

A little later he spends six dollars of the money he has won on a maroon sweater. But a gloom falls upon him, courses through his veins and mingles strangely with that fierce belief he has that everything is his. He must *win*, he thinks, through his sadness, his long-fingered brown hand clenching with anger.

Later still he stands on the Avenue, and watches while two men pile out of a shiny black car which, long-snouted as an alligator, noses into the pavement. The wind whistles down the street as he stands, with shoulders hunched, near the bus stop. He sees the two men pose like kings on the sidewalk and greet a third man, who is fair, except that the color of his skin is too dark to be white, too muddied to be pure Latin, and his hair's extreme flatness has been dyed or processed to an unnatural red, which seems, even to Loper's unsophisticated eyes, an unpleasant brand . . . Yet this man's clothes are impeccable, his features are heavy and authoritative and, as he greets the other two with "Hey men . . . how you doing?" . . . "Hey Duke" . . . "Say, baby, what's happening?" he gestures also with a broad hand weighted with rings.

It is this kind of man whom Loper admires, a man who looks and acts as though he owns the world, a man who watches others with an amused masculine smile, and is dark, handsome, mustached, behatted, beringed. Loper remembers how he himself has often been standing outside the bar on Moon Street while some man clutches at a passing girl and holds her familiarly between his legs for a moment, caressing her shoulders, and saying that he is 'her man.' Loper remembers how on one such occasion the girl had broken from the arms of the older man, and tousled Loper's hair, saying teasingly over her shoulder for the benefit of that bolder, older male rival, "Leave me alone. I'm Loper's girl. Loper's real *pretty* . . . and when he grows up he's gonna be my pimp!"

Now as he stands at the windy corner, he realizes that these pimps are just like businessmen stepping out of some hotel in

New York City, conversing for a moment in the wary, joking way of the elect, slapping each other on the back, handing out cigars, making contact with their kind.

"Yeah," he hears one man say, "yeah—things might be worse!"

"Heard you copped Alice last night."

"That's a fact."

"She's a good girl. There's nice money there."

One of the men shows his gleaming teeth and throws back his head, flapping a pair of leather gloves across his hand as if to emphasize something, and the other shrugs expressively and announces: "Sure is."

"I took a shot at her myself, but she wouldn't give me any action," complains the one who has not been lucky enough to 'cop.'

"Well you do all right, baby," the redheaded man says expansively, "you do all right . . . That 'Eldo' didn't cost peanuts . . . How many 'hoes you got you make that kind of money?"

"Not so many, man, not so many . . ."

"Shi-i-it," the other mocks.

"I got five," the man with the gleaming teeth confesses, "five good bitches."

"A nice stable," comments Red.

"And how's *your* racket, Red?"

"Can't complain." Red hunches his shoulders. "But Clara sure was hittin' it on the hip. Ah had to send her up to Paragoula for a rest cure."

Loper, alert to every word, knows that Paragoula is the State Reformatory for Women, and he wonders how Red can *decide* to send Clara up there.

"Mighty handy," one of the others comments. "They get cleaned up, cured of clap, well fed, and come out with a process . . . How you work it, man?"

"She broke parole, didn't she?" gibes Red. "Angel—she made a lot o' fuss, so I sent Clara up . . . Could sure do with your Alice, man."

"Anyone could do with *her*," the other grins.

"Worth two cars *that* size." Red indicates the Cadillac at the curb. "I hear she's a real stand-up broad, too. Like the time she backed up poor old Blondie."

"You mean the time the Feds booked her on that dry beef?"

Her new owner nods reflectively. "That was a good job. All she'd of had to do was mention her man's name."

"But she took the weight and did the trey?"

The other sounded sober. "She sure did."

For a moment all of them seem to be aware of how much they might be at the mercy of their women; and in the half-dark Loper catches on their faces expressions of acute discomfort.

One of them says at last: "Well—so long."

"So long—glad you copped, man."

Their voices fade into the spring wind, and Loper, alone in the dusk, wedged now in the doorway of an empty store, gazes enormous-eyed at the gleaming Cadillac and feels warm with ambition. He who had first possessed only a dollar cadged from Opaline and now is better off by a maroon sweater, he who had obtained in one night and without effort a gun and a bicycle, he who is caught by the girls on the Avenue and petted and kissed while they murmur, laughingly, "Going to be my man someday, Loper baby, going to be my pimp," understands clearly how these captains of the street have ascended such pinnacles. Not, he reflects, by dreary labor in factory and shop, not gritty-eyed at dawn from all-night sweeping on the subways, not as a runner on the garbage truck, nor from waiting in restaurants, nor janitoring in schools, nor carrying around the collection plate in churches— not from any of these things, but from climbing, climbing, climbing upon the smooth naked shoulders of their women.

Like Loper, Beppo is more part of the street than she is of institutions. Like Loper, the street got her early.

By the time that she was eighteen and serving her first sentence at Henry Street, her sophistication had far outstripped that of the compulsive car-stealing Harriet (also eighteen) and the masochistic amateur prostitute Brenda (seventeen). She was already at that time considering her future, and seeing herself in it (as one sees images of power divorced from practicality), a Sphinx-like prince, owner of a rich harem, and wearing black corduroy stovepipe pants with a tunic of gold lamé. Yet her early history had been an earnest one, and years had been needed to turn her into this girl, who in the day room of Henry Street was pointed out with respect as 'Man Delgado.'

In 1954, Beppo's mother, Maria, had moved her family from the St. Lawrence Project to an apartment on top of a sagging house in North City's Negro ghetto. The apartment was less hygienic than had been the one in the Project, but there were more rooms to it, and it was cosier. In fact, Beppo's mother was happy as she pasted imitation-tile paper over the dirty walls of the kitchen and painted the trim in the living room a shiny black. When she went into the hospital to have a periodic 'breakdown,' she was always to say: "My rooms are done in black and gold." She was also accustomed to tranquilize herself during these breakdown periods by making 'fabulous' black and gold place mats, or crocheting pot holders with gold and black cotton yarn. In the living room there was not much furniture, but there was a cupboard which was filled with white and gold china, and with white and red wineglasses—the china bought by the first money Beppo earned when she was a 'vegetable girl' (assistant to the old vegetable man who parked his truck at the corner)—and the wineglasses bought a little later when she had gone 'on the street' and developed a taste for elegance.

This little vegetable girl had been at eleven rather tall for her age, but with so slight and wiry a body, and so determined, fierce, and prowlike a head, that many a housewife interested in extracting the cheaper beans and cabbages from the rusty belly of the old truck would watch instead the child in blue jeans and blouse who, the autumn wind tossing the bangs of her long Indian hair and paling her profile, had stood astride the green produce, holding the vegetable scales at the end of a thrust-out arm, like a statue of Justice herself. The job on the vegetable truck had been her first, and had coincided with that time of her life when she had been set free from the despairs of the school at the St. Lawrence Project, where she had been regularly called 'nigger' and thus just as regularly induced to fight an urgent battle with her tongue, her fists, and her feet. Every afternoon during this St. Lawrence period, she would return to her mother like some battered and weary warrior, her face dirty and sometimes bleeding, her knuckles bruised, her books scattered and lost. If this experience had tilted her aggressive chin still further and warmed a smoldering fire in her dark oblique eyes, it had also hardened her muscles and covered her psyche with an armor hard to pierce.

On the truck she was free, as she was now free of the school in which she had been a minority. In the old sagging apartment in the ghetto she was also free, and ready to take the position of leadership for which she had been well prepared. After school, she walked the fresh-smelling markets with the old man, choosing and discarding vegetables, hauling boxes, exchanging jokes and obscenities with the marketmen, feeling herself as good as any of them, and cadging from them the cigarettes which, from that time on, were never to be out of her mouth. Ironically, this job, which according to the law she should never have had, was one of the more positive aspects of her life.

. . . It is one o'clock in the morning, and Maria Delgado climbs the long, dark staircase to the apartment. She has just heard of the death of her husband in Florida, and she feels a certain bewildered relief, since there had always been a saying in her family: "Mother is a matter of fact—father is a matter of opinion." Now there will be no handsome rambling itinerant musician to spend a symbolic ten minutes in the bosom of his family, and go away leaving her pregnant again. Now she will be the director of events—not only practically, as she has always been, but emotionally as well—no longer psychically tied to someone whose touch has meant the ambivalence of love and disaster. She is a short plump woman, a little fat for her years, but with a still-pretty face, a small hooked nose, and burning slanted eyes. Short of breath, she toils up the dark stairs toward the eyrie of an apartment into which she has packed her brood of children. As there is no doorknob downstairs, there is also no light in the ceiling of the stairwell, and four flights later she fumbles with her key at the dark scarred door where a faded printed sign states "God Bless Our Home." Once inside, she puts down the package of leftovers from the restaurant where she works, kicks the shoes off her swollen feet, hangs up her wet jacket, and turns on the gas under the coffeepot on the stove. She hears almost at once the alert, insistent voice of Beppo in the room next door. "Mums . . . Mums . . ."

"Coming," Maria says, "for the love of God . . ."

A little later she is sitting on the edge of the double bed which Beppo shares with the two smaller boys, holding a cup of coffee, while her eleven-year-old daughter, thin and swarthy-looking in red-and-white-striped flannel pajamas, warms her palms around a cup of cocoa.

"So—what happened today?"

"Nothing much." Beppo's eyes devour her, are fierce and intent in the short, flat face, where the skin at the temples and at the sides of the eyes is misted with a slight grayish-white, like the white bloom over the brown of grapes.

"You fightin' today then?" her mother asks.

"No . . . don't fight any more . . . not since we left the Project."

"You sure? No good to fight, Beppo . . . You hold it in."

Maria regards her with pride—the competent, disciplined little housekeeper who cleans the apartment, does the marketing, and bosses her brothers, while she, Maria, works the late shift at the restaurant. She is proud of all her children, who seem to have escaped her own dumpy figure and to favor their tall Portuguese father. Yet intimate as she is with her daughter, there is an uneasiness, a suspicion.

"You didn't jump school?"

"No, Mums." Beppo eyes her with a guarded interest. "You tired?"

"Some." Maria slumps on the bed, and sips at her coffee. "Your father's dead."

"He is!" Beppo sits up straighter.

"He is."

"*When?*"

"Two days it seems."

There is a silence.

"It were an O.D.," Maria says.

"What's that?"

"An overdose."

Maria feels that the sudden death has its poetic suitability. Any resentment she has felt for this handsome irresponsible male is thus eliminated, and it is suitable that he should die young like this, suddenly and without mourners, of too much heroin, in a seedy segregated Southern hotel room—this man, the irreverent father of four children he scarcely knew.

"It'll be better for you, Mums," Beppo says with a sudden unsuitable pity, "better than messing you up like that . . . Men only mess women up anyway . . ."

A little shocked, Maria says: "Daughter, that's life." She doesn't know how Beppo gets such ideas, but is vaguely disquieted and displeased.

"No Mums, I mean it. Now there is just us. We can get along without him . . . I hated it when he came." She hunches up her knees in a way she has, and her expression is defenseless. "I'll help you, Mums."

"Why child, you help me now."

"I'll help you more."

"No need for you to help more'n you do."

"I will."

The dark, straight, coarse, shiny hair, Indian hair, falls around her like a tent, and the bangs dance over the flat brown nose starred with freckles. The secretive stubborn expression returns.

"You won't have to worry. I'll do all sorts of things. We don't need *him*."

"He was your father, after all." Maria's tired throaty voice fades with the fatigue of the early morning hours. "But he *sure* were a Rambling Rose," she adds.

"My father, you're telling me," Beppo says. "How often I see him?"

"Well . . ." Maria fumbles with the blanket to cover her daughter. "That's the price of being fabulous."

. . . Beppo's life is more complicated than her mother imagines. Indeed Maria's appreciation of the tidy apartment, the boys' ironed shirts, the washed-up supper dishes does not include room for the realization that her eleven-year-old daughter is competent enough to do all this and carry on another life as well. Beppo goes to school in the morning in a pleated skirt, a white shirt and sweater, and socks pulled up to knees pallid from the cold. She wears a rough boy's jacket and heavy shoes, but her glorious hair hangs almost to her waist, and it is not surprising that the grimy street on which she lives notices and watches her boyish beauty. The older man who rents the apartment across the way stares at her from his window. The prostitutes who operate upstairs above the liquor store on the corner comment about her in the late afternoon as she straggles home from school or from Mary's Lunch down in East City. The policeman at the subway station gets to recognize her among the groups of rowdy youngsters who cross on their way to school, and he sees her hair flying like a flag whenever the gang 'gets the wind' and streaks up the opposite hill. And an older girl named Pat, just out of Wentworth, runs into her near the apartment door and, looking at her reflectively, says as if it were a prophecy: "You'd make the cutest little boy."

Sometimes when she peeks through the window of the guy across the street, he beckons her in and gives her one of the 'sticks' he is accustomed to smoke. Dizzy and laughing, she smokes it and envelops herself in a new and distorted world, while he jokes about her hair and says teasingly: "I bet you don't got any down *there* yet!"

"What you bet?" Beppo demands promptly.

"I bet you five dollars."

"You'll give me five dollars?"

"Sure will," the man says.

Beppo shows him. She lifts her school skirt and pulls down her pants and proudly shows him the little dark fleece which shades the apex of that brown triangle between her legs. Afterwards he won't give her the five dollars and Beppo stares at him reflectively.

"I spill things very easy," she taunts. "My mother lives acrosst the street."

"Looky here," the man coaxes, "here's three. I haven't got no more."

"You can give it me some other time," she says magnanimously. He is conscious of having met his match . . .

The girl Pat, who is sixteen and has been to Wentworth, and who first takes her to Mary's Lunch, recognizes this strength of character which has so little to do with age, and she coaches her accordingly. "You can do lots of things," she tells her, pushing her into her brother's blue jeans and setting the belt down low. "You're a real cute boy." She kisses her, and smoothes her long hair back behind her ears, and takes her, as a sort of mascot, to Mary's Lunch on East Mackay Street.

Although the basic structure of this restaurant is that of a primitive sandwich shop, some slight effort has been made to decorate it by painting a clumsy mural on one of the walls, and by putting a string of purplish draw-curtains along the windows above the booths. The jukebox plays loud rock 'n' roll, and occasionally the girls jump up to dance with each other in the easy laconic manner of the times. But the chief advantage of the place is its proximity to the bar next door, so that the customers can overflow from one to the other without difficulty. For Beppo the excitement is that she is allowed there at all, and that she is not sent home by the older girls as being too young to be interesting, but is instead kissed and petted and complimented.

One day Sandra takes her home with her. Sandra is twenty-two years old and lives alone in an apartment on the Hill, where the ghetto borders on white areas, and where Negroes and whites intermingle in an indeterminate world of passing on the part of both races—a world of tolerance and crime. Her three rooms are at the top of an old wooden building with an octagonal tower, and for all their ghetto origin, the windows look down like eyes upon midtown North City's overprivileged spires. Sandra has a great white bed, and to Beppo's unsophisticated eyes, a magnificent if slightly grubby blue carpet. The room spreads a garden of forget-me-nots, touched with snow, and includes prim mantelpiece decorations of artificial flowers. There is a cupboard in which all of Sandra's clothes are laid out—shoes like jewels, and dresses like rare tapestries, slacks of orange and black, suits of aquamarine and cherry, a black-satin sheath, a coat of blue-dyed rabbit, two-tone knit suits in which her breasts and hips seem to have made gentle contours. It is these contours which Beppo is now to learn, as earth curves are explored by geologists . . . And she is to learn them not because Sandra's form has intrinsic value, but rather because it is '*the*' form, the final one, the form of 'commerce.'

This distinction is made, not because Sandra has not been *attracted* to Beppo. Indeed, there is something about the burning-eyed, somber, hard-kneed little girl which she lusts after. But she is as well occupied with the practicalities of the thing, with a traditional and well-tried pattern, so that she has no need to justify her actions by exploring their moral implications. She has found out only what it is necessary to find out, what has already been disclosed by Pat—that Beppo's mother works each day from 1:00 p.m. to midnight, that Beppo has no father, that Beppo herself is an intelligent, controlled, and silent little girl, who has already been trained by her mother to "hold it in."

"Now we are going to take a bath," she says to the unwilling Beppo, whom she presses against her knees.

"Why?" asks Beppo restlessly.

Although she goes to Mary's Lunch and sits interminably with Pat and Sandra and the other older girls, it is partly because of status needs, and not because she would not rather be running the streets with the gang or working for the old vegetable man. (She had given up this job at the insistence of Sandra and Pat, who hand out dollars every time they see her, and tell her, laughing and exchanging glances as if there were some invisible link between action and statement, that she looks like a "good gay kid.")

"Yes, we're going to take a wonderful hot bath," Sandra is saying, as she unbuttons Beppo's shirt, and the hooks and eyes of her school skirt, "a bubble bath."

"Do we have to, Sandra?"

"Sure we have to . . . It's very sexy . . ."

Beppo watches as the tall blond girl, so much older and so much more developed than she is, wriggles out of her dress and stockings and stands like Venus in a pink slip made of silk and lace.

"Well—*you* take one," Beppo says indifferently. "I'll go home."

"No . . . no . . . I'm going to teach you things."

"*Teach* me?" Beppo eyes the door, which suddenly represents freedom. "I have enough of that at *school*."

"Not like this you don't," Sandra insists as she goes on getting out of her slip and panties and stretches voluptuously in front of the big mirror hung on the wall. "Come here."

Beppo comes unwillingly, even with distaste, for a moment almost afraid of those breasts and hips—so blond and pink—so forbiddingly female—so arrogantly displayed before her. She shrinks. She feels Sandra taking off the last of her clothes and leaving her straight brown body naked. And although this represents nothing to her in itself, she feels anger at the intrusion, as she has felt with the old man who tried to cheat her out of five dollars.

"I don't *want* a bath," she insists, the dark eyes turning sullen and resentful, her body resisting Sandra's hands which propel her toward the bathroom. "I'd rather go home now, the kids are waiting."

"It's only four o'clock," Sandra is declaring above the running of the bathwater. "I'm gonna play you records later . . . Besides it's a bubble bath."

"That's only *soap*." Beppo is scornful, but she has some slight interest in it all the same, in the technical process by which the bubbles mount higher and higher and, filled with a rainbow light, foam toward the ceiling.

"It feels good," lures Sandra. "Get in."

In the bath Beppo is at once afraid and relieved. The heat soothes her tenseness, but Sandra's hands are demanding and insistent. However much she squirms and resists, they won't let her go, but insist on rubbing and caressing her body, and making sure of a standard of cleanliness never dreamt of before.

"You see we wash like this," Sandra says earnestly. "We always wash every little corner—every bitty *tiny* corner—and make sure that everything is *terribly* clean . . ." She laughs, throwing back her head with its tied-up blond curls and hugging Beppo's elusive narrow body in sudden victory. "You see you like it, don't you?"

"I do *not* like it," Beppo insists, climbing out of the bath quickly. "I think it's silly . . . Who wants to bathe in the middle of the afternoon? I don't anyway."

Sandra wraps a big white towel around her, and a pink one around herself.

"I'm going to show you something you *will* like," she promises. "You'll wonder how you ever did without it . . . It's a game . . . and I'm going to play you records as well."

Amongst the blankets Beppo feels warm and sheltered, although she is aware of a world which slips away from her, a world which is bright and sunlit and filled with the natural energy of youth, and which fades now down a dark passage and loses its reality even as, held by Sandra's relentless hands, she struggles to return to it. She is a small animal—a rabbit, a hare. She has been captured and caged. Sandra kisses her immature breasts.

"Now we do this," she says.

Sandra breathes into her neck and ears.

"That tickles," protests Beppo sullenly.

"We play like this," Sandra says. "Don't be scared, baby. You do just like I do . . . Afterwards you do it to me."

"It's like school," Beppo says with disgust, struggling again.

Sandra caresses her body and her small hard buttocks, and parts her muscular little legs. It is only then that Beppo's interest is aroused. She is aware of a sensation which grows and spreads, which begins as a molten warmth, which becomes intolerably delicious, which expands and envelops her, and then, like some convulsive explosion, seems to tear apart her immature body. She is conscious of jerking and shuddering. Tears force themselves between her eyelids— She lies at last, like an inanimate doll, between Sandra's controlling arms.

There begins a period for Beppo when money is no longer earned by work, a time when luxury and even satiety are forced upon her. She finds herself with new shirts and shoes, with a boy's wristwatch, and with fine imported silk and woolen scarves. She has a leather wallet which is always stuffed with bills, and linen handkerchiefs which Sandra likes to see peeping out of her blazer pocket. She is showered with records, cigarettes, candy, and tickets to the sports arena—and in case her mother should suspect this new-found affluence, much of what Beppo thinks of as 'loot,' is kept in Sandra's apartment where she is expected each afternoon after school. This, she is told, is the gay life and worth by implication, as much as all other kinds of lives put together.

"Jump school—what good is it doing you?" Sandra suggests, and indeed, when Beppo is supposed to be at the library, she is now—the original situation reversed—lying between Sandra's legs, and getting there what education she can.

She is at first fascinated and a little horrified, and then, as the distaste fades, she is still fascinated. And finally she becomes addicted . . .

Her ordinary child's life seems to be a dream. Although she goes to school each day, it is only with half her attention that she hears the teacher's voice. She looks pale and listless, and the eyes set obliquely in her face stare with a clouded and inward-looking expression toward some foreign horizon. She wonders about herself during this time, wonders why she is different, why she does all these things which others apparently don't, why she is 'gay'— as Sandra and Pat now tell her she is—why she is inside in the apartment while her old companions still run the streets in hilarious freedom. Now she walks to school instead of running, is alone instead of with the gang, listens with a bored expression to the gossip of her contemporaries. When she can escape from Sandra, she walks grimly, her hands stuck into the pockets of her jeans. She walks and walks, head bent into the wind, long hair streaming, a perpetual scowl upon her puzzled face.

Yet slowly she is absorbing the mores of the cult which has adopted her. She is being taught that women are superior to men —better, kinder, less demanding, cleverer at love-making.

"No sweat—" Sandra says with a laugh.

"Men—I don't give them the time of day," Pat comments. And then, with profound truth, "Who needs them?"

"An' if you're in a spot," warns Sandra as the lessons proceed, "don't take no shit."

"A spot?" inquires Beppo warily.

"The way to get on in this world is to be hard, baby. Don't you take nothing."

"I *don't* take nothing," Beppo growls, remembering her daily fights in the school playground at the Project.

"Okay, don't you *never* take nothing. Don't you take no shit."

In the apartment Beppo finds her mother looking at her with sudden mistrust.

"What's this—you always tired? You draggin' around, child."

"I'm all right, Mums."

"Maybe." Maria has little time to consider whether anyone is really all right, herself included. "You worrying about your father?"

"*Him!*" There is contempt in Beppo's voice. "I'm glad he's not here to mess us up. Men always mess women up, Mums. Don't you understand that?"

Maria is distressed. "You too young to have ideas like that."

"I don't want you ever to have anything to do with men again," Beppo says with a strange seriousness.

"You don't understand," Maria dismisses it.

She picks up a paperback which is lying on the floor by Beppo's bed, and which Sandra had given her as part of her education.

"What's this?"

The book is called *Lesbian Loves.*

"Don't read it," Beppo urges, snatching it away.

She is not frightened, but wants only to protect her mother, whose dumpy bowed figure seems to need protection. Her mother must be kept innocent, she feels, yet at the same time she must be treated tenderly as only women can treat her. Beppo wants suddenly to go to Sandra's apartment and collect all that Sandra has given her and give it to her mother instead.

"Look what he did to you," she says to her mother, throwing the book down and indicating the next room where the sleeping boys are lying. "Look how he messed you up."

"It's natural, daughter," the bewildered mother protests.

"He gave you the kids and left," Beppo says. Her voice is slightly tearful. Her dark eyes judge her mother. "You took too much. You don't want to take nothing from nobody . . . No man is worth that sweat . . ."

In the afternoon Sandra accompanies Beppo to the barber and has all her hair cut off. On the floor of the barbershop the hair lies like strips of black silk from which the life ebbs slowly. If one knelt on the dirty floor and put one's finger under the hair, it would cling gently as if desirous of reattaching itself to something. Beppo regards her small short-clipped head in the mirror. She looks with her dark, dead eyes. She trembles. She gets off the barber's stool and marches out without looking at Sandra. She wanders streets without seeing their names, streets where no one knows her. At dusk she creeps home and goes up the back stairs and gets an old cap out of her drawer. She wears the cap in the house. For two weeks she wears the cap. She doesn't go to school. She wears the cap at home as well as in the street.

The same luminous sky which covers all innocent children covers Beppo. But at a specified time, and almost without warning, the shadow falls. Her joys can no longer be spoken of; they remain tangled with the dying strands on the floor of the barber's shop.

Sandra's motives in seducing her are the ambivalent motives of the street—on one side the loneliness and desperation of the prostitute, the need for company, the perverted sexuality; on the other, the highly developed commercial sense, which sees all human interchange as translated into hard cash, and each new friendship as a contribution to the life. (Those with whom you exchange sexual pleasures are closest to you, are those also over whom you have most control, and therefore those whom you 'cop' [catch] and subsequently exploit.) Sandra introduces Beppo to cocaine, and with this the circle of material wealth is closed by a sensual pleasure almost too exquisite to be borne. So that Beppo follows Sandra now, as a child follows the Pied Piper . . . She is thirteen, and after morning school is over, she slips out the back gate and goes with Sandra and Pat to a 'party,' held most unsuitably in the mid-afternoon at an apartment on Upper Evans Avenue. Here the décor, for all its touch of the department store, is further individualized by a collection of weapons—bows and arrows, swords, spears—which hang on the wall of the living room, above the blue couches and the little tables inlaid with beige, white, and brown mosaic. Today Sandra wears one of her pink knit suits, and the coffee-colored Pat is dressed in a brown corduroy box jacket and corduroy slacks, a costume which is more poetic than that of a tall white Irish girl, who appears simply in a harsh man's suit and a white shirt held at the neck with a stud. Beppo, in her schoolgirl skirt, her knee socks, her blazer, is the mascot of the party, and is solemnly introduced to the apartment's owner ("Hey Nina, this is Beppo—Beppo, this is Nina, the 'Queen of the Lesbians' "). Nina is a voluptuous rounded girl wearing a black dress, her waterfall of black hair held back by big clips studded with brilliants.

During the afternoon the Irish girl in the man's suit is forced to call Nina into the kitchen, where Beppo hears her reprove her for flirting with Pat, and tell her: "Please don't do that no more;

we have company and I don't want to knock you down in front of company . . ." Beppo also manages to explore the apartment, and to marvel at the different bedrooms with their colored phones —red, black, white and, in the bathroom, orchid, to match the orchid towels. Sandra confesses that she doesn't like orchid, screwing up her fair features in disgust, and murmuring: "My aunt died and was laid away in orchid, and I never liked orchid since." But she agrees that the place is 'high-class' and seems to say to Beppo: "You see how this is the life, baby?" even while she gets angry with Nina, who shouts out above the din her guests are making: "Listen you—shut up all of you. This is not a *motel!* . . . Hear me, I don't run a *motel!*"

. . . When the police break into the apartment, the cocaine has disappeared, already wafted up the nostrils of the girls, leaving clear and innocent the mirror on which it had been divided with a razor blade. But Sandra and Nina are naked to the waist, and Beppo's school skirt is flung over the back of a chair. Three girls who had come in during the afternoon are fully clothed, but the police arrest them as being on parole from Wentworth, and although Nina tries to brazen it out, by wrapping herself in a shawl, and insisting that the Irish girl is her boyfriend, the entire company are transported to the police station and booked for 'I and D,' and 'Unnatural Acts' . . . Beppo does not find out until several months later that her mother had gone to the police, alerted by the school superintendent who had learned that the thirteen-year-old Beppo had been buying cigarettes with $50 bills at the Spa near the school. Nor having taken, young and blindfolded so to speak, those giant steps toward sensuality, does she understand her own relief to find herself in Wentworth State School for Girls, where a certain security and order surround her, and where she is accepted as if she were not as experienced as she actually is, but had only truanted, and smoked marijuana, and lost her virginity to a clumsy boy in the back of a car.

. . . At the end of a year, the street waits. Sandra and Pat are both in the 'big house'—Paragoula, the State Reformatory for Women, and Beppo is alienated from her old school friends, not only by her experiences but by her lack of interest in academic work, and by that stigma which is attached to the 'alumnae' of Wentworth. She drifts toward Moon Street, where she makes friends with Frankie's cousin, Opaline, and although her mother has found her an after-school job at a shoe factory, she shoplifts occasionally and, in return for a share of the proceeds, 'plays chickie' for two of Sandra's male friends when they break into a delicatessen. The destructive forces of the street, which had first stripped her of her innocence and then of her hair, and finally had begun to make inroads upon her body itself, the cocaine scorching her nasal passages and burning the delicate membranes lining her sinuses, now begin to harden her psyche. There is still something moderate about her, a controlled energy, which is later recognized and used by the various institutions in which she is incarcerated—a discipline seeming to hark back to early training, to that time when, however heavy the demands made by regular attendance at Mary's Lunch and by the afternoon sessions with Sandra, Maria had come home to washed dishes, folded clothes, and a clean apartment. But it seems only a matter of habit and will, a veneer which controls those deeper impulses, those indulgences and resentments which had been aroused and encouraged by Sandra . . .

Maria had hoped that Wentworth would have 'cured' her daughter, but now, beginning to be dependent on barbiturates herself, she makes only sporadic and half-hearted efforts to guide her.

"Don't start anything with my girl, or I'll have your head," she says to a slipshod woman called Mrs. Green (whose husband, serving a term in the federal penitentiary, is known as 'Sleepy Green') at whose house she found Beppo soon after her release from reform school. "Your own girls, both of them with two children, and one boy out drinking every night. Do you think I'll have *my* girl there? She may want to go, because there is no excitement in my house, but I'll have your head, you encourage her."

"You keep her home then," Mrs. Green had retorted, secure in her image of Beppo striding around her house in pants and shirt, and sleeping at night curled up in the bed of her daughter. "You keep her home then," and Maria had tried to do just this, filled with the anger stored up during months of anxiety, turning on the tall calm girl who stood by the stove in her usual costume of jeans, shirt, and head handkerchief.

"Your brothers came home," she said ominously.

"So?"

"They'd heard things in the street."

Obsidian-dark eyes wary under flat shining bangs, Beppo looked at her mother. "Such as?"

"Someone tells Harry: 'Your sister's a dirty Butch.' "

Beppo said nothing, only her mouth twitching a little, her fingers fiddling with a box of matches.

"So you got nothing to say."

Her mother advanced on her.

"Get a hold of yourself, Ma."

"A *hold* of myself." Maria's short stocky body thrust itself aggressively against Beppo. Her trembling hands grabbed her daughter's arm. "So you're telling me to get a *hold* of myself! What am I to do? . . . I can't kill you, Beppo. I can't *kill* you . . ."

She retreated and clutched at a broom. "See this, daughter! Am I to beat you with it? . . . Tell me, am I? Tell me what to do?"

Beppo drew away from the stove. Her eyes were frightened and her lips moving, as if she were conscious not only of her mother's lack of control but her own. "*Don't* . . ." she cried loudly. "*Don't*, Ma . . ." She saw her mother's face, the dark skin drained and gray, and the trembling ridiculous hand clutching at the broom. She reached over and took the broom and threw it down. "I can't stand noise," she said in a low voice. Then she added in a monotone: "No need to try and change me. I don't want to change."

Two weeks later when Beppo is picked up by the police during a raid on a bar which has been serving liquor to minors, and is sent back to Wentworth, Maria feels relief—not now because she hopes the reform school will reform, but because she knows that it can scarcely be worse than the street. It is during this second stay in the institution that Beppo reverses Sandra's lessons and tries to establish herself as an aggressor, as—in the language of Wentworth—one of the '*in* crowd.' After a disturbance in Martha Washington Cottage, Miss Turner has her put in isolation, where she manages, well taught as she is, to find her own satisfactions and rewards.

. . . In the Wentworth clinic—an annex with three or four bedrooms, a kitchen, a dispensary, and officers' quarters—the light burns in the passages all night long. Beppo is restless and sometimes prowls around during the night, asking for attention, persuading Miss Allison, the big, fat, pretty-faced nurse who is on duty during the night, to let her help bake cookies or put on the beans for the following day. Beppo's simple reward is a glass of milk and a piece of banana bread, seated at midnight at the kitchen table. Miss Allison is persuaded to give her a cigarette to smoke in her bedroom. One night when Miss Allison comes in to tell her to turn off her light, Beppo grabs her, and kisses her, at which the bewildered and mountainous Miss Allison, appalled by her own breach of discipline, begins to cry.

"Get out of here," Beppo commands, laughing.

She lies back on the narrow hospital bed, slender, muscular, and unmoved, while Miss Allison retires in ignominious defeat, ruffled and tearful . . .

"It's ridiculous," Beppo recounts afterwards to her confidantes. "She gets three days off and doesn't come on duty for a week. She won't speak to me, and it sort of builds up. I just get the urge to beat her down . . . I am alone over there and I'm a weak-hearted slob anyway . . . After a while, she comes in and gives me a cigarette, and I kiss her all over again. I push her right down . . . She gives me shirts; she brings me fried chicken from home . . . I take her to bed . . . It's real ridiculous. I can't find it, in all that fat! . . . Well she wants to learn, and I teach her. Gee— she must have given me hundreds of dollars in that time. She gets

so she'll hang out the hospital window to watch me play basketball. Once when I got out she didn't hear from me, and she comes
to Mum's apartment to find me, and she's dressed just in a nightgown with her coat over it . . . I get up and I says: "Come
on . . . ," and I takes her to Callendall and puts her in a hotel
room, and I refuses to make love to her, and she's in floods of
tears, like a baby. The whole thing's ridiculous . . ."

It is customary, after a time, for the authorities to give up the
attempt at rehabilitation. Fed by numerous sources, the Niagara
of juvenile delinquency presents an overwhelming and discourag-
ing picture to those who can no longer see those gradual stages by
which the clear page of childhood gets scrawled over and de-
faced. By the time that Beppo is back on the street again, she is
sixteen, and not only have the youth authorities lost interest in
her, but she is associated at Wentworth with scandal and trouble,
as she is at the local courts with insults and obscenities. With her
aggressive instincts now in full control, she makes advances to a
girl on Moon Street and is cut on her arm by that girl's jealous
partner. An anonymous telephone call warns her mother: "I wish
I'd cut her deeper," the woman said. "Tell her next time no doctor will save her." In desperation, and because of the bad example presented to the boys, Maria makes Beppo move out of the
house.

Now, for the first time, she is seriously depressed. Afterwards,
describing her subsequent addiction to heroin, she is to tell someone that during this period she tried to kill herself with a pair of
scissors—but she said this with a slight laugh, as if it were not
really true, as if she had just picked up the scissors and looked at
them longingly and put them down again. She doesn't at first have
a bad habit, and even in her worst moments she keeps 'clean,' as
she says—though this is the term used, and not without reason, to
describe an addict who has kicked his habit. "But I got so bad,"
she explains later, "so bad . . . that I'd take off if the phone rang
. . . or if the dog barked . . . Anything . . . anything would
make me shoot . . ." "Yes," she adds quietly, her eyes level and
expressionless, "yes . . . the ticking of a *watch* was too loud for
me."

It is two o'clock in the morning, and she is considering picking up a man. She does this only when she is desperate, since the very shape of a man, his very perfume, has become repulsive to her and, rather than turn a trick to get her fix, she is readier to steal or gamble. On this winter's night she wears a black dress, black heels and, over her short hair, a wig of piled-up curls. Her features are tense, however, and her eyes narrowed painfully against the light, while she stands quietly at the bar beside an awkward graying man who is obviously a little drunk, and relies upon her looks rather than upon more obvious advances. After a moment or two, she places her hand somewhat tentatively on the polished bar near his half-empty glass. He stares at her; and she smiles. Then she moves her hand to touch the glossy cap of false curls.

"I like your type," the man says heavily in a blurred voice, "a real womanly type!"

Beppo smiles again. She is trying to control her sense of acute discomfort—the crawling of her skin, the beginning of cramps in her stomach.

. . . An hour later she returns to the bar. At the 'trick house' her attention had been caught by what seemed an unnatural swelling on her drunken partner's foot. Exhausted by love, his gigantic form had been completely at Beppo's mercy. Deftly, with a razor blade extracted from her compact, she had slit the sock just over the telltale bump. Gently, she had extracted a wad of $100 bills. Then, just as gently, her shoes in her hand, she had slipped out of the room, leaving him passed out on the bed.

In the bar, Terry, who has been watching for her, tells her that she is out of her mind.

"That trick you left with . . . know who that bastard was?"

"No."

"Arturo Moravio's father."

"That so?" Beppo looks at her with dead eyes. Arturo Moravio is one of North City's minor gangsters, and she immediately pictures herself lying in an alley with her broken limbs spread at grotesque angles.

"That's not all," she says.

"What's not all?"

"I beat him out of some money."

Terry asks for the second time: "Girl—you outa your mind?"

"I didn't know who the motherfucker was," Beppo replies tonelessly. She feels faintly cold, and her eyes search restlessly around the room. "Terry, I gotta cop."

"Hold it, honey. You betta get outa here . . . There's a dozen witnesses that you left with him."

"Not until I cop," Beppo insists.

"Wait."

Terry disappears.

Beneath the black dress and the wig of piled-up curls, Beppo remains what Sandra has made her, but her defiance, and her firm conviction that all she needs to do to succeed is to 'take no shit,' stops short before the power of the underworld. Hasn't her long education in self-control meant just this? That she no longer needs to try to beat them, and is ready to join them? But now, by getting hooked, she has become so strung out that she has put herself at their mercy. With great effort she remains standing at the bar, her fingertips gripping the polished counter, and her mouth set. Finally Terry returns and murmurs: "Pom-Pom's waiting for you upstairs."

As she is going through the back passage from the bar, and mounting the dirty stairs lit by a single 25-watt bulb, she is thinking to herself the grandiose thoughts which comfort the victims of the street . . . "I've got my automatic at home . . . They really try to mess with me, they'll meet something . . . Those big apes of Moravio are men like other men . . . *Their* asses don't stop no bullets."

But in the bathroom while she prepares the injection and ties the tourniquet around her arm, she is beyond imagining possible vengeance. Her forehead sweats; she begins to shake. The hand holding the hypodermic trembles and can scarcely find the vein;

so that she is forced to press against the wall and to bring one hand to guide the other.

A week later, Maria is called to the North City State Hospital at four o'clock in the morning, to find that Beppo has been picked up unconscious on Holloway Avenue (where she had fallen between the car tracks), and although for some reason no narcotics charge is being pressed against her, she tells her mother that 'Brown Betty,' Mrs. Green's daughter, had given her a shot.

"I don't know if someone gave her orders—one of her men was tight with Moravio—but when I passed out she left me there . . ." "I will say," Beppo adds with her toneless cynicism, "she left me on the tracks where I'd be found, or I'd have froze to death."

Maria now feels fatalistically that Beppo will follow her husband. She cannot imagine how long ago it had started, nor understand the opposite poles between which her daughter has swung. She has all that she can do to cling to reality herself, to keep up with the mechanics of living, to look after the rest of her family without the competent aid of her daughter, aid which is now removed. Maria feels that she endures—like an eroded rock, through which the beating sea bores holes and caverns—endures and lives out the years of her life.

But Beppo returns from the hospital with a greater patience and a new will to become competent in her profession. She keeps away from her addict acquaintances, and tells them that she intends to be 'clean.' In her well-cut jackets and slacks, in her long hand-sewn boots made of soft leather, she roams through the bars and streets, intensifying her hunt for girls, and trying to get—in Marxist terms—more and more 'surplus value.' Her business gamble is greater than that of most capitalists, because she burns up the funds in her own wiry body, but she is able to employ enough patience and cunning to gain entree to one of the hotels on South Spring Street where she has come to an understanding with a Negro representative of the Syndicate. And this is her first real success.

She is not yet eighteen, but she is persuasive and reliable, and she manages to interest the representative in a girl called Lillian, whom she has trained to be receptive to moderate cruelty. "I carved my name on her," she boasts afterwards.

> *Shorty would take me to groovy, frantic scenes in different chicks'*
> *and cats' pads, where with the lights and juke down mellow,*
> *everybody blew gage and juiced back and jumped. I met chicks*
> *who were as fine as May wine, and cats who were hip to all hap-*
> *penings.* From the *Autobiography of Malcolm X*

On her return from Wentworth it is only Opaline in whom Frankie wishes to confide, Opaline who is now married and whose richness and luster is demonstrated by glossy piled-up hair and a mouth purpler than ever. Yet Opaline seems indifferent, and compliments glance off the security of her large pale-skinned body as verbal assaults glance off her passive good nature. In quiet acceptance she waits—contemptuous, amused—for the nervous attacks of her smaller cousin.

"Married! How you stand that?" Frankie comments. "I don't want no man hanging over *me* too tough!"

"I got real well setup," is all that Opaline will say. " 'N' you—you better put some flesh on, baby."

They walk the familiar streets in a comradely way, but Frankie is jealous. She sees Opaline now as Beppo might have seen her long ago, and that part of her nature which yearns for power torments her and crushes her easiness. She wants to control Opaline as she had controlled Lacey and Candy, she wants Opaline to look at her provocatively as had Ana Pulaski. And now she boasts as they saunter down Moon Street of her conquest of Baby when they were in the County Jail.

"Them broads sure snapped to attention . . . I tell you, Opaline, it killed me . . . I couldn't figure out what they wanted—not for the life of me—and then it struck me that they wanted me to be a little *boy*, that's what . . ."

But Opaline is only interested in material possessions. Her life seems to center around dressmaking, baby's furniture, afternoons in some women's club, and good times during the weekends. For full measure she talks about a new skin bleach, a backyard barbecue, and white-walled tires. Then she says: "I gonna get me one of those hats this summer. You seen them little caps, only made with flowers on net, sort of poppies in cream color all over, to go with my new silk suit. Madeline got one over at Sayer's, and she got too the cutest thing to hol' her shoes, all padded and ready to hang."

"How you stand a man pawing on you—is what I don't know," Frankie says with exasperation.

"Oh it soon over! It not too tough!" Opaline's yawn shows her splendid teeth. "Harry's ready to throw his pay check in my lap, and I got no stink coming."

Alva Ford has grown thinner and narrower than ever; and her low depressed voice is no match now for her daughter's, which has sharpened in the verbal tussles at Wentworth. She has her own troubles with her husband, and is torn by the conflict between father and child, as a martyr is when tied between two wild horses. "Don't play around," she warns Frankie from the depths of her own experience, "you'll get a child, or you'll get VD. Walk the straight and narrow. Listen to the voice of the Lord." And she watches her daughter to see what change there is, in her movements, her growth, her attitude toward men, understanding only that a stranger has been returned to her, a stranger who swaggers in tight skirts and boyish blouses, who laughs hysterically, inordinately over the telephone, and tells her obliquely afterwards that it is "just something about that fellow, Sugar."

Alva can see that the street holds many resources, that the very pavements are speaking to Frankie, that soon it will not be the old half-scared truancy with which she will have to deal, but rather an impenetrable 'cool.' And because of this she is frightened. She tries to draw Frankie into the family circle, to interest her in shopping trips with Rosina, and helping to run a tea to raise funds for the Moon Street Boy Scout Troop, of which Bobo is now a member. She buys tickets for the Ice Capades, only to have Frankie refuse laughingly: "No Mama—I don't want to go to no *Ice Capades!*" And when her husband misses $10 from the pocket of the coat he has left on a kitchen chair, and associates it with a visit from Pepper and Pug Nose, she remonstrates faintly and persistently, telling him that the "girl will leave home again."

"Be honest yourself," she protests, "who knows who took it? Support the child and you'll get your reward. You can't do right and wrong at the same time."

"You want that bunch make a sucker outa me?" her husband roars. "Those gaolbirds got no right coming here in the first place. It's against probation."

And for once at least, her husband is right. Because her religion has made her so fatalistic, Alva does not yield enough importance to the influences which surround Frankie. Considering herself saved, she remembers how God had stepped in to elect her from amongst her sisters (of whom Jeanette was already a prostitute, and Miriam in the dubious profession of 'night-club hopping and finger-popping'). And now she feels that prayer alone will make her strong enough to wrestle like an angel, for the soul of her daughter.

Once Frankie is missing for a night, and on the tip of a neighbor, her mother follows her to the subway where she sees her on the other side of the tracks with a gang of girls, all of them drawing attention to themselves by shouting and laughing. Helplessly Alva sees Frankie strutting and dancing on the opposite platform, sees her small face distorted into a caricature of false gaiety. She sees the neat little figure—small-boned and petite—with its slightly rolling walk, dressed in leaf-browns and burnt orange. She sees the straight profile, now changed into a grinning mask . . . She calls across the tracks . . . Frankie turns her head. Her whole face hardens and goes dead, so that it seems a skull with dark holes for nostrils. Then she is swept up with the group and into a passing train . . . Alva, out of force of habit, begins to pray.

The Burrow is a club situated on lower Evans Avenue, on the outskirts of the central city and so closer to the Hill than to the ghetto. Its membership is most elastic, and its reputation shady. Although many of those who frequent it know that it has a back staircase which leads up to a suite rented out for parties and dinners, few know that conveniently just around the corner and linked with The Burrow by one of those secret commercial understandings so common in the underworld, there is a basement shooting gallery where addicts can get a fix.

Yet the club is not without its own kind of refinement. Its clientele and especially its position at the foot of the Hill, make it a suitable center for the kind of Bohemian aspiration which seeks to integrate the races (at least on the sexual level), and to boost the cause of such pseudo sciences as astrology and yoga. It is relatively quiet—unlike the low bars on South Spring Street, which are frequented by crews of itinerant cargo ships, lonely drunken service men, and workmen with belligerent ideas; and although young colored and white prostitutes, at least half of whom have seen the inside of reformatories, are to be found there, as they are in the bars on Mackay and South Spring streets; at the former, they will be quite probably of a superior type, with an interest in jazz and art, and with intellectual pretensions of a limited but intense kind. The males present at the club form part of a racial rainbow in which one finds Indians from India, West Indians with the noble names of their British progenitors, occasional Puerto Ricans or Latin Americans, and Negroes with light skins. The women are more varied, having in common an interest in their own sex which is more uniting than any other single interest, as well as an almost universal tolerant tendency to look upon the male as scarcely necessary though helpful to social existence. Here in The Burrow there is not only talk of the life and the gay life, but talk about Wentworth and Paragoula, Townsend and Bancroft, and, in special booths, and on special occasions, one might even overhear the names of Plato, St. Thomas Aquinas, Nietzsche, and Sartre. The truth is that most of those who go to The Burrow go there because it serves a secondary purpose in their lives, because it is like a post office, for instance, for those who have no telephones and write no letters, because it is pleasanter and less defined than the bars in the ghetto and on the Hill, and because it is a step up for those looking for status. Indicative of the line it draws is the fact that Sugar, with her dark skin and lack of education, would be uncomfortable there, that Beppo, who is attractive looking and quiet mannered but who never went to high school and is too restless to read, would only frequent it for some particular purpose, and that Pepper would find it boring. Lower-class white girls like Polish Ana Pulaski and Irish Brenda O'Reilly would only be there by accident, and would in any case prefer the beer joints in the honky-tonk zone down off Mackay Street in the center of town. But for Frankie, who is still not sixteen and looking for an identity, it is perfect. Here her thwarted and immature intellect can receive stimulation. Here she can join in talk which touches upon that creativity toward which she yearns. Here she can bone up on material symbols—sandals, leotards, cravats, polo shirts, guitars, books on astrology, philosophy, and the racial struggle—of a life which might seem to her superior to what she has so far known. And here she can pretend that it doesn't matter that she has been shut up in Henry Street and Wentworth, and that she hasn't finished high school, since here she can be 'with it' all the same.

It is one day when she is on her way home from a visit to The Burrow that the power of the street touches her in a more direct way. A big Cadillac slows beside her, and she hears the loud beat of jazz enveloping the sidewalk, even while the enormous white shiny fender looms up, intruding, pushing closely enough so that she reaches out and puts one brown finger on its glossy surface.

"Jump in."

She looks hesitantly at the driver, a heavy, handsome black man with a little mustache. It is Wally—the man who is a legend in the family—the pimp who has had her Aunt Jeanette for so long, and made himself rich in the process.

"Jump in," he says authoritatively.

She climbs into the car, and he flips open his silver cigarette case.

"It's Frankie, isn't it?"

"Yes."

She is flattered. Even while nonchalantly taking a cigarette and lighting it from the proffered lighter, she feels inferior, rustic, unfinished. She feels that she is too small for the car she is sitting in.

"Do you know me?" She gives him her most dazzling smile.

He smiles back, showing an arc of white teeth. "Known you since you were an infant." As if drawn by a pencil, the hairs of his mustache are neat and black. His cravat is in perfect taste.

"You rode with Jeanette and me once, when you were so high . . . Your aunt's a fox!"

"Sure is," admits Frankie.

"And when are you coming out?" the man banters.

"What you mean?" Frankie is smiling because she knows very well what he means; but it is a nervous smile and she feels the loud beat of the jazz which comes welling up from an expensive-looking radio set in a glittering panel between the two front seats.

"What you mean?" she repeats.

" 'Bout time you came out," the man says. "Be a pretty fox like your aunt."

He is driving very slowly and looking ahead and smiling so that she sees his profile and the chipped edge of one snow-white tooth. He is cool and hard like a piece of stone, and she has the uncertain feeling that he is a little contemptuous of her. Yet at the same time she enjoys the soft red of the upholstery, the easiness, the music, and the strange sense of complicity. *This is for me*, she thinks, and strokes the infinitely soft red leather with her brown paw.

"Yeah, your aunt's sure one of the steppers." The man looks at her with an amused glance. "You're nearly the same size, and they say the best things are wrapped up in small packages."

———————

. . . She remembered how Jeanette had greeted her on her return from Wentworth. Jeanette had seemed to assume now that Frankie was no longer innocent, so that when her niece inquired

about an old friend she answered with less than her usual protective discretion:

"A rookie was gunning for her, and she found herself in the pussy court."

After this remark she had measured Frankie with a disparaging glance, and asked, in a low unaccented monotone: "Baby, when you goin' to *dig* yourself? When you goin' to get a hole of yourself?"

"What you mean?" Frankie was half indignant. "What you *at*, Jeanette?"

"Get one of these *fellas*," her aunt said, "and get some *clothes* on you"—a suggestion which had, as Frankie explained to Opaline later, sent her 'di-rectly to the moon.' It was not that her own aunt should advise her to get herself a man and get some clothes on her back, she expatiated, but rather that her aunt seemed to have looked at her and sensed that she was different, older, and more knowing. As if her aunt had flung open a door and said: "Okay, you're ready now—get going!"

"What's in her head?" she asked Opaline. "She say that in front of my *mother* she get something."

And again she was conscious of the difference between these two sisters; the one who prayed and cried, the other who seemed proud of the life she led, but to whose apartment the city ambulance had several times been called because of abortive attempts at suicide. Frankie, still having little clear idea of the strength and power of the street, interpreted it to Opaline in a rather romantic way:

"It was because of some man she was hung up on."

Now Frankie feels Wally's candid appraisal, remote, yet touched with sexuality. Abruptly she says: "Aunt Jeanette's in the hospital."

He doesn't seem particularly interested. "That so?" he says.

Frankie remembers the reiterated emergency in the house on Moon Street. ('*Jeanette took pills again*'—'*She got no reason to live*'—'*How come she don't stay in Christ!*'). She remembers that this time she had said: "You needn't hide in front of me, Mama. I

know about that dope. They had it in Henry Street . . . Oh
man, did that girl cry!"

Her mother had corrected her ". . . not dope; it's pills Jeanette took. That's three times now. The second time the Lord
saved her by a miracle. This time Mrs. Kernutz, the landlady,
found her . . . Mrs. Kernutz was sent by God."

. . . Frankie looks sideways at the man beside her. She wonders why he doesn't show some emotion. But at the same time she
admires his cold self-control. She sees how he sits there, so handsome, so well dressed, smiling faintly.

He's cool, she thinks.

Two streets off the car lines, in the semi-industrialized section of
East Williamstown, the O'Reilly house is drowned by the summer rain. Water pours from the gutters, from the sticks of the
just budding forsythia, from the wires which, like taut umbilical
cords, link the house to that fount of electricity and communication which is the city. Water pours onto the narrow strips of
hungry ground which separate this house from the next.

Brenda, discharged from Wentworth six weeks after Frankie,
sits at the table in the kitchen, and allows her little sister Molly to
tie up her long coarse shining hair on pink plastic rollers. A black
handkerchief is then carefully tied around the rollers. The extra
bobby pins are gathered up into a Sampler chocolate box. Brenda's empty coffee cup is put tidily into the sink, and Molly's
round childish face appears satisfied.

"You looked like a big ape before," she comments. "Now you
look like a nun."

"Thanks a lot. That's just what I want to look like."

Molly beams. For weeks she has been praying to have her
older sister at home again.

"Will you do mine this-after?"

"Yes—when you get back from music school," Brenda promises. She lights another cigarette.

Molly pauses on the threshold, her music under one arm.

"Promise you'll hang around." Doubt touches her voice. "Promise you won't go off with one of those niggers."

"Stop saying fine things." Brenda's eyes are sad under the pink plastic curlers, and the black handkerchief. "Niggers are as good as you are."

"I wish you'd be a *real* sister to me," pleads Molly. "It's lonely here without you."

"Wait till you're older." Brenda (who is 'Baby' to her contemporaries, and does not want to be an older sister) thinks vaguely of some future date when she will be in control of her destiny, and able to be what Molly wants. She remembers Sugar and her eyes fill with tears. The walls seem to close in around her, and she waits for her mother to leave the house so that she can call Frankie.

"I always mope if I can't be loud and crazy," she explains on the phone a little later, ". . . I can't take it, Frankie. I can't keep it in no longer. I feel I want to hurt myself when I get to thinking . . . I only been out once since I got here, Frankie . . . No, my probation officer is real strict, and she'll hang me if she knows I'm talking to you. Sugar's at Paragoula, did you know? She got six months. Yes, she sent a kite by Turkey, and Turkey telephoned my cousin, and my cousin told me. Oh boy am I fed up!" Her words began to trip over themselves in her haste to communicate. "No . . . only once I was out dancing. Turkey and me wuz up at The Crimson, and an officer comes in and says: 'I won't have you girls dancing the twist together.' Can you beat it? She was going to have us up for L and L. I said to her: 'You can't put lewd dancing on *us!*' Turkey was going to fight, but I got her arm and dragged her outa there . . ."

Frankie is laughing and murmuring at the other end of the line, and Brenda begins to mimic her mother. "Ma says I must get *work*, and I must get in at a *reasonable* time at night. And I must pay *fifteen* a week for my room and board."

"Better play 'long with that," Frankie advises.

Brenda's voice grows tearful again. "Ma says I'll be standing alone in court. I said to her if Turkey stands alone, then I stand alone—I was real hurt, I can tell you. She always gets on my weak side. She says I have to get a job. She says I'm givin' her gray hairs . . . I tell you, I want to get a place by myself. I'm fit to climb up the walls . . ."

In the supermarket Brenda's mother buys the food she thinks her daughter will like. She loads the basket with cereals, bacon, grapefruit, chicken, whipping cream, and Delaney's cheese cake. She dreams unreasonably that Brenda will stay at home, and she plans to do her daughter's bedroom over. She considers plastic curtains with roses on them. Brenda is far away from her, but in despair she pretends that this is not so. It is all an error, a bad dream . . . Long ago when the child was fourteen, she had had a birthday party. Two Negro boys arrived with the other guests. "They're drinking in there, Ma," Dennis had told her. "They're goin' in the bathroom, and they got vodka—I can smell it." She had called Brenda to ask her if the boys were drinking and Brenda had said that they weren't. Mrs. O'Reilly had gone to one of the colored boys and said: "Stand up," and she'd opened his coat and there was a half pint of vodka in his inside pocket. She had said: "Come boys, get out—or I'll call the police." Dennis had taken on a grown-up role and said to his brother: "We've got some work to do," and he'd marched to the front door, flung it open and said to the two boys: "Will you go peacefully, one at a time, or will I have to throw you down the stairs?"

They'd gone quickly like two tall gangling dark shadows—but afterwards Brenda had been hysterical and had said that the party was no good and she was going to her girl friend's, and in spite of her mother forbidding her, she had pulled on her coat and rushed wildly out of the apartment. For one moment Mrs. O'Reilly had thought of sending the boys after her, and thus subjecting her daughter to the same discipline to which she had subjected the Negro guests. But she had hesitated for too long . . .

She pauses now in the aisles, her wire basket loaded with food, and her eyes sorrow amongst the canned goods, the spices, the chocolate . . . "I am at the end of my rope," she whispers . . .

She remembers the sudden changes in Brenda—the rudeness, the hysteria, the lapse of interest in school ("She sits and stares in school," the teacher had said in a puzzled manner, "she no longer concentrates"), the accusations against her family, her sudden disrespect of all they represented ("Pa's nothing but an ole' drunken bum! . . . He can't order *me* around"). In the aisles of the supermarket, the mother pauses as if in a maze of doubt. If it wasn't the niggers, then what was it? Where had it begun? What had changed her biddable, quiet, religious daughter into this rude stranger?

Outside the supermarket she sees Officer Shannon directing the traffic, and rests her heavy bags on top of a parked car as she waits to hail a taxi. The officer comes toward her, his badge flashing in the sun, and tells her that they want to see her at the station.

"It's only the juvenile officer to have a word with ye. He sees that you've got the girl home and has some words of advice . . . You'll find him to the right of the main door."

"It's O'Toole then?" she asks in her low worried voice. "It's the same one that was such a friend to Brenda."

"That's right. Why don't you go along then, Mrs. O'Reilly? Keep to the right of the main door and there you'll find him." His voice is heavy with a special concern, as if the whole matter were a blot on the Irish.

At the police station, Officer O'Toole motions her to a seat, and closes the door.

"Yes—I know that she's back and I want to tell you that we've got new information on that friend of hers, the one that used to be in the Project."

"That Rachel?" Mrs. O'Reilly feels the anger and disgust of a rejected mother. "That's the one whose face I could smash in."

"She's the one that rented the house in Leland where Brenda was found after her first run. Remember that?" The officer bends forward and lowers his voice. "Well, we raided the house, you know, and just two weeks ago we raided it again. Officer Brown up there at Chicoba kicked the door down and they found three or four girls in there, both white and colored."

Brenda's mother regards him from under the crown of her graying hair. Her sad eyes stand out against her pale face, that face which has at once a German stolidity, an Irish melancholy.

"What was going on then?"

"That's it . . . One of them was booked for possession."

Mrs. O'Reilly stares at him.

"Narcotics," the officer explains. "Brown found several rooms with beds in them—but hardly any other furniture. In one room there was a table with makeup and a mirror. He says there must have been fifty or sixty dollars' worth of makeup there—and in one room there was a TV that you or I couldn't afford . . ." The phone is ringing constantly, and now he lifts it up and talks into it, gazing reflectively at a pad upon which he jots down notes and telephone numbers.

Brenda's mother feels the panic of one who realizes that she is part of a universal disaster, that her own troubles are not unique and that therefore they cannot claim exclusive attention.

The officer puts down the phone and says with emphasis: "Inside the refrigerator there were hypodermics and several capsules of heroin." She sits uneasily, her face blank.

"That means that someone there was using narcotics," the officer explains patiently. "For instance, your daughter may have been exposed to drugs . . . There was very definitely an addict or two in that bunch. Rachel seems to be the brains of the outfit."

"How can I find out?" Mrs. O'Reilly demands flushing. "How can I know if Brenda uses things like that?"

"It's unlikely she's doing it now," the officer says. "She's just out of Wentworth. It's what she's been subjected to . . . You're going to have to watch her . . ."

The minutes tick by in the brain of Brenda's mother. She is used to anxiety and pain, but now she doesn't know what is expected of her. This is something new.

"Watch her," the officer is saying.

"To watch her all the time," the mother begins, "already it's like she feels my eyes on her . . ."

"She'll be slipping out. But when she goes out you should go with her." The officer's voice is insistent. The phone keeps ring-ing, and it is obvious that he has a busy day ahead of him.

"Why can't they stop it? Why can't they shut them up—those that sell it? Where did that Rachel get it in the first place?"

"They did shut Rachel up," Officer O'Toole is saying.

The phone is ringing again.

. . . On the way to get a taxi, Mrs. O'Reilly passes the Sports-mans' Bar and Grill down on the edge of the tracks. In the dirty and uninteresting street, its neon lights make an unsuitable spot of color, purple, green, orange-red, climbing a neutral wall as if try-ing to set fire to the roof. Out of the corner of her eye she sees the dried-up flaxen-haired woman who goes into the bar, good-quality clothes hanging on her obscene figure—an overripe figure topped by a raddled and masklike face.

A chill catches the mother's breath and she touches her throat where the gold cross of childhood still hangs. *I pray she'll be taken, she thinks . . . I pray she'll be taken if this doesn't stop . . . Quickly, while she's still young . . .*

––––––––––

Two nights later, Brenda has a fatal quarrel with her father, who has been drinking all through the summer afternoon. The late sun glitters on the car tracks in front of the house, and Mollie plays noisily with some children in the street, their shouts—loud, un-controlled, disconnected—echoing through the windows of the living room where Mr. O'Reilly walks to and fro, his coat off, his feet bare.

"I don't want that Turkey coming here," he says.

"Turkey's my friend, Pa."

"What d'you mean, she's your friend? She's colored and I know the type. You think your Ma and me—that we're fools, that we don't know the type? . . . I don't want her here. Haven't we had enough trouble?"

"You live your life, Pa, and I'll live mine."

"You call it a *life* . . . ?"

Brenda suddenly wants to attack her father, to hurt him as much as she can.

"And if it's not a life, what do you *care?*" Her heart constricts. "What do you really care about? You sit there drinking with your little Irish bald-headed self!"

Mr. O'Reilly's pale hairless forehead turns red with anger and shame.

"So *that's* what you call me!"

"And what do you call *me?* Everything but a child of God!"

There is a silence for a moment and Brenda turns away trying to control herself, biting her lips, snapping her fingers in exasperation.

"There's got to be some discipline here, that's what there has to be," her father interjects. "We've got Dennis away in the mental home . . . You running with the scum of the streets. I tell you sometime you're going to be found with your throat cut . . ."

"And if I'm found with my throat cut, what does it matter to you? . . . I've taken this crap so long that I can't take more of it . . . What's this about the colored anyway? I been with Negroes so much I wouldn't know how to act around a white man . . . Oh no, I'm not fascinated by nothing. It's just I like them, that's what. White men are *savages!*"

"So white men are *savages,* eh?" Her Irish father descends upon her with his fists up. "You say that again, my beauty . . ."

Brenda backs away. She is breathing hard.

"As far as I'm concerned I'm colored," she cries. "And you might as well know it now. I don't know how to be anything else, Pa!"

Some truth in this penetrates through his anger and his drunkenness.

"Brenda—"

"I *don't,* Pa . . ."

It is as if there were some plea for help in her voice. "You stay with them," he warns stolidly. "You stay with them, girl, and you'll find yourself . . ." He pauses and there is a drunken sob in his voice. "You'll find yourself dead—with your throat cut, daughter."

"If I do . . ." Her face is pale, and she is no longer angry. "If I do, it'll be a Whitey does it."

"It'll be a Negro," warns her father.

"No . . . it's *not* gonna be a Negro. Anytime anyone finds me dead, it's gonna be a *Whitey*."

She turns away, cold and resolute . . . In the morning she has disappeared.

Oliver Jackson is one of The Burrow habitués. He is a short blond boy with a gliding walk, his silver-fair features have a Nordic regularity, and he generally wears turtle-neck sweaters—black, brown, russet—with tight hip-hugging pants. When he gets to The Burrow, he sometimes changes his street shoes for handmade sandals fashioned by Krafto-Link (Krafto-Link is the tradename used by his friend Victor, who has a jewelry and sandal shop in New York City in the winter, and another jewelry and sandal shop on the Maine coast in the summer). That he, Oliver, frequents The Burrow, which is a hang-out for girls rather than for men, is not surprising, since Oliver himself has experienced a sexual metamorphosis, and as such feels sympathy for all sexually vacillating creatures—whether male or female. Indeed, he is attracted to The Burrow in the first place, not only because of Joel, the barman, who is also gay, and because of the other gay men who drop in from time to time, but because he also likes women, and here in The Burrow he can toy with the idea of paying one of the 'Fems' as a prostitute, or even (and this particularly appeals to him) seduce one of the little near-Lesbians who are just out of reform school and not yet sure of their preferences.

Like most of the habitués, he has his own particular ax to grind, since as an agent for Victor, he has been able to do a flourishing trade in sandals and birthstones (slung in cradles of silver wire and worn on chains around the neck). In fact, it is through one of these birthstones that Oliver meets Frankie in the first place: since Pepper has bought one and given it, in an excess of generosity, to Frankie.

"Who's your friend, dear?" inquires Oliver.

"This is Frankie," Pepper explains. "She's a way-out kid."

Oliver warns Frankie about the implications of being born in August, and about the dangers of August fourteenth in this particular transit.

"It might be a fatal day for Virgos," he says in his soft voice of a maiden aunt.

Frankie is impressed by Oliver's sandals, and the topaz in an ornamental silver setting which he wears on the little finger of his left hand.

"What's going to happen to me?" she asks him. "Don't tell me I'll have to go up to the joint again, because I think I'll lose my marbles."

"I don't know exactly what might happen dear," Oliver says, "but you should be careful."

He adds earnestly: "In the present cycle of Venus, dear, love will flourish in the little acts which show your attention to matters pertaining to them . . . Venus vibrations reveal a transit which can establish contact with one who is destined to be a lifelong companion . . ." He looks into her eyes fixedly and adds: "Seek to communicate with one who has been hard to find."

"I gotta go," Pepper says.

Much as she likes the jewelry which Oliver sells, she doesn't care for his conversation, and besides always feels uncomfortable in The Burrow, preferring to make her headquarters in one of the drugstores downtown or in the Prince of Pizzas.

When Pepper has gone, Oliver is able to comment about Frankie's orange shirt, the violet stone which swings around her neck, and the darkness of her eyes. "I like your colors," he says. "They're really exotic."

"What's *your* month?" she asks.

"Well I'm a Libra myself." He shows perfect teeth in his moon-clear profile. "We're known for our moderation, our fairness. It's a *neutral* sign . . ." He looks at her to see if she has noted this remark, but she is still concerned with August four-teenth.

"If it's a dangerous day, I'll stay at home and read."

"Do you like to read, dear?"

"Yes, I love to read; that's about all I do."

With a gentle erotic intonation he inquires: "What are you reading now, Francesca?"

"I'm reading *The Sign of the Swastika*—about Hitler."

"And isn't *that* something!"

"You've read it?"

"I've read it all, Francesca, absolutely all."

"What do you *make* of it? . . ." Frankie gazes at him with somber eyes. "How'd they let it happen?" She knows that there is some meaning for her in this historical event, some meaning which worries her unduly. "All those killings make you sick to your stomach."

"They certainly do," Oliver agrees blandly.

"Hitler even had syphilis eating away at his brain . . ."

Oliver nods. "That's true, dear."

But she is brooding about the power of evil, caught in a con-flict which seems integral to her, the conflict between her mother's God and her father's paganism.

"He only had to *stand* there, and five thousand people raised their arms . . ."

"He was sick, dear."

"I know that, but people *followed* him." Frankie is trying to involve him in her own fantasy. "I know it from myself . . . At Wentworth all the girls would snap to attention when I went by . . ."

"We just can't *understand* people like that," Oliver declares.

"He was no worse than Herod," Frankie says aggressively.

"Herod . . . I never thought of that." Oliver is not at all in-terested in politics, and Frankie finds herself dissatisfied with his answers. Seeing her looking at him with disgust, he excuses him-self and goes to join the barman.

Left alone, Frankie hears the gossip from the next table which enlivens her and makes her feel part of an active world. A wild-looking dark girl with an aggressive manner and short hair is scolding a little blond creature wrapped in a fluffy sweater. "You got me by that little shit you pulled," she accuses. "There's not a damn thing I can do about it . . ."

"Those are the breaks, dickeybird," the blonde answers in a small voice, "those are the breaks . . ."

"Why you instigating it? That's what I want to know. Why you instigating it?"

"I'm not instigating," the blonde protests.

Frankie gets up and makes her way to the ladies room, swinging her hips in the tight tweed skirt which she wears whenever she feels she shouldn't wear pants. She passes a table where three earnest effeminate-looking young men are talking about 'soul.'

"It's got nothing to do with the *mechanics* of music," one of them is saying, "nothing, I tell you. You have it, or you don't."

"Spades have it, and whites don't," another answers in an infatuated voice.

The only colored boy in the group drawls a protest: "Frankie Sinatra has it, and *he's* white."

"Sinatra sure has it," one of the others has to admit.

Inside the ladies room, smelling of cigarette smoke and so small that only two people can fit inside at one time, Frankie pulls a letter out and rereads it. Candy, who is still in Wentworth, has smuggled out a childishly written note, with several spelling mistakes, and filled with those phrases current in institutions set up for adolescent lovers.

'*My darling . . . my secret love . . . It's not the same since you're gone, and I cry in my bed every nite. Without your arms to hol' me. When are you coming back Frankie. I've had 2 write-ups since you're gone. Even Mrs. Casey give me a write-up. This is because I don't care about nothing my love. Only you. Yours for ever Candy.*'

Frankie puts the letter back into her pocket, does her hair, and returns to the bar where Oliver puts out a restraining hand and holds her waist.

"Wouldn't you like to see my photographs, dear?"

"You photograph?" Frankie is intrigued, associating photography with art, and art with status. "I'm interested in art," she adds.

"I don't do the photography," Oliver confesses with his white smile. "I model for Preston Blake. He does jobs for all sorts of high-class publications. He's just got a big assignment for *Noon*. You'd *dig* Preston's work, Francesca."

She is flattered by the attentions of this young man with the marvelous profile, although she would have claimed that he didn't exactly ring the bell for her.

"We'll play records at my place too," he encourages.

"What kind of records?"

"Jazz," Oliver suggests, "Jimmy Smith, Monk, Horace Silver."

"I'm supposed to work . . ." Frankie's probation officer has insisted that she get a summer job, and she has recently been taken on for two months at the Morton Belt Company in Moon Street. "It's the four-o'clock shift, but I sure could use some of that funky guitar."

"We've got two hours," Oliver suggests. "Perhaps Preston can pay you as a model, too. Let's go."

Already Frankie hears herself tell her mother that she has given up the job at the Morton Belt Company because she is modeling for a photographer—and, indeed, at five o'clock that afternoon when she is late for work, and is drinking beer at Oliver's apartment, his employer, Preston Blake, does come in, and at Oliver's urging tilts her head from side to side, as if looking for a suitable angle from which to immortalize her. "You've got a smooth eye line, a very smooth eye line," he says several times. In Frankie's mind, she is moving upwards in the world, simply because she is in Oliver's apartment which is in an all-white area near the university, and which is hung around with pictures of nude young men, and with shots of Oliver from the waist up, modeling all kinds of shirts (polo, button-down, Swiss-Velour, and Casual Sports).

H

After Preston goes, Oliver suggests that they try to find Pepper, who claims that she has some customers for him, and he begins to call Frankie "Darling," telling her that if she ever has trouble with her parents she only needs to come to *him*, because he has befriended many a girl who is in trouble at home, and never wanted anything from them either. And at seven o'clock when the disillusioned foreman at the Morton Belt Company (*I thought I was doin' that kid a favor*) has just crossed Frankie's name off the shift list at the factory, she and Oliver are sitting at a table in the Prince of Pizzas, facing Pepper, whose red lips are twitching and whose mass of unmanageable hair is crowned with an odd little hat given her by a cousin who's just returned from Italy. Pepper is slightly drunk and invites Oliver to dance to the jukebox, which they do to the tune of "Mama Said," and to a round of applause from the pizza eaters.

But Oliver, although he finds himself excited by her rich hourlong obscenities, cannot make what he calls 'spiritual contact,' and finally persuades Frankie to leave, which she does to the sound of Pepper's half-angry protests: "What you want with that motherfucker, Frankie . . . ? What he goin' to do for you? Eh . . . ? He promised to give you *head*?"

An hour later, Oliver's car, shadowed by the trees in the far reaches of the park behind the university, is the scene of a seduction. They are drinking whisky out of paper cups, and Frankie, warmed by the liquor, and dazzled by Oliver's regular features and silver hair, is expatiating about his physical beauty.

"You built like *Atlas!*" she cries.

"You think so, dear?" Oliver pushes up his sleeve and shows the muscle of his upper arm.

"I *think* so," Frankie admits, "I *dig* it."

"You're beautiful and exotic your own self, do you know that?"

"I don't know it, until I see those broads hitting on me," Frankie says. "Even in that Burrow there, one or two of them are at it. D'you see that redheaded broad in the booth behind you today . . . ?"

"The homely one with the stick-up hair?"

"She sure *is* homely . . . Did you *smoke* that onion?" Frankie affects exaggerated horror. "She'd make somebody cry . . . Can't go near her without your eyes watering! . . ."

Oliver begins to laugh, and draws Frankie to him in comradely amusement. He likes her as much for her quick tongue as for her petite figure and beautiful eyes.

"She real *plain*," Frankie comments, pleased by her success . . . "Ef Moses'd seen that broad, I tell you there'd been another commandment. She was *truly* whipped . . ." Oliver laughs louder than ever. Frankie sees his almost white lashes and his even, pearly teeth.

"Is she as bad as *that?*"

"I tell you, Oliver . . . couldn't nobody love her but *Jesus*."

He buries his face in her neck, filled with an amused half-sensuous affection, asking her what she thinks the broad wants.

"She horny," Frankie says wisely. "Bent for a lick and a rub."

Oliver caresses her further, her words inflaming him, his ego pushing him to prove himself a man—and she, for a similar reason, because she wonders deep down whether she is indeed a woman, allows him, almost without any sense of danger, to kiss her and to play with her body, especially with her buttocks ("You've got such beautiful little brown buttocks"). Yet as he gets more excited and forces sexual intercourse upon her, she struggles in panic, like a small wild cat, and is only subdued at last when he pushes her down on the seat with his muscled arms and closes her mouth with the pearly teeth she has admired so much.

The next day she wakes in his apartment again, where photographs of her new lover look down upon the bed she has refused to share with him—Oliver in profile, swathed to the chin with Rattan and Myers polo shirts; and Oliver in full-length little-boy postures, grinning, with hands in pockets of Smith and Sons raincoats. She has broken the code of her group, and gone to bed with a *man*, although she is not so sure that it is a real man, and the

tears she had shed the night before are like pearls strewn in payment for an act forbidden her. Something has been desecrated and
she cannot believe that good can come of it. She is still sufficiently
unformed sexually to ponder with interest about a rapturous
pleasure which never comes, almost as if she were saying to this
man-woman: 'I'm giving you a chance—dig—try to knock me
out.' But partly because of the passivity to which Oliver has become accustomed, which makes him so much less suitable a lover
for a woman, she is always disappointed and wishes only, when
she yields to him again and again, that he would "hurry up and
get through with it."

Yet as the days pass she experiences some happiness. She likes
the money he gives her, the free drinks, the flavor of a world
which is attractive to her. Oliver is friendly with all sorts of people whom Frankie knows nothing about—other models, both
male and female, admen, radio commentators, disc jockeys, dress
designers, and even publishers' assistants. And although she considers his literary tastes poor, she is pleased that they both lie
naked on the narrow couch in his apartment, while she recites to
him from Walt Whitman's "Song of Myself" ('That man Walt is
my heart') or from the Bible ('Jesus is just on the other side of
that door, Oliver'), pleased that Oliver pays tribute to the part of
her which is perennially hungry for the things of the spirit. The
truth is that he is better than the ghetto, he does something for
her ego, he is built like Atlas, and he is white! At the same time
she can so little believe in his masculinity that it does not occur to
her that she can become pregnant.

It is only when her mother—several months later—watching
the strange blossoming of her daughter, the rounding of her figure, the languor of her movements, asks, in a voice strained and
low: "Don't you know that you are going to have a baby,
Frankie?" that this idea even occurs to her. She shrinks back, her
eyes thrown up, her shoulders retreating from a meaningless burden, putting out her hands as if to ward something off. And she
sees her mother bend and rest her face in her hands for a moment,
murmuring: "I have a lot of grace to withstand trouble . . . but
this is too much."

As Frankie stands there like a statue, a somber shadow creeping over her set face, Alva adds prophetically: "Your father will put you out!"

Miss Bailey knocks at the door of the apartment in the Project, and hears the furious barking of dogs. The clamor is so loud that she can scarcely distinguish the faint swish of rubber tires on the other side of the door, and when the door is at last opened by a cautious hand, it is as if she were physically assaulted by the eager snouts pushed through the crack, and the apartment's close urine-laden breath.

A wheelchair is standing in the doorway. A small thin face looks up at her from under a thatch of once-blond hair, the flesh hanging from the cheeks and the throat. A whining wistful voice, suspicious eyes, a cramped body—its upper part clothed in a grubby white sweater, its wasted lower limbs wrapped in a flowered skirt.

"Who is it?" the face asks.

"I've come to see about Ana."

"Who is it?" repeats the hostile whining voice.

"I'm from *Wentworth*, Mrs. Pulaski," Miss Bailey says.

"Oh come in, come in, dear." The voice becomes ingratiating, the wheels of the chair reverse, the door opens further, the hysterical dogs yelp louder, and leap higher.

"Down—down," the woman in the wheelchair is saying, "down—down."

Miss Bailey sees that one of the dogs is tied by a long leash to the leg of a lopsided table. She steps back fastidiously from a pool of urine on the floor. She looks longingly at a window, as if she would tear it open.

"Pull the shade down, dear," Ana's mother begs. "Please pull that down for me . . . I've been alone for two days and everything is out of order . . . Please pull down the blind for me, dear. There's a lot of nosy people around here, only wanting to mix in with your business . . . Oh . . . it's broken on me again . . ." Miss Bailey has pulled at the blind, only to have it come out of its socket into her hand. ". . . Oh do try again, dear . . . No *don't* get up on the table, dear. . . Not that one, the leg's broken . . . Try the *chair*, dear. That's it . . . Good." Reassured, the woman's voice changes, becomes more relaxed. She knows now that none of the neighbors can see that she is being visited by someone from the State School at Wentworth.

"You was Ana's Friendly Visitor?" she inquires cautiously.

Miss Bailey smiles, and lets her think that this is so, her efforts to speak drowned in any case by a torrent of protest from Mrs. Pulaski.

"Well *I* don't know where she is. I can't tell you *where* to find her. She's out with those so-called friends of hers—she calls them friends but I guarantee they're only acquaintances . . . Leaves me alone like this for two days and more at a time . . . That's what she does! . . . And the *animals!* She's got all her animals in here. I must say this for her, she's lovely with animals and children . . . There's a big Siamese cat locked in the bathroom. What do you think of this place? Look there—look at the *roof!*"

Miss Bailey looks at the peeling roof.

"And they call this a *Project* apartment. What do you think for $50 a month, eh? I'm like a prisoner here. All I have for view is the washing in the court. Why I can't even see the Fords going by . . ."

Miss Bailey agrees that Mrs. Pulaski, tied to her wheelchair, might indeed want to watch the Fords going by. "But if the apartment were cleaned up . . . ," she begins.

"Oh dear, how am I to clean with my legs like this?" The thin wistful crafty little face peers up, and in the pale-greenish eyes and the weak mouth, Miss Bailey catches a buried likeness to Ana.

"It's MD, my dear."

"MD?" the social worker questions.

"What is it, dear? What did you say? I can't hear you . . ."

Miss Bailey realizes at last that Mrs. Pulaski has hardly heard a word since she entered the apartment.

"My hearing aid's off being mended . . . What did you say, dear?"

"I said what's MD?" Miss Bailey shouted.

"Speak up . . . speak up . . ."

"MD?"

"Yes, I've got MD, dear. That's muscular dystrophy . . . Ever had it, dear?"

"Good heavens no!"

Miss Bailey withdraws herself into an island in the room, feels her limbs shrink from touching anything, is conscious of the controlled horror of the healthy. She thinks: *Why am I a social worker? . . . Why in God's name? . . . I want to leave here . . . I want to get outside . . .* Instead she flips an inner page from an old newspaper lying on a chair, spreads it out on the table, and determinedly puts down her coat and pocketbook.

She then begins to gather together the soiled plates scattered around the room, and to place them in the sink. "I think I'll help to clean a little."

"Oh *don't* bother, dear . . . Leave that . . . Someone will do it. It's the apartment, that's what it is! The manager he says it's my fault the walls peeled like that. Why don't you open the windows, he says. When you first come you should have opened the windows. When you moved in . . . As if one wants to freeze to death." Her voice rises again in whining complaint. She begins to wheeze as if out of breath. "Oh dear, it's my chest . . . Sometimes I can't breathe." She sits there gasping, and finally she goes on, "I haven't *done* anything . . . Why should I be here like this . . . I haven't done anything *wrong* . . . I tell you I might as well be in *jail* . . . See that pipe over there? . . . I burnt myself on that pipe, and was in the hospital for two weeks. My son from California, he came and he said: 'Ma . . . Ma I'm going to take you out of here . . .' "

The wail ceases for a moment. Miss Bailey gathers together a great pile of garbage and grimly sweeps the floor. She tries not to draw the air into her lungs, and is glad of an excuse to go with the garbage to the outside incinerator.

" . . . and so Ana hangs out with those friends of hers, and doesn't come back nights half the time. My son says: 'Ma . . . I won't have you alone like this. You'll come to live with us.' My son took me to his home up there in Murmaine County, and you should have seen it. Beautiful it was, like a home in Hollywood. In the Cartage and Storage Company he was. What beautiful floors he had, all polished, you could eat off of them. Wall-to-wall carpeting in the front room, a TV to one side, and a big aquarium all along one window . . . I was in the upstairs too. I can't wait long for the bathroom these days, and when I have to go, I have to go. And I'm sitting there in my chair . . . and my son says to me: 'Ma, what's the matter?' and I just look at him, and he says: 'What's the *matter?*' and I say: 'Son, I have to go . . .' and he had two of his friends there and he says: 'Come on, fellers, give me a hand,' and they lift me up, chair and all, and carry me upstairs to the bathroom . . ."

After Miss Bailey's second trip to the incinerator, Mrs. Pulaski is still talking about the bathroom in her son's house in Murmaine County. ". . . I tell you it was like a star's bathroom . . . glass and the tables and bottles and all . . . Everything electric . . . And here I am living like a pig."

Miss Bailey has fed the dogs which are now lying quietly, and —somewhat impressed by her own unselfishness (since housekeeping is scarcely part of her duty)—she is making Mrs. Pulaski some tea.

"But he loves me, my son does, and he says: 'Now we're going to California, Ma, and we're hoping to bring you out as soon as we're fixed up . . .' And my older daughter she was here for the first time in seven years, and that Ana went off with her so-called friends the second day and didn't come home. My daughter was planning to take Ana back with her, but she missed the boat . . . My older daughter, *she* won't stand no nonsense . . . One day *I'll* go, and *then* that girl'll be left alone . . ."

Miss Bailey now has her notebook out, and is trying to get some information as to what Ana does with her time.

"She *goes* . . . that's what she does . . . She *goes* all the time. As for that Margie she calls such a friend, *she* has a terrible temper you know. When she's here, Ana's absolutely changed. One night that Margie, she was here and she says: 'What've you got to eat?' and I said: 'I don't know what we've got. There's something in the icebox I s'pose.' Well she opens the icebox and she says, as fresh as you please: 'Haven't you got any *meat?*' And when I says we only have franks, she grabs the franks and she grabs the eggs, and she acts like the place is hers. Can you imagine the *nerve?* . . . So I say to Ana: 'I don't want that girl here. She stabbed somebody and she sets fires, and I don't want her here. She grabs things as if they were hers' . . . She borrowed Ana's leather jacket without so much as a by your leave, and we've never seen it since. I told Ana: 'Keep that girl away from here . . . If she thinks she's going to hang with us, she's mistaken' . . . I tell you I was afraid to fall asleep in front of her . . . Sometimes I'd doze for a moment, and when I looked up, I'd see those evil eyes staring at me."

Miss Bailey asks if Ana still sees Margie outside of the house, and Mrs. Pulaski says that Ana is so fascinated by her, that anything Margie says goes.

"She's breaking parole," Miss Bailey suggests.

Mrs. Pulaski's face changes, as she realizes, perhaps for the first time, that Miss Bailey is more than a Friendly Visitor and may have some official post at Wentworth. Ana's daughterly care is almost nonexistent, but if Miss Bailey turns her in again, then there will be no one at all, no help, no company.

"She's young, dear," she soothes. "The young have to go."

"But with no one to supervise her . . ." Miss Bailey objects.

"What did you say, dear? . . ." She is having difficulty with her breathing again, as if the nerves of her throat and chest, wasted by the disease, refuse to respond.

"It's my throat," she explains in a wheezing voice.

"I'm very sorry." Miss Bailey feels uncomfortable, as though her very presence were an insult. "I'm here because her probation officer is on leave, and the department asked me to check on what Ana is doing . . ." She looks at Mrs. Pulaski who sits there in her wheelchair, her eyes alive and anxious in her thin fallen face, the loose folds of skin at her neck moving with the effort she has to make in breathing.

"The young won't stay in these days . . . You can't keep them in, not these days you can't."

"It is difficult," Miss Bailey murmurs.

The mother seems to be thinking of something. Her face lights up with a faint dim joy. "Ana loves to dance. I have to give it to the little devil . . . she *can* dance."

At this very moment Ana is standing outside Perry's Drugstore, where Mackay Street cuts across South Spring Street. The hair which had been so long and red when she first entered the County Jail, and which at Wentworth she had worn in a fashionable bubble bob, has recently been bleached until it looks almost blue and contrasts oddly with her pale-greenish eyes, the contrast making her look older than her sixteen years, although it is much in favor with Alec (the boyfriend whose seriousness is expressed by his refusal to take her to bed).

"I never went with him in my life," she says now to Kathie, one of Margie's friends.

"Please—" she adds in a shocked voice, rolling her eyes upwards.

"Never *once?* Not even that time we wuz at Bony's Pond?" inquires Kathie.

"He wouldn't let me even if I wanted to," boasts Ana. "He says wait till we're married. I've tried to get him to a few times but he won't . . . Oh Alec don't mean trouble for me." She teeters to and fro on her heels, hugging her little blue jacket around her, casting provocative glances over her shoulder at some nearby sailors (the sailor's uniform sets off a triggered response in her as immediate as that of a match touching a trail of gunpowder). And then she adds with a childish carelessness: "It's you girls mean trouble for *me*. Alec takes me everywhere—parties, shows, Chinatown, pizza, movies. *That's* no sweat."

"Okay," Kathie says jealousy. "Why you hangin' with us?"

"I'm s'posed to be meeting him, but he's awful sometimes because he won't tell me *when*. Sometimes when he's got duty he don't let me know, and here I am waiting on the corner. I'm waiting here an hour perhaps." Her round childish face clouds and she glances disconsolately up and down the street.

"Let's go up the U.S.O."

Kathie, who is an unattractive girl, knows that she is more likely to pick up a serviceman if she is accompanied by the tiny but rotund Pug Nose.

"No, I gotta wait for Alec, I tell you."

"Last night I wuz to Bony's Pond," Kathie confides in a low voice. "Gigi tilted the cash register, and we got a bottle o' vodka an' a case o' beer. I went out and I called 'Hi Mac' to that truck driver Penny wuz going with, and we all piled in an' went out to Bony's, and we got kinda drunk an' danced and everything . . ."

Ana's face falls.

"Gee, I don't do nothing no more," she mourns. "Even I go up to Margie's my mother hollers. As for them cops, five of them brought me back to the Project last week, and there they was pounding on the door till everyone in the Project knows . . . It was the Big Guinea and my mother says he has no respect. She says that I sure got that big ape's ego . . ."

Kathie speaks with her usual lack of sympathy. "They watch out for you, they sure can't miss that blue wig of yours!"

Ana touches her hair self-consciously. "Gee, I wish Auntie Casey could see it. "*She'd* sure flip!"

"Who's Auntie Casey?" Kathie props her lanky frame on the fire hydrant.

"She wuz head of my college," Ana announces proudly, referring to her time in Wentworth. "I was in Florence Nightingale College."

"You like it there?"

"Gee I *loved* it," Ana speaks with conviction, unable to understand why she had ever left that big school where all had been so ordered and so busy, where there had been so much to do, from ice-skating to waiting on table in a lavender uniform. "But Margie had done her time, and so I was glad to go home too . . . Besides I was lonely without my kitty cat . . . Ma shuts her up in the bathroom all day 'cause of the dogs, 'cause they all fight and dirty up the place. And my kitty she gets real nervous from being shut up. And she scratches something terrible."

"Hey lookit," Kathie urges, interrupting, "lookit . . ."

"What's the big news?"

"Lookit . . ."

Ana sees a couple going into Perry's, a tall mousy girl with a wide lipsticked mouth and wearing a silk dress, and a stocky belligerent-looking little midget in pants and a sweater.

"See our new *couple?*" Ana questions. "Guess who wuz at the dance Saturday? *They* wuz . . . Betty's broke up with Lou, and here she is with *that* Butch!"

Ana sounds lofty and disinterested.

"Oh they wuz all loving funny in Wentworth . . . But you wouldn't catch *me* risking going into Secure . . . No 'Rec' or anything . . ."

"It cracks me up," murmurs Kathie. "She's been with about fifty girls. They must think she's *Paradise.*"

Ana sighs . . . Although she is not really interested, it seems that she is always waiting for something. Her impatient nature, her voracious little body, her weak intellect—none of them can guard her from the life which surrounds her. If Alec doesn't come soon, she knows that she is going to do something foolish, something which will get her into trouble with everyone, her probation officer, her mother, and of course the Big Guinea whose dark menacing face and squat figure, tightly encased in its police uniform, fills her with delicious fear. She hears the Big Guinea's voice saying loudly: "All right you bunch of tramps—get off the corner!"

"The only father I have is Harold," she says suddenly.

Kathie stares at her, and then begins picking at one of her long brittle painted fingernails.

"Harold's down at the golf course where we used to hang," Ana says. "He used to talk things over with me. Alec tries to talk to me and the social worker tries—but they're only playing with my mind . . . Harold's different . . . It was nice down there at the golf course . . . no sweat . . ." Her voice tails away. "I'm goin' in to get a Coke," she adds with sudden energy and defiance, and she pushes her way into Perry's with Kathie trailing after her. Her hips swing energetically, her small body lurches on its ridiculously high heels.

"I'm not gonna wait for Alec all *day*," she announces over her shoulder . . . "He'll find out."

At one of the tables inside she is hailed by a thin pimply youth and two sailors whose faces appear bewilderingly young above their navy uniforms. The three of them smell strongly of beer, and the young man is saying: "Meet my buddies," while Ana, happy to find that the vacuum of the afternoon appears to be filled, says in her turn: "Meet Kathie, my girl friend."

After the refreshments, two hours are spent drag racing on the expressway—Ana in one car with the two sailors, and Kathie in another with the thin pimply youth (who detaches the back plates before they start racing, in case anyone should try to take down the registration numbers).

When the sailors win the drag, the pimply youth claims it's a foul, and while the sailors disappear into the dark interior of the Palace to treat Ana to a surreptitious beer, he rips up the upholstery of the sailor's car with a bottle opener. The Palace is famous for the two scantily clad dancers who gyrate wearily inside the red-painted cages which are suspended from the roof, and here the sailors proposition Ana as to some further entertainment, so that after slight resistance she agrees to go with them (when it's dark enough) to a secluded spot outside of town. Finally, spread out casually on the slashed back seat, she satisfies them both for the sum of fifteen dollars, and is returned to the Project at last with her blue-bleached hair disarranged, with pieces of white fluff from the car's seat stuffing sticking to her clothes, and with the skin of her buttocks under the tight pegged skirt red and scratched from the sharp plastic edges of the broken upholstery.

Mrs. Sheila O'Reilly gets out of bed, puts on her dressing gown with infinite slowness, her knees aching with the arthritis which is intensified by sleeplessness, her eyes heavy from worrying about Brenda. She pads into the kitchen where the kettle has been set on the gas by her husband, and pours the boiling water onto the coffee. Then she opens the kitchen door to let the cat out, feels the October chill in the air, and closes the door abruptly. Something beats incessantly in her brain, *I will get her back . . . I'll go out into the streets and get her back.*

"So you're up, Ma?" Her husband stands in the doorway in a dark-blue flannel dressing gown, his gray, level eyes slightly rimmed with red.

"Did you sleep?" she asks him.

"Not much." His face closes over as he accepts the coffee cup she hands him. "Not much."

Together they stand in the kitchen, mutely exploring this hole in their lives, dark, with its jagged edges of fear and mistrust. Their eyes become evasive.

"Sometimes I'd smash her face in," the mother murmurs.

"Okay . . . okay," the father says mechanically. "I'm going to get O'Toole onto it again."

"O'Toole's known for two months, and hasn't picked her up."

"Give him a chance, Sheila."

Curiously Mrs. O'Reilly reflects. "You know it didn't seem to bother her to leave the house. As if she knew all the time, and only came here to have our custody."

"We can't keep her here, unless she straightens out," her father declares firmly. "She's got to know this is her home . . . she's got to behave decently."

There is a silence as it becomes clear that this remark is not realistic, the whole thing having gone much further than this, into realms where simple orders don't penetrate. The mother turns around helplessly, her fat face grieving and distorted. She gives a sweep with her arm, indicating the tidy kitchen and the comfortable living room beyond, with its upholstered chairs and polished tables, and she inquires in a broken voice: "How could she, Paddy? How could she leave such a *fabulous* home?"

Her husband rubs his hand over his forehead as if the skin hurts him.

———————

Brenda at this moment has been asleep for two hours. She shares a bed with Sugar's cousin, 'Pokey,' a gigantic Negro girl with some of Sugar's grace but none of her good nature; and in the adjoining room two white girls are sleeping, their hair tangled on the same pillow, but their backs turned to each other as if in mutual hostility. On the table nearby there is an almost empty wine jug, and a host of dirty glasses. Under the sink in the small kitchen, numerous bags overflowing with garbage, are flanked by piles of empty beer cans which roll along the wall and spill out onto the available floor space, witness not to the thirst of the apartment renters, who have their own preferred way of getting high, but to that of their numerous visitors. The core of the matter—the 'works' and a single deck of heroin—is hidden in a specially marked beer can, in the midst of all this refuse (Pokey's theory being that the 'squad' doesn't like to play around in garbage and trash—and that if they do try it, *this* particular can may never be detected). Through a thousand garbage removals, therefore, the one can remains.

In the front room, Brenda's black sheath dress and slightly bent-over black pumps—blank adjuncts to her profession—lie on the floor where she threw them at five o'clock this morning, and she looks, as she sleeps, exhausted but healthy, while her dark companion and the two white girls in the room next door seem all to be plunged into nervous twitching comas, the skin of their faces curiously dead and blank, their veins protruding from the flesh of their throats and hands. Of the four sleepers, only Brenda is not an addict, and it is upon her coarse but youthful strength that the others feed like parasites. Even in their sleep this fact seems to be expressed, for the three other girls lie huddled, faceless and loglike, while Brenda, the victim, lies on her back, her foolish freckled face exposed. And the history of the past could also be read here, as fallen monuments sometimes lie like stark reminders on the grass of empty plains. For if one could have turned over the bodies.of Clariss and Lily, one would have seen, echoing that system by which cattle are branded by their owner's name, the single word *Pokey* tattooed into the flesh of their upper arms.

And Brenda herself is not unmarked, because she wears the imprint of Pokey's fist at the corner of her mouth, and bruises on her arms where Pokey's angry fingers have so often caught her, and spun her around.

Two months ago she had been safe and healthy in her mother's house, plump from good food and regular sleep, cured of all minor ailments, fresh from the guardianship of Wentworth. But after a single night on the street, after several drinks in the bars of Mackay and South Spring streets, after an hour's conversation with old acquaintances, she had found herself falling victim to big, dark Pokey's blandishments, and ending up by going back with her to her two-room apartment at the foot of the Hill. Pokey has reminded her of Sugar, as Sugar had reminded her of King; and the cycle has closed around her loneliness, as the long-fingered dark hands encircle her body. Too drunk to be conscious of what is going on, she does not realize that one room opens into another, where Clariss and Lily lift heavy eyes as Pokey enters quietly, shuts the intervening door with care, and announces proudly: "Well, I copped me a fine white girl!"

After that Brenda loses count of the days. She feels the noose tightening as Pokey demonstrates a brutality which even King has never shown toward her. She is driven into the street in the middle of the afternoon, and abused if she returns before dawn with less than $100 to show for her labors. Clariss and Lily, emaciated and dope-hungry, have neither the strength nor the heart to protect her from Pokey, whose physical resistance is such that she can burn up the 'stuff,' keep the trio subservient to her, and still handle the relatively strong Brenda with one hand. Pokey's secret seems to lie in a harsh tyranny which combines strangely with an abased but animal-like attachment to her three girls. Brenda learns to parry the blows and arm twistings, to remind Pokey that the color of her skin is an asset, and to appeal to whatever distorted protectiveness she senses buried deep under an insensitive exterior. Yet the pace is too fast for her, and she is unable to appease that insatiable desire for money.

"So bitch, why were you late?" Pokey had asked her at five that morning. "And only a lousy eighty bucks to show for your trouble? Are you getting funny ideas—is that it?" She had waited until Brenda began to explain.

"I couldn't help it, Pokey . . . I tell you I was duckin' Mercatti because I promised him to keep off the streets . . . Honest to God, the jive roller was after me while I was with this trick . . . I had to blow the trick even . . . I *swear* . . ."

And at this point Pokey (as if she understood very well the loneliness in her victim's mind, and the desire to make contact with old friends) had drawn her fist back, and punched Brenda on the mouth.

At four o'clock Sheila O'Reilly calls her sister Shannon and begs her to meet her at seven that night. "I'm stumped," she tells her. "I'm fit to collapse. I tell you I've got to find her or I'm going to have a breakdown!"

"But what can you do, Sheila?"

"What can I do? I don't know. But after all those wonderful promises she made in front of the parole board, I'd as soon see her behind bars, I promise you."

The sister begins to smoke numerous cigarettes as she listens to her on the phone.

"You can't put her behind bars if you can't find her, Sheila . . . And if O'Toole can't find her, nobody can . . ."

"O'Toole will send an officer with us and he'll take us to the bars where they hang out." Shannon hears the panting breath in her sister's short fat body, and she imagines the perspiration breaking out on her skin. "I tell you I've got to try it, Shannon. I may be fifty but I've got to find out how life really is . . . What's got into her out there? What she's after that she wants to leave her parents and her home? What's she got out there?"

"The Holy Saviour alone knows . . . But where will we go and what will we do?"

"We'll go with the officer and he'll show us the bars. He says we may be able to find her better than he can . . . He says that a man stands out in these places . . . I tell you if I find her I'll half kill her . . ." The avenging angel with the sword hovers before the mother's eyes. She begins to cry.

"Don't upset yourself," soothes Shannon.

"I can't . . ." sobs Sheila, "I can't . . . She's my daughter after all . . ."

"No Sheila, it's no good to upset yourself. I'll go with you. It's something to do, isn't it? But don't get your hopes up."

"I'll smash her face in . . ." Sheila sobs.

An hour later Pokey is waking Brenda.

"You'll be late for work."

From the bed Brenda feels them watching her, their eyes empty, their hands passive. They all seem tentative, restless, like birds gathering around a special area mapped out on the ground. She herself hovers in the sky, and she sees the bird-shapes arranging and rearranging themselves around some unspecified carrion. The shoulders of the girls hump like wings. The wings lift, then droop again.

"A-a-ah," she murmurs unintelligibly, feeling sick, resentful, indolent, burying her face in the sheets.

"Get up, you bitch," Pokey suggests, stripping off the bed covers, and exposing Brenda's large naked legs. "Get up."

While Brenda dresses she longs for coffee, but none of the other three seem to care to eat, and now they are all around the kitchen table bent on carrying out the ritual of shooting, their faces caught in expressions of calm desire, their eyes blank but watchful. There is an exquisite fairness about it, a calm that is impregnable, the kind of silence which one keeps in the death house. The tourniquet is tightened. The flame of the candle burns under the spoon. The precious liquid is poured into the dropper. The plunger is pushed down slowly. The faces one by one relax, lose shape and sharpness.

Only Brenda is tense and alive; and she is worn out by the fatiguing labors of the night before, and by the knowledge that twelve whole hours on the street will not be enough to satisfy the trio before her. Now, while Pokey is out of the room, she cries: "What you think we're doing?"—trying with a remnant of good sense to draw the other two girls into league with her against their tyrant. "I can't carry you *all* . . . It's getting next to me . . . What we think we're doing?"

"We're burning *everybody*," Lily murmurs in a low voice, but with a burst of fading energy, "just like you're screwing everybody. How'd you think we did before you came? I told fantastic lies to my mother, and Clariss was making up to her old man . . . Just to get the bread, that's what. We're *junkies* . . . Don't you know the scene?"

Brenda goes into the kitchen. It is true that she does not know the scene. She has prostituted in one way or another for the last two and a half years, but she is not yet a true professional, and this is the first time she has fallen into a nest as abandoned as Pokey's.

She hears Pokey come out of the bathroom. She hears Lily protest to her in a low voice, with scant emphasis but with a certain sincerity.

"Baby, dig yourself," she hears her say, "you're pushing that broad too hard . . . Lighten up on her a bit . . . You only had the broad five weeks or so, and look how you're shoving . . . Cakes are *nice*, Pokey. State we're in, we can't afford to blow them . . ."

Brenda hears Pokey reply in a surly tone. "Fuck that bitch . . . There's plenty more where she came from."

"Yes, baby," Lily answers mildly. "But don't get beside yourself . . . Look how we're situated? I sure don't want to go out there. I'm too *strung out*."

Her voice fades. Brenda hears Pokey's heavy tread. And then, like an expiring sigh, the light lost voice of Clariss: "And I *truly* can't make it!"

"So what you want *me* to do?" Pokey growls. "Give the broad a blow job? Do a Jeff Davis?"

"No, baby—No, Daddy," Lily croons persuasively. "Give a little 'spect, that's all."

In the kitchen Brenda determines to leave that night. And as if even through the wall Pokey has read her mind, there is the sound of heavy footsteps, and a large hand at the neck of her dress.

"So . . . what's with you?"

"Pokey—I'm *going* . . . this very minute I'm going . . ."

"You're going, bitch! . . . But don't get any funny ideas either . . ." Born in Trinidad, Pokey has a certain clarity of speech inherited from the English owners of her slave grandparents, but her language itself is violent and aggressive. It cuts the air like a whip curling about Brenda's head. And the intensely black and polished face, with the thick scar to the left of one eye, which had been inflicted during a teen-age gang war in Harlem, bends now over her frightened victim.

"You know I'll find you, bitch . . ." she promises. "Wherever you go I'll *find* you . . . Remember I ain't but two minutes off your ass!"

In her worn and unbrushed black shift with pieces of dust sticking to it, with her heavy dark hair stiff with pomade, and her freckles coated with makeup, Brenda searches restlessly through bar after bar—the dim lights throwing off an occasional dull sparkle from her hair—table after table, feeling the anxious drumming of her fingers. She knows that Sugar is still in Paragoula and that Rachel has been sent up to Townsend. But she hopes to find Frankie, or Pepper, or at least one of the girls from Wentworth, and she searches with a blind frantic haste through the darkened bars, as if she were in a race with time itself. This feeling is justified since by nine o'clock Pokey will be out after her, checking up on her prowess, urging her on, trying to calculate her gains, stripping her of enough to go out and buy stuff for the next day —and should she suspect any kind of loitering or double-dealing, thinking nothing of attacking her in front of everyone, and slapping her into submission. Because of her anxiety and haste, she finds none of her friends; but the waitress at The Oracle—a short-haired, hard-fisted young woman in dark-brown shirt and slacks, who knows her by sight—warns her that her mother is looking for her.

"My mother!" Brenda recoils in horror.

"Officer Werner comes in." The waitress is anxious that there shouid be no trouble. "He asks for you, and I say I haven't seen you for days . . . Then later your mother comes in."

"How d'you know it was my mother?"

"She asked for you. She said did I know Brenda or Baby? And she's the spitting image of you, too . . . Then I says: 'Any message if I *do* see her?' And she says: 'No message. And it's tonight I want to see her, or *never*.'"

"God in Heaven! Mary, Jesus, and Joseph!"

"You better get out of here. Let her find you anywhere but here . . ."

. . . Brenda walks the streets, besieged by memories of home. Something has happened? "Pa is ill . . ." she murmurs aloud. "No, Ma's after me, that's all . . ." She feels a disgust for the life she is living but is unable to imagine going home to something she has left behind her. In some ways she is more at a loss before her mother than she is afraid of Pokey and the street. She is filled with suffering, but she does not see her suffering clearly. It is a wall against which she bends her head, and at which she helplessly beats her hands . . . In the Golden Girl she hears the same story. Two older women were looking for her. She is convinced that the second woman is a policewoman who is going to take her in. She rushes out of the bar and walks on the dark side of the street. It occurs to her that the best way to elude capture is to hide out with a man, and she accosts two truck drivers who take her to a hotel and book her a room. She bargains for an all-night price, and sinks back on the bed with a feeling of relief, almost unaware of the young man who stands taking off his clothes on the bed's other side—as if he were a statue, a block of wood.

"Where d'you come from?" she asks mechanically.

"Florida."

"Let's see your health card."

He produces it.

"Thanks." She waves it away. "Hurry up."

It is as if she were in the streets still, hastening along to avoid capture. Her mother is at one end, and Pokey at the other. Her mother has promised to smash her face in, and Pokey has also promised to smash her face in. Down corridors and through alleys she hastens, breathless, her high-heeled black shoes loose on her feet, her heart thumping. She looks for refuge and defense, and feels the man trying to kiss her as if this were happening on some far away fleshly perimeter.

"I don't kiss tricks," she says sullenly turning her face away.

He turns his attention to her body, to her big breasts and her ample peasant hips, and with a perfunctory impatient gesture she hastens his pleasure, in order to dismiss him the more readily from the room.

"We've got a long time," he pleads. "You've got the room for the night now . . . Sweetie, spare me another fifteen minutes."

"No—get out."

"You've got a nasty attitude," complains the man.

She shuts her eyes and pulls at the dress which she still wears (as if by doing this she denies the act of love and makes it more clearly commercial). She is wondering whether there is something wrong with her mind. Her brother Dennis had been shut up for quite a while. And they wouldn't take him in the Army. Then there'd been a cousin who'd gone crazy over in Ireland, and they'd had to shut her up too. Brenda remembers how she'd sat on her bed often, clutching at the sharpened file she carried in her stocking or her shoe.

She ignores the man pawing at her body.

"I want my money back," the man says suddenly.

"What you doin' . . . ? Juggin'?" Brenda asks in surprise.

"It's no fun turning a trick with you." He lifts his face from her waist and she sees a broad angry nose, and a sunken belligerent mouth. "Why d'you pretend to turn tricks when you don't like it?"

"*Like* it—you don't think I do it because I *like* it, do you?"

She shakes her shoulders like a dog emerging from water. "Now get out."

"I want my money first," he mutters.

"I got your money, and I'm planning to keep it . . ." Brenda turns her back on him and busies herself with her hair. "Ain't no need for your coming over this way again," she adds rudely, "not going to beat your nuts here. Send your pal in."

When he doesn't move, she swings around angrily, her voice hysterical. "Go ahead . . . *Blow* it . . . Get *going!*" she orders.

And in the meantime, and indeed ever since seven o'clock, Sheila O'Reilly and her sister Shannon have been in and out of the bars which (according to Officer Werner) are those frequented by Brenda and her friends.

"She's supposed to be with a girl called Pokey," he tells the two women.

"Well, if you know as much as that, can't you put a hand on the girl?" asks Shannon.

"We pick up people from time to time, and we get the latest news . . . but we don't get the addresses that easy."

"Can't we get it in Brenda's case?" her mother asks.

"If we could put *one* man onto it." His voice is a shade defensive. "There's only six of us in the squad, and I tell you we work an eighty-hour week. All night and then in court in the morning." His eyes are indeed swollen from lack of sleep, and he is nervous while he's with the two women, because he is neglecting the beat he's responsible for. "We cooperate as much as we can," he adds in his calm rolling voice, "but it's the work of her probation officer."

"She wouldn't even get out of *bed* for her probation officer," Mrs. O'Reilly cries indignantly.

She wears her dark suit, thinking it more suitable than anything gayer, and followed by her slightly less substantial sister, she moves through the dark bars like a respectable navy-blue cruise ship moving through strange waters. She peers at the tables crowded with girls, and at the dark corners where couples sit close together, staring into each other's eyes. She is amazed that so many women should crowd together at this hour of night simply for the pleasure of being together, and soon she becomes uncomfortable under the hostile or derisive glances which greet her as she pauses bewildered beside some booth more than usually lost in shadow. Many of the girls are young, and most of them are in slacks. But whereas some of them have close-cut hair and wear mannish sweaters, pullovers, or shirts, others have hair which streams over their shoulders. These last go in for earrings, pancake makeup, lacy blouses, brilliantly colored sweaters, or delicately made shirts with frilled jabots. The girls who take the masculine role sit slouching at their tables, their legs thrust out immodestly, their sleeves rolled up to show the tattoos on the muscled part of the forearm, cigarettes in their fists. The more delicate girls sit hunched, their eyes drooping with mascara, their necks weighted with chains holding coins, birthstones, or replicas of the signs of the zodiac. They affect flirtatiousness, disdain, boredom, or mystery, and their partners view them with the same curious attentive look with which real men, absorbed in solving a perpetual riddle, are apt to view the women who accompany them.

From time to time a couple get up and do a brief illegal dance to a tune on the jukebox—some quick variation of the twist or the watusi—the male girl being seen then to dance with a vigorous lack of self-consciousness, and the female more delicately and with a show of hands and gestures. Occasionally, too, a quarrel drifts like smoke through the chatter and noise of the rooms—heightened voices, shrill laughter, accusations, a few obscene or rude expressions . . . Or someone gets up and pushes her way resolutely through the tables and out of the swinging doors, her shoulders expressing a certain violence or hysteria, something which is not quite normal but which in this context seems natural enough . . . The door to the telephone booth bangs perpetually . . .

Sheila begins to feel lost in this crowd of distorted femininity and to wish that she were not there. She catches Shannon's hand and draws her along with her, and would retreat were it not that she thinks from time to time that she has found Brenda, that some erratic gleam of blue-black hair, some pale profile turning there to the left of her belongs to her daughter. She is filled with a frustrated anguish, something between rage and horror, and as she proceeds resolutely cleaving her way through the semi-darkness, her indignation grows. What a situation Brenda has put her in! Look at what her mother has to do! How can this happen? How is it that her own child draws her out into the streets and low bars searching for her? She thinks with an anguish which has a terrible clarity. "If I don't find her tonight, I'll never find her. I know it . . . I just know it . . ."

At The Burrow a party has been arranged in the upstairs room. If all the habitués of the bar are not invited, it is rather because of various animosities between individuals than because of the exclusiveness of the party itself, which has not even the exclusiveness of sex, since it has been organized by Trigger for the twenty-first birthday of her longtime friend Mary, and Mary has insisted upon inviting the 'men' (though these men are of the same type as Oliver and his friend Victor, up from New York City). A few interracial couples who live on the Hill have put in their appearance; and odd types, such as Fleur, a college student, who is enamored of the musician who plays the trumpet in the band hired for the occasion, as well as Pierre, a French orphan from Martinique, who arrives accompanied by a Filipino businessman (respectable but lonely), who is surprised to find himself in a dirty room above The Burrow where there is no furniture, but an odd collection of people, mostly young women in slacks. He is also surprised to be accosted at the door by a nervous Negro with a wispy goatee, who stands handing out joints at a dollar apiece and murmuring at the same time: "Come on . . . get with it . . . Come on . . . you're lagging." This young Filipino is even more surprised as he drifts around the room with Pierre to hear parts of a conversation of which he can understand very little, most of it seeming to be about someone who was 'caught in a snowstorm,' and 'riding the wave,' and then had suddenly found himself a 'fresh fish,' and landing in 'the can, to live on angel cake and wine.' But as he moves on further, in search of what is more familiar to him, he is completely confused to hear a serious bearded man with a shock of white hair say that the philosophy of St. Thomas Aquinas is just so much dreaming, whereas Nietzsche might have been a controversial fellow, but that he still had sound ideas.

"God is dead," the man says decidedly, drawing at his 'stick' with an expression of satisfaction. "That's something anyone might reasonably think. It's more suitable to think that God is dead . . . than it is to think that God is living and all-powerful. Agreed?"

"Agreed—agreed," says Fleur's trumpeter, a small Negro with a black beard, black pants, and a black shirt. "Absolutely agreed."

And Fleur herself, a thin blond girl wearing a purple leotard and a little scrap of a skirt, nods decisively, hanging on his shoulder, and saying that while she adores Nietzsche she has been introduced to Sartre lately—by Oliver actually—and she absolutely 'digs' Sartre.

"Do you, Fleur?" Oliver asks happily. "Do you really, dear?" Well I knew you would . . . I knew you'd just *love* Jean Sartre."

"Fleur'd dig anything that goes against society," Oliver's friend Victor contributes.

"Oh, d'you *know* Fleur?" Nick the trumpeter inquires possessively. "You knew each other before?"

"Since *when*," Victor affirms.

"Since I bought my sandals from him," Fleur says, looking at her feet as if they were flowers.

"Sartre is the epitome of nonconformity," adds Victor, "and Fleur is the epitome of nonconformity."

Frankie has now joined the group, and Oliver puts his arm around her shoulder and introduces her to the others, adding in a tone of gentle guidance that she too must read Sartre; but Frankie—looking in her black slacks and black shirt like a smaller edition of Nick the trumpeter—feels embarrassed by her ignorance, and only shrugs a little. She is elated, however, to be in such intellectual company, because this is always what she has wanted—to be in intellectual company, to listen to the prophetic words spoken around her. Yet although she does not know it, some years are to pass before she is to hear Sartre's name spoken again, and had she become more familiar with it, even during the next few months, and used it as some sort of talisman, it is doubtful that it could have prevented her from treading the paths she was destined to tread. Having smoked several sticks of marijuana, the scene around her has lost its sharp focus, and the people who are so handy with the names of philosophers have dim outlines and might as well be angels. She remembers the cell in Henry Street, and resolves to call up publicly the words and images which surrounded her then.

"It's Walt Whitman," she cries. "*He's* the one I dig. He pounds down the words like someone hammering nails . . . Oh I love him to *death* . . ."

Oliver looks at her proudly, filled with a momentary tenderness which transcends the bounds of sexual differentiation. And he is glad that he has insisted that she come to the party, although he knows that she is not yet sophisticated enough to be part of *his* group, and although the presence of Victor has made it a little delicate. Now, like Pygmalion, he is proud of that portion of her which he thinks is his work, and he dreams of teaching her more, dressing her in some sort of livery and keeping her as his perpetual page. He is ignorant of her pregnancy and of the fact that his Nordic seed has already created within her a folded inch-long form, more potent for change in her life than any of his egotistical and romantic notions. Because he does not know, however, he cannot be frightened, and is able to protest to Victor later on when, loosened up by the turmoil of the party, Victor makes some rather crude allusion to her—"Baby, what do you *think?* She's a cute and clever little Spade, but I tell you, I'd as soon fuck a baby cow!"

As the evening wore on, the women in the dirty but transformed room outnumbered the men more and more. Trigger had thought of bringing up some of the lamps from downstairs, lamps which were made in the shape of crystal roses and painted red, so that an illuminated blood-red blossom now bloomed on the floor in each corner. The overhead lights had been turned out, and in the near-darkness couples danced to a music which was so slow as to be almost stationary and which rendered the steps of lovers sticky and weighted, as if they were trapped in molasses. The intellectual conversations which had occupied Oliver's group for a few moments had soon been blown away by the more solid inroads of the girls' gossip and the inarticulate obscenities of those who had a long acquaintance with the street. Polite heterosexual phrases heard earlier, such as "Hey Fleur—how are you? Come to think of it, baby, we've never been to bed together, have we?" had given way now, murmured in the thick of the dancing crowd, from a Butch to her 'Fem,' to such brief commands as "Get my cookie, baby—get it."

Long arms lolled over the shoulders of the feminine partners. Hips moved slowly. The darkness showed only a smudge of faces, the pallor of shirt or dress, the whites of eyes, hands outspread on hips—all of them tinged with the faint red light from the eye of the illuminated rose . . .

It was during this night that Frankie tried to tell Oliver that she was pregnant but was restrained by the noise and confusion, by Victor's evident possessiveness, and by the fact that she was constantly claimed as a dancing partner by a pretty little girl who had been told by Pepper about her 'rep' in Wentworth. She was tortured through the evening (in the midst of the naïve questions of the girl, who obviously expected great revelations and whose gaze had the shallow clarity of water trickling over sand) by visions of a swelling belly, upon which she must brood through long months.

She danced away, confused by the fumes of marijuana, and unaware that while she danced Oliver was being persuaded by Victor to return with him to New York City for several weeks, and that soon the two of them would unostentatiously leave the party, thus severing forever the fragile relationship between Oliver and Frankie.

. . . It is also during this night that Beppo runs into Ana 'Pug Nose' Pulaski, in The Burrow's ladies room. Beppo has looked in at the party because Trigger has urged her to do so for old time's sake. Ana, on her side, has heard of the party from Pom-Pom, one of the cage dancers at The Palace, and she has tagged along with Pom-Pom and several other girls, hoping that someone won't find out her age and turn her away at the door. All dressed up in a long pink sweater, dangling earrings, and tight slacks of duck-egg

green, Ana is rapturous about running into Beppo again, whose
legend on the street is less vivid than it is in Wentworth but still
glamorous enough in the world of Ana, which does not extend
further than the Project, The Palace haunt of lonely lower-class
servicemen, and 'hanging' in front of Perry's.

"Well, wadda y'know!"

"It's been a long time." Beppo looks at her reflectively.
"You've cut off all that hair?"

"D'you like it?" Ana turns around in the tiny space between
the toilet and the washbasin, fluffing up her blonded bob. "Don't
you think it's a *bad* color?"

"Real *bad*."

Beppo lounges back and lights a cigarette, while Ana sits on
the toilet. "Okay baby, don't stay there too long, might give me
ideas."

Ana shrugs self-consciously, rolling her big green eyes, the
lashes heavy with mascara. In spite of the makeup and the crudely
bleached hair, she still has a touch of naïve innocence.

"So what's been happening to you?" Beppo asks, infusing her
voice with tender amusement.

"Oh hanging . . ."

"Where d'you hang?"

"Oh, Perry's, or The Palace, or at my girl-friend Margie's."

"They sent you up to Wentworth, didn't they?"

"Sure they did."

"Well how *is* that place? Still got that bitch Miss Turner?"

"Sure thing, she's the super . . . Oh I *loved* it. I was in Florence Nightingale College."

Ana pushes at her hair, and watches Beppo out of the corner
of her eye. "Gee, the girls all talk about *you* there. They think
you're the *greatest*, Beppo. When you sent me that card I'd have
thought they'd die . . ."

"Nobody raped you there, eh?" Beppo smiles at her small
plump victim, wondering whether it will be worthwhile to cop
her. She is becoming more and more discriminating, and is not
sure whether such a dense little broad is going to be worth the

trouble involved. But she knows now that as long as her habit controls her she will always need money.

"Nobody raped you?" she inquires again.

Ana squirms in discomfort.

"I never loved *funny*," she protests flirtatiously. "Gee Beppo, I got my fiancé Alec . . ."

"So you're a square, eh?"

"I don't like hanging any longer," Ana confesses rather pathetically. "I get tired of running, honest. If the police see me, they bust me . . . And Connie Topper—she barboushed with Schafer and gave him the clap, and whose golly great name did they pick out of the hat but mine! . . . I had to go to the doctor again and everything . . . It was like Henry Street before. It wasn't me at all and I got a paper to prove it . . . It's just that I'm a ringleader."

. . . The noise of the party above penetrates even into the tiny downstairs ladies room. Someone is pretending that he is a bird and is hopping heavily about on the floor overhead, while his friends try to prevent him from flying out of the window.

"You're lonely, Ana," Beppo says gently, remembering that the girl had always wanted to be called her real name instead of the nickname Pug Nose. "How'd you like to live with me?"

"You're kidding!" Ana pouts a little, retreating from Beppo and pressing herself against the wooden partition. She thinks that it is like a dream, to hear the famous Beppo suggest that she, Ana, team up with her. Unconsciously, like a weak flower precariously blooming, she leans toward Beppo, the stronger, sturdier, flowerless plant.

"I'm hard," Beppo warns, "and I take no mess."

She thinks to herself that Ana has certain coarse physical charms, that she is too shallow to demand much of her sponsor, that she, Beppo, will be able to con her easily and not have to expend much energy on love-making. After she's been copped she will learn the ropes rapidly, and become as rapacious as necessary. She may make a good durable sturdy whore. With those green eyes and that dead-white skin, Beppo may be able to get her into one of the hotels. *If she's not too dense*, Beppo qualifies to herself. Her conscience does not move her, because it is only occasionally, when she sees the light of intelligence break over a girl's face, that her conscience operates.

". . . Come here, Ana," she commands, and sees the girl shrug her plump shoulders and sidle nearer, like a fascinated rabbit.

"What's the matter . . . you scared?" Beppo looks down at the coarse white little face, with its eyelashes quivering, and Ana looks up to see the inscrutable dark eyes, the flat Indian hair dangling over the strong, flat freckled nose.

"Ye-es," she admits shrinking.

Beppo smiles, showing her even teeth. "So you ought to be." Then she warns caressingly: "I take no mess."

"I know." Ana fidgets in embarrassment.

"I got no time for t.l.c.," Beppo adds. "It's not as if you was a virgin."

A little giggle shakes Ana's plump body, which Beppo thinks is like a rotund cask filled with a sweetish wine.

"And what about this Alec . . . ?"

Impressionable and weak-minded, Ana feels excited by Beppo's closeness and her bold staring eyes. Swept away with the novelty of it all, she discards Alec without another thought.

"Oh I can't be bothered with *men* . . . They play around with my mind. An' Alec's always leaving me hanging on the corner . . ."

Tears touch her voice, and pathetically she flutters her lashes.

There is a silence in the tiny room, and the music reiterates its beat, intruding from above and wrapping them both around with an artificial and temporary warmth, not unlike that warmth they both know, of the cells, the reformatory, the 'Secure.' The approach to love, being made so appropriately in this ladies room, reassures them that for a moment at least they are a '*couple*,' and soon perhaps to be '*one*.' Even Beppo feels some sexual excitement.

"D'you want to go to bed with me?" she inquires.

Ana nods, still keeping her head down.

And it is also during this night or rather early the next morning, that Brenda, refreshed after her uninterrupted sleep in the hotel room the night before, and eager to get ahead of the game financially so that she will be independent of Pokey, goes out looking for business in a street not far from the building where the party at The Burrow is still going on.

She sees a shiny new cranberry-colored coupe drawn in near the sidewalk and approaches it tentatively, strolling a little past it, and then pausing and searching in her pocketbook as if to get out a cigarette. The man in the car stares at her, and the blaze of the streetlight falls obliquely across his face.

"Looking for a good time?" she inquires, smiling provacatively and walking back a few steps.

"What were you thinking of?" the man asks.

She leans down and places her hand on the rim of the rolled-down window.

"I was thinking about twenty-five."

"What's your name?" he asks. "I think I've warned you before."

His hand fastens onto her wrist, and she feels it strong and authoritative, the practiced hand of the law.

"Mary, Jesus, and Joseph!" she exclaims under her breath.

"What's your name?" he asks again. "O'Reilly, isn't it?" His face shifts, and with the light full on it she recognizes the blunt features of the incorruptible O'Malley, terror of all the North City prostitutes south of the Bay. Dazzled by the cranberry-colored off-duty car, she has been cruising a cop!

"Is that your own hair, Mary?" he questions next.

"What's it to you? And my name's not Mary."

"What is it then?"

"Elizabeth," she lies hopelessly.

"Well, Elizabeth, you'd better come back with me."

"Don't take me in," Brenda begs.

"I remember seeing you a month ago. And I warned you then." He gets out of the car, still holding her wrist in that iron grip, and she flinches back, conscious of a group of squares waiting for a taxi on the corner, and watching the scene with interest.

"The captain's in that squad car up there," he warns, "and that's where we're going."

"I don't care if the Pope's there." Her voice rises with the old uncontrollable hysteria. "I know *you*—you'd bust your own *mother*," she cries.

"Is *that* so . . . ? My mother was never on the corner . . . Let's go along."

His grip is hurting her arm, and she sees the staring faces of the men and women.

"Let go of me," she mutters in a low voice, "let go of me . . . Okay I'm busted, but let go of me . . . I promise I'll walk like a lady."

———————

Two hours later, which is a little after 3:00 a.m., her mother is awakened by Brenda's voice, begging her to come and bail her out from Henry Street Jail.

But Mrs. O'Reilly, who, while she toured the bars the night before, had felt raw and hurt as well as ashamed, and who had been unable to sleep for most of this night as well, and who has only that day been informed by Officer O'Toole that one of the department's men has identified Brenda's roommate as 'Pokey,' a *'young Negro woman with a very dark skin, who always wears men's clothes, and is known in all the bars for her belligerency,'* is now seized with some final disgust. She has had no time to digest this new information, to adapt herself to it, and she only knows that Brenda is doing it again, seeking out those 'niggers' instead of her own kind.

With harshness and in tears, she cries out to Brenda across those gulfs opened up long ago, and now opening wider and wider: "Brenda, why don't you get your half-breed friends to bail you out? . . . I'd as soon . . . I swear it . . . I'd as soon see you stay where you are."

I

IV

Townsend—Wentworth—Bancroft

Harriet stands in the little kitchenette at the Townsend Hospital and feels that she is in a place without furniture. This bareness, this emptiness, clothed only with the disturbed cries and confused conversation of the patients, seems like the stripped landscape which one sometimes sees in dreams.

Although color has come back into her face and she moves more easily (without using that old gesture of hers, that flexing of her muscles to lunge at the wall), she knows that she is still a prisoner, and that she only experiences a travesty of liberty when she sweeps the outside passage, or accompanies Miss Clover to the kitchen to help her bring dinner for the ward, or goes with old Mr. Smith, the porter, on his rounds to deliver the mail.

Even if she were able to put a dummy in her bed some night, she thinks, and manage to elude the night nurse, and slip into the elevator, and get downstairs to the reception room—even then, there would remain two doors to get past, as well as the eagle-eyed receptionist herself, and the grounds man (who has a two-way radio in the car with which he makes his rounds, as well as a phone in his office in the basement).

It does not occur to her that she is supposed to be mentally unbalanced and that that is why she is shut up. She always thinks of herself as a prisoner rather than as a patient, and dismisses with scorn those tiny fading scars which are the result of that moment long ago in Henry Street when she had pushed her wrist against the blunt end of a wire spiral on the cell cot. But in spite of this dismissal, she is aware of uncertainty, conscious of ineptitude, conscious that she is trained for nothing but mechanical tasks and enduring silence. *I'm different from other girls,* she thinks.

She has even lost her spoon, which she had managed to hang on to through the transfer from Henry Street to Townsend. And since the ability to withstand disintegration of the personality is closely linked to material symbols, to the relics and signs of a past life, to toilet articles and cooking utensils, to the tools of half-forgotten trades, Harriet is unduly upset by this loss. After so many months of good behavior, she is famished for want of using the tools of escape, for want of the slow laborious business of sliding the metal plate out of the lock of a door, or delicately inserting and turning the curved spoon bowl under a bolt. She needs to use this skill because it is one of the few skills she has . . . There is very little else she *can* do, and almost nothing which releases her from herself and proves her superiority to others. She is obsessed, therefore, with the mechanics of freedom.

"Harriet," Miss Clover says, "we're going to have tea. All the ladies in the ward together."

"I don't want to," Harriet says.

Miss Clover protests. "Now you always say that you don't want to go in the yard, you don't want to play bingo. Always 'I don't *want* to.'"

"Well, I don't—it's all stupid."

"There's a movie tonight," Miss Clover says. "Will you go to that?"

"Not if it's a *love* movie." Harriet's voice sounds disgusted.

"Why don't you like love movies?"

"Because they're *foolish.*"

Miss Clover encircles her shoulders with one arm and gently pats her.

Harriet jerks her shoulder away.

"I'm no two-year-old."

Miss Clover smiles faintly.

One of the other patients comes sidling up, holding onto the wall with both hands, as one might clutch the grab-rail on the deck of a ship. She is a slight young woman, rather smartly dressed, and with graying hair worn in short fashionable curls; but her face, which has a ravaged look of anxiety, breaks up into tears as she approaches Miss Clover.

"I can't *find* anyone," she complains with a half moan. "I can't *find* anyone . . ."

"We're all here," the nurse comforts her.

"I'm a salty nurse . . . I'm from the salty sea."

"I know it, dear," Miss Clover accepts.

The girl's nose and mouth screw up in an agony of despair, and she begins to cry, standing there, her hands outstretched on either side of her pretty dress.

"Now Marcie," Miss Clover warns, "none of that crying!"

"I can't find anyone."

Miss Clover is playful. "We're going to have tea now. On deck, Marcie!"

Marcie, who had served in the Navy during the last war and has not been the same since, records her terrifying past in disjointed sentences.

"I'm a salty nurse . . . Salty . . . I'm from the salty, salty sea . . . They picked me up, nurse. I was in the tank, you know . . . Did you know that, nurse?" She tags along, ready to ward off the attentions Miss Clover is about to pay to Harriet. "Nursie . . ." she begs, clinging to the white-clad arm.

"Marcie, please behave yourself . . . Go and get ready for tea . . . Go and brush your hair."

Marcie puts her hands to her hair with a moan and retreats to the other end of the ward. The prohibition against being untidy or careless, which had been instilled during her Navy years, still rules in her confused mind.

"Come," Miss Clover says to Harriet, "we're all going to have tea together—all the ladies . . ."

Harriet protests again: "I'm no lady." But with a faint feeling of relief, she follows Miss Clover into the annex, obediently passes around cups of tea, fluffs up the pillows of older patients, brings a special tray for a young girl with a withered arm, and offers plates of cookies.

She even smiles as Miss Clover pats her again on the shoulder and tells her that she is her "right-hand man." When the head nurse comes in and whispers to Miss Clover for a moment and she sees them glance quickly in her direction, she thinks that it is because they are commenting about her good behavior and she feels a weary pride, as if a light from far away had warmed the mere surface of her flesh. She is surprised, therefore, and a little shocked, when Miss Clover approaches her, draws her apart from the other patients, and says to her: "Harriet dear, your father is downstairs. He has come to take you home for a while."

"My *father!*"

"Yes." Miss Clover looks at her with interested blue eyes. "Are you *glad?* Isn't this what you wanted?"

Harriet blushes. Her neck and her round, fair face are flooded with crimson.

"I'm salty . . . I'm salty," the patient Marcie cries suddenly from the other side of the room. "I'm from the s-a-l-t-y . . . s-e-a—"

"Hush, Marcie," Miss Clover calls.

Harriet is sober, seeing herself as dissociated from the other patients. She is not mad as they are. She had only stolen a car.

"Yes . . . I want to get out. They can't keep me here for *ever*, you know," she adds, looking at Miss Clover. "The doctor told me that I was all right. He said—he said—that I was quite well . . ." She stumbles a little. "I'll pay my father back because he had to get a lawyer."

"I'll help you to pack," Miss Clover says.

Two hours later as the car speeds through the familiar countryside, through Leicester and Coletown, past the big dairy with the enormous red silo and the white barn (SUNNY LANE DAIRY—the RICHEST milk), through Green River Valley with its rolling wooded sides, Harriet is aware that she is free again. The ground has been soaked by rain and melted snow. The trees are etched and still budless against an April sky. Past Tasseldone, which Harriet knows best because some of the girls have been in jail there, along a strip of Route 471 (lined with nondescript houses, small shops, florists, laundries, furniture stores, real-estate agencies and package stores), and finally, where Thornton's traffic lights are blinking, a turn-off from the highway which follows along a red-soil ridge where the earth is still raw and wounded, where new houses painted white or pale green or pink sit forlornly in unfinished gardens, and one gets, across empty fields and as far as a blue line of mountains, glimpses of a raped countryside (rivers bridged—curves scarred by highways —hillsides become quarries). Here at last Harriet is within that familiar magic circle which encloses the comfortable wooden house which had been bought and furnished by profits from the Brun Cement Block Company, the bus stop from which she had first gone to school, the liquor shop from which she had bought her first pint, the parking lot from which she had stolen her first car. Her father is telling her that they will try to make her happy, that she has a good home, that his business is doing well, that she must settle down and be contented. She is aware that he is nervous and insecure, just as she can see that his big red hands grip the wheel anxiously, and that his reddish face under the thatch of white hair is the closed face of a stranger. She remembers the times when she has been afraid of him (*If he had had a knife he might have killed me*). She fantasies about him chasing her along lanes, and over the roofs, and through windows. On one occasion when she had been fighting in the street, he had come after her. On this occasion, however, he had not touched her. Instead, he had not spoken a word to her for a week. Sullenly, she thinks that he should have helped her when the police took her. He should have explained to the cops that when she left the Killian jail with Marie she would never have stolen another car if the cops had not taken *hers*. Her mind operated then, and operates now, upon so simple a level that she cannot adapt to the complications of the property law. (*Don't they know what a car means to me? Don't they know that I have to have a car?*) Yet, even had she been able to express this adequately and thus side-step the anger of her father and the demands of the law, the whole question still remains academic, because no word of this gets spoken. She simply sits beside her father in silence. When she does steal a glance at him, it is to think to herself that she must earn money and pay back every penny which she presumes he has spent on a lawyer. She is not going to be under any obligation to *him!*

"How much did the lawyer cost?" she asks.

"Plenty . . ." Her father smiles with satisfaction as he always does when money is mentioned. "He got a doctor's affadavit that there is alcoholism in the family. You'd never have taken that car without alcohol in you," he adds. "You're just like your Grandfather Brun . . . Can't take a drop without getting out of control." Again there is silence.

"Your mother's well," says her father.

Harriet nods without interest.

"She's looking forward to having you back."

They drive on.

"Where's Billy?" asks Harriet abruptly.

"He's got a job over North City way," her father says.

For the rest of the drive they sit in silence.

———————

Six months later she has saved up $300. She keeps it hidden in various places around her room, almost as if she were keeping it hidden from her parents, who by paying her so generously for her work in the cement yard are her allies in some future escape. As she has been released from the hospital, so now she must manage some release from her home, an attitude which is implicit in her bearing so that her mother, timid and ineffectual ('miserable' is what Harriet says, seeing how she submits to her husband) demands nothing of her daughter beyond the fact that she cause no trouble. Harriet does no housework, cooks no meals, carries on no conversations, and is forced into no new relationships. Her male role persists. She dresses like a boy, works like a boy, and spends her spare time playing golf or listening to TV. But in spite of this external simplification, new elements have entered her life, offshoots from that secret and inarticulate past which had once found expression in a car hidden in her uncle's yard and a hideaway shared with Marie in the woods, and which now flowers in an identification with the worlds of Henry Street and Townsend. Having tasted prison and a mental ward, the taste lingers. She tries it with her inexperienced senses. She absorbs it, and is slyly, even vindictively curious. Am *I a criminal?* . . . She thinks, as she had thought lying silently on the cot in Henry Street. Am *I mad* . . . ? she asks of the walls in Townsend. And when no answer comes, she whispers a tentative "Yes" into her clenched fist.

"What are you doing?" asks Billy, home for the weekend, watching her as she sits hunched forward staring at the television screen.

Harriet answers, absorbed: "This is the *best* program. It's Clancy A." She scarcely turns to welcome him, but her eyes flicker hotly with the hard brilliance of the screen. "Look, he's getting her . . . He's up there climbing along the ledge, and she thinks she heard a noise, but isn't sure . . . Her husband's gone out . . ." Billy thinks that it is always like this when he comes home, that there is never anyone really to talk to.

"Why do you watch those crime things all the time?" he asks in a disgusted voice.

"They're *cool*," Harriet says. Dressed as always in shirt and slacks and sweater, she hunches before the TV set, not turning to look at him. In her room upstairs—mute testimony to her preoccupation—there are piles of crime clippings which she has cut out of newspapers and magazines, and the ham radio which she has persuaded her father to get her so that she can listen in to the calls sent out by police cars and airports. Sitting in this room with the chintz curtains and the tidy bed, she is in reality intent upon the world of escape and capture.

. . . One day she runs into Marie Budette again, and Marie stares at her with delight.

"Oh *Harry* . . ." She clasps her hands together in that emotional way, which, in spite of the fact that she pretends indifference, has always delighted Harriet.

"Where you *been?*"

"In the nuthouse," Harriet answers gruffly. Bending down and drawing a $10 bill from her shoe, she persuades Marie to wait for her while she buys a pint of whisky. "We'll go somewhere," she suggests. Marie, now two years older than she had been during her last escapade with Harriet, is still only a little more worldly-wise. With the same faithfulness she waits on the corner while Harry buys the whisky, and then they walk together in the back street, stopping to drink out of the bottle in solitary doorways, Marie just sipping, but Harriet—as if she had a tremendous thirst—tossing the liquor down her throat. Almost immediately Harriet is drunk. The control of the past months, the long period of inaction in the hospital, vanish in a burst of determination. She roves the town with Marie at her heels, looking at various cars, contemptuously dismissing them as unsuitable, striding along, whistling, with her hands in the pockets of her jeans, appearing with her short tawny hair like an attractive and well-built boy. Finally she chooses a small Chevrolet pick-up truck, conveniently parked near a supermarket, and she sends Marie to buy soft drinks and cigarettes while she works on opening the door. She proclaims that she's sick of Thornton and that she's off to California, and within fifteen minutes the truck, pointed in the direction which Harriet thinks is west, is speeding down a main highway.

"I never *been* nowhere else but Thornton and jail and hospital," she calls out above the sound of the engine. "I tell you, Marie, we get to California and no one will be able to hold us." And Marie answers, clasping her hands again, her murmur lost in the rush of the wind past her burning face. "I know it, Harry . . . I love it . . . I just *love* to travel."

Afterwards Marie tells the police chief at Chicopee that she had tried to restrain Harriet.

"I don't know why she lit the papers inside the truck and tried to burn it, Officer. It's just that she got so she was happier and happier. When we wuz out of gas she says: "That truck's no good!" and she piles up all these papers on the floor and lights them. After the truck we pick out this Ford coupe up the street, and we drive in that . . . And six o'clock *that's* out of gas, too, and Harriet pushes it off the highway and makes a big pile of all the maps in the car on the floor in the back and sets it alight . . . She's singing and everything . . ."

In the cell that night she is still singing. It is as if the liquor has unbearably inflamed her brain and set loose some forgotten tragic merriment, so that she swaggers around the cell, singing "America the Beautiful" and other songs which had been popular when she was in that first and only year of high school. The tearful Marie, who can't sleep, sits curled up on one of the bunks with her head on her knees. When songs fail, Harriet alternately throws punches at the walls and at the battered iron door, or calls out again and again with a wild tremor of laughter in her voice: *"Hullo all you fucking people . . . hullo out there . . . hullo . . ."* She is greeting everyone. She is saying 'I have come back again. I have come back to prison again.'

"I dig myself and come up with the idea that there are politics in everything," Frankie declares.

It is her first day back at Wentworth, and with a certain relief she sees again the well-known institution buildings, the long avenue of bare-branched trees, the ice pond in its frozen fields. Four months pregnant and ignominiously recommitted, she is like an exhausted runner, driven to confinement and protection, glad to be overtaken at last.

"Yes, I dig myself and come up with that," she admits to Merry Davis, a tall Negro girl who is known as the school "politician," and who claims to be a member of the Black Muslims. "Because everyone's equal, that's why, but Whitey's not admitting it. There'll always be politics and strife until Whitey admits it."

Merry talks of Big Bill Brent, the Negro who has won the state lightweight championship, and who after being converted to 'Allah' and rechristening himself William X has been barred from competition.

"He cleaned himself up physically and morally," Merry claims. "Now he's William X and he knows just who God is. But they're discriminating him as far as his religion is concerned. Some say they're going to put him outa the League."

"They can't do that," Frankie argues. "It's his constitution right to worship as he chooses."

Merry denies that this will make any difference. "The white

man won't give him rights. The record shows the white man never done that yet . . . The white man's a devil with blue eyes." Her voice takes on a hypnotic sing-song quality. "He stole our mothers and fathers from a culture of silks and satins, and brought them here in chains . . . So, since they kept us all here, making us hewers of wood and drawers of water. And forced their family name on us and their God with a pale skin, making that 'black' was a curse . . . Well I tell you now, the white blue-eyed devil's time is running out."

Frankie listens, as she has listened before, to the catalog of the white man's wrongs. "All the fiery hell the white man heaped on us," Merry prophesies, "will be heaped on him. Going to get that white creature off our backs. Going to hitch him to the plough an' make him plough his own fields. God is *black*, that's for sure. An' we all gotta clean ourselves up, and be like William X . . ."

"Why is William X so shining an example?" Frankie asks argumentatively. "Boxing ain't no example! Bruising and maiming your fellow man for sport isn't so shining—whatever way you look at it!"

"He did what Elijah Muhammud tells us," argues Merry. "Elijah Muhammud makes it plain that now we know who God is, now that we have found Allah, we got to learn to love and respect and bring ourselves outa the slums and the prisons."

Frankie is not particularly aware of the wave of history, of the fact that '*the time of the Negro has come.*' She knows about Martin Luther King and the philosophy of nonviolence, but she is not aware of its historical importance. More familiar to her are phrases from the extremists, phrases which she had heard echoed in The Burrow and in the militant black nationalist newspapers, now being sold in the stores on Moon Street—"THE AMERICAN NEGRO MUST FIGHT THE BATTLE OF ARMEGEDDON IN THE WILDERNESS OF NORTH AMERICA"—"THE TIME OF THE BLOOD-LETTING IS NIGH"— "DON'T EAT OF THE POISONOUS FOOD OF THE WHITE MAN, EAT THE FOOD OF YOUR HOME COUNTRY." Now she says to Merry: "Some of my friends in The Burrow went into Islam. And I dig myself, and ask shall I go in too?"

"You come into it with me, Frankie," Merry urges. "You're dumb and blind until you come into Islam."

But Frankie is not sure that she sees it that way. She loves to listen to Merry's talk of the silks and satins of her ancestors, and she is able to get enthusiastic and boastful about the Ashantis, Timbuctu, and the bronzes of Ife. She also feels warmth when she thinks of the Negro bookstore on 125th Street, the Temple at 116th and Lennox, and classes in Arabic. (This is all food for her glory-starved ego.) But in her longing for status she is more anxious to identify with the powerful white man than she is to rant and rave about the enslavement of her ancestors, suspecting that William X, for instance, is just one more dumb nigger. (In any case, she is too independent to want to join the masses who lift their arms in the salute. *She* wants to be the leader.)

Lost in conflict, she turns toward immediate gratifications. In music she is able to forget her pressing sense of race, and she goes around with a small transistor radio held against her ear, listening to jazz and gospel songs, to 'oldies but goodies,' to station W.I.L.D., and to tunes from the sawdust gin mills. Lifting her heavy lids in enchantment, she murmurs to herself: "He really tears it," or "That record couldn't be tougher!" or "*Bad*, Baby, *bad!*" Dreaming to the beat, she pretends that the race question doesn't exist, that she is outside it all, or able to rise above it.

But in the nation at large, all through that winter of 1961–2, the armies of the future gather: when Malcolm X defies the Ku Klux Klan on its home territory (the Fruit of Islam posted on the rooftops along the route to Atlanta's Magnolia Hall, which now flowers with the blackest of black blossoms); when the sit-ins pray in Birmingham, Alabama, and aggressive black onlookers decry the whole business (saying, "we want to *own* the store, and the ground on which it sits"), a warmth and gaiety creep into the voices of the black waifs of the white society; there is wafted from the inarticulate ghettos the breath of a satiric laughter.

Frankie feels an interested discomfort because some of the others hate the white man so easily; she is disturbed because she bears within her not only the blood of the white man, but love for him too. She accepts this love in her own body, without thinking of it, without even knowing it (as she had accepted Candy and Baby and Oliver, and even the white Italian rapers of her earlier years). She looks upon the tiny white spot on her skin as a sign that she was meant by God to mingle and be equal. This is not because of charity now that a long antagonism has been 'brought to light,' but simply because she *feels* equal; and feels as well, caught up in a general human problem, far beyond politics.

She can look back upon many betrayals, betrayals which she has scarcely protested, accepting them in their extremity, as if they were completely natural, yet none of these betrayals has had the flat intimacy (accompanied by cups of coffee, poetry readings, and trite comments) which characterized her relationship with Oliver. Nor can she hide from herself, as she dutifully presses her stomach, records her nausea, details to the doctor the exact dates of her past menstrual periods, that in this betrayal at least she has played an active part.

As the horrified watcher of a murder, hidden perhaps behind curtains or shrubbery, absorbs through his senses, and almost without the help of intelligence, the details of a crime, so Frankie has watched the course of her impregnation. Little as she has admired Oliver, and casual as she had been all through that encounter, she wishes now ardently for his love and fantasies many times the scene in which, seated as they had so often been in the half-dark of The Burrow, the blue smoke of a cigarette almost obscuring his silver-cold profile, and the shadows blending with the wrinkled neck of his black polo shirt, he asks her if what he hears is true, that she really bears his child. "Yes, yes, I am pregnant," she says to him, and his weakness is then glorified by his acceptance of fatherhood, as is glorified also his white skin, which he throws like a mantle over the unborn child . . .

"Am I to put myself so low," she asks herself, "that I need to run to a white faggot, and tell him that he put a baby in my belly? Isn't it that he's no friend if he went off like that? And why isn't he more of a friend? . . . Is it because I'm colored?"

She feels that it is not his surprise that she wants, nor his aroused sense of guilt, nor even his financial assistance, but rather his disinterested friendship, the assurance that she is his fellow human being. But his silence, his sudden disappearance, has made this assurance untenable. He has made it impossible for her to seek him out.

Her return to Wentworth in this dependent and conflicted state is a return to external controls, but above and beyond that it is a return to misdirected emotion, to a deepening of the split in her psyche.

All she can do here is to indulge in the familiar verbal camouflage until the words grow like weeds over a grave which loses its outline (just as her body begins to lose its outline under her full woolen dress).

In her dilemma she does not see herself as one of many others betrayed. There is no one to clarify these emotions for her, to help to translate them into positive attitudes. Even her letters—in which she expresses the bitterness of a young female, vulnerable because of her sex, made pregnant by an irresponsible male, and therefore renounced by her family—are censored by the institution, and never reach their destination.

"*I've been a stepdaughter,*" she writes to her mother. "*And you sacrificed me to please Daddy. But I won't always have to suffer. God is not that cruel . . . I will finish school if it takes twenty years and make something out of myself . . . You won't have to pretend to your friends then. Somebody had a hand in helping me to be what I am now whether they admit it or not . . . If I have a daughter I'll be proud of her . . . God willing she will be beautiful and lovely. You and Daddy don't care . . . If they gave me ninety years it would probably be all right with you two. When I sit here behind bars, I wonder can you look out of your window without thinking of me . . . ? Just call 'the man' and everything will be all right, that's what you and Daddy do.*"

This bitterness flows from her like a dark river, stains the days and nights, but is lost in the impersonal desert of the reform school.

As time passes, she takes on—as have so many before her—a dual role. She is at once protector and exploiter, creator and destroyer, victim and victimizer. She works to make the school honor roll, but is constantly demoted for infractions of the rules, for smoking in the corridors, for swearing at officers, for encouraging Midget to start a fire. It is as if two Frankies live side by side in one body, and sensing this division she makes an effort to integrate them but is immediately filled with so outrageous an anxiety that she searches for security by plunging herself into a world she despises.

"I'm not wrapped too tough, baby," she tells Candy, who has welcomed her back so ardently, "but I sure am settling down." And with another girl, she tries to dismiss the trauma of her pregnancy by discussing Oliver with calm objectivity, and putting the choice of events upon her own shoulders.

"I don't know anyone can speak to me strong enough," she complains. "I want a man to be *mac* and aggressive, and not just a yard dog like they all are. But when they're strong I want to break them . . . Why, Oliver I wouldn't even let him touch my tits . . . and now here I am pregnant."

"That's how the ball bounces," the girl replies.

This girl, whose real name is Jane Stanislas, is known in the institution as 'Stan,' and now she spreads large expressive hands. "Alice Admonson, ask her."

Frankie grins. "*That* bitch still here?"

"Sure she's here—she only goes out to come in. She's seventeen, but she has two kids already."

"Who's got the children?"

"Her mother's got one, and the last one's up for adoption."

Frankie becomes aggressive. "No one's going to adopt *my* child."

"Alice's father says she bring another child home, he'll beat the skin off of her," Stan explains.

"I were his daughter," Frankie protests, "I'd rap till times got better. Don't she know she's a *juvenile?*"

"She don't know *nothing!*" Stan, heavy-browed and large-faced, frowns in concentration, but Frankie, always ready to philosophize about the rights of minors, declares authoritatively: "Well, she won't get anywhere lying down under him—the victim breeds the brute."

. . . How can one not feel pity and admiration for those who try heroically to direct the course of their lives, for those who bare their breasts to a miscellaneous assortment of weapons, and seem to say: "Self-determination or death!" Frankie feels in her clearer moments that she is only experimenting with life, and that she can accept nobody's reality but her own. In the old schoolroom at Wentworth, from which some of the early magic has fled, she sits down to write poetry again, haughtily denouncing passivity, gloomily fearing some violent end.

> There is nothing in, to or for life,
> But reality,
> To attain it is your business,
> Your ecstasy or agony,
> However you attain it,
> By crucifixion or renunciation,
> Or fantastic experience,
> Is your affair,
> And no one's affair,
> But yours.
> To have attained it is,
> To have achieved all that is,
> Worthwhile in life,
> For it is a supreme knowledge,
> Of adjustment—
> The only accomplishment,
> That takes life,
> A step further onward,
> Or,
> For some people,
> Ends it.

And this acceptance soothes her, giving her, if only for a few days, a sense of direction. But the tides of Wentworth, rolling ceaselessly toward some future shore, are unable to pause for phil-osophical debate, and they bear Frankie relentlessly toward a status role. As if in bravado, the older and more sober girls, most of whom claim to have chosen the gay life, pile up protective barriers around themselves—as rich men pile up posessions—talk-ing about their 'need for bread' and their power of 'giving protec-tion.' Yet while they lead this campaign against the uncommitted, forcing them to choose, their eyes seem compulsive and fright-ened.

"You *gotta* be a Butch," Stan advises Frankie, "a *stone* Butch."

"I'm no tackhead," Frankie evades.

"You're no Fem either," Stan compliments. "If you're not a Butch, you'll do hard time on campus!"

Frankie is undecided. In the boredom of institution life, she now feels a dawning excitement, a conviction that life need not be dull, that her old desire to live out of books, to finish school and go to college, to know everything about art, literature, politics, is impractical, but that in Wentworth she can at least live 'the life.'

She has always given love to Candy, but now, as if to offset this, she pursues Alice Admonson, the hysterical overdeveloped redheaded seventeen-year-old (mother of two) who sleeps in her own old bed in Florence Nightingale Cottage, the girl who had been, long ago, the recipient of the note which had puzzled and upset the Wentworth staff. Having captured this girl's attention, she then—perversely—pretends disinterest, wavering between the love of drama and the love of Jesus Christ. And one day, she ven-tures further. Fully clothed, and armed even to the extent of the knife hidden in her stocking, she drops on her knees beside Candy (when they have been left in the afternoon to weed the rows of plants in the greenhouse) and experiments in satisfying her. It is a late tribute to desires roused months earlier—desires still present-ing a preverse challenge.

"I'll get boss at it," she boasts, hiding her fears. But she is so afraid that her fear paralyzes her, as if she crouches at the head of a dry valley, her face set into the mask of the sly gamin of the street.

"I can't say I like it," she admits, "I don't . . . I can't . . ."

And behind her mask she is tortured because she is more alone than ever, because Candy, giving everything up to Frankie, is silent, pleading only with her enormous eyes. And leaning over her, Frankie feels herself pushed against her will into that world of female wonder which those pale maturing limbs suggest, into a warmth which softens, contracts, responds, seems indeed to be something she has always longed for, something which answers, curiously and upon some deep unspoken level, to her need. This need is not to lose herself, not to forget her power, but to heighten her identity through Candy's subjugated body. And caught in this desire, she begins to imagine these material objects —the locked door of the greenhouse, her own costume of continence, a handful of Candy's underclothing—as forever allied to her courage.

"You satisfy them as much as a man—you *are* the man, see?" Stan's slow heavy voice falls like the tread of a mature male upon the floor of the future. "You hold *off*. They fight you for that control, but you don't let 'em get it, or they got something over you and you won't get nothing out of *them*."

Stan is passing on the philosophy of the street—the theory that all sexual contact must be oriented toward profit. She wants to draw Frankie to her side, to have her partake of the underworld's values, here suitably softened for a juvenile institution. She wants to help Frankie to absorb, as she herself has absorbed almost without consciousness, almost by osmosis, the essential skills of the pimp.

But Frankie, having already received all of Candy's adoration, insists: "I don't want nothing out of Candy."

"You give head, but you don't *take* it," Stan urges with her somber black seriousness. "You give up the work."

This last ironic phrase, which Frankie has been hearing all through her institution days, has a logic of its own: since "work" is generally paid for, and if *you* alone work and expect nothing from your partner, then you alone get *paid*. This makes you 'tops,' the 'boss,' the 'leader.' In the spirit of the competitive street, you earn your living by your sexual prowess, your ability to 'cop,' your power to instill fear. (Although it is not in such clear terms that the delinquent thinks, but rather boastfully and freely, like a child who, with borrowed weapons, plays cops and robbers.)

"And is *that* how you get to be Sky King?" Frankie drawls with a studied sophistication.

Stan ignores the question. "You don't let her do *nothing*," she insists, as if this is the very first thing to be understood. "You give up the work . . . You make 'em *lie* there."

"*Every* time?" Frankie gets some vague glimpse of the avenues of containment and concentration which this new life will demand of her.

"This place is no place to *dream*," Stan warns as if afraid that her pupil might escape her. She suggests that they stand in a purgatorial terrain where the terrorized landscape is set in volcanic shapes. "You gotta keep on top in a place like this."

Frankie laughs at the appropriateness of the simile. "*You're* not kidding."

Yet in the final sense, it is not Stan's exhortations or this "you give work, and you get the edge" philosophy which altogether determines Frankie's development. So much has been demanded of her in her childhood ghetto that she shrinks in alarm from a true interchange. She has found already that it is easier to act than to interact.

"No—don't touch me," she begs Candy. "Lie there—I must prove this. Don't touch me, doll."

Candy shows a certain desperation. "I don't want you to be away from me, Frankie," she pleads . . . and Frankie's own loneliness is a desert, her body grows dry in this climate of thirst. Inadequately nourished as a child, of small and doubtfully stable stock, the trauma of her adolescent experiences have produced in her a sexual anesthesia, which now—since Stan has drawn for her a map of 'love in the life'—fits her needs. She begins to follow the cult to the letter. She pretends to care nothing about reciprocal physical love. She is 'Frankie'—that 'stone Butch from Martha Washington,' 'bigtime' in the school, the one that gets kites by the dozen, the one for whom the girls say they are going to cut themselves.

Compulsively she lives up to that image. In spite of the affection she feels for Candy, she practices seductive glances on a throng of immature worshippers, and diverts her literary talent to making up amorous verse. She loiters one day at the end of the dinner line, until she sees the voluptuous red-haired Alice Admonson approaching her self-consciously, her hips swinging, her shoulders wriggling. She presses a note into her hand. The note says boldly:

> You think you're bad
> And bad you may be,
> But if you're all that bad
> Bring your bad ass to me!

Again, by some strange repetitive logic, this note is intercepted. Again it is thought wise to remove Frankie—not only from the cottage, but from the institution itself—so that she can no longer be a source of contamination.

The Bancroft Hospital stands at the end of a long avenue of trees. Its sprawling buildings with white porticoes, its pale yellow paint, gives it the familiar look of a great shabby Victorian establishment once inhabited by an extended family with droves of children and relatives. Yet now it is not a particularly cheerful place, occupied as it is by so many of the near-dead—chronic cases with little hope of recovery, patients with age-weakened bodies and lingering illnesses.

Frankie, who has been sent there to have her baby, sees it as emphasizing her segregation, throwing her weakness into relief by the absence of contemporaries, who, by reason of their own difficulties, could support and mitigate her own. Yet her egotism shrinks as she helps the nurses in the chronic wards, squeezing between the close-packed beds to change the sheets of old shrunken incontinent women, of terminal cancer patients, of childlike visionaries who play with dolls and are so cut off from the modern world that they have never seen an airplane. In this haven for the sick and the disturbed and the old, she feels a patience and resignation which is momentarily humbling; as if a sharp knife had cut through the indifferent patina of her own delinquency to reveal some scene of universal suffering. *"They are my heart,"* she wrote to her mother as she described these patients. *"They look for me to come every day, and they call out my name and ask me how I feel . . . I love each and every one."*

Frankie does not know what connection there is between her own world and this shuttered world of the Bancroft Hospital. As Harriet had thought that she was not 'mad' like the other patients, Frankie thinks that she is not 'ill,' that she is only going to have a baby. But uncomfortably she senses a link somewhere and searches the old, the suffering, the vacant faces, as if looking for a revealing answer. Now in her eighth month of pregnancy, she walks down avenues of sickness, her stomach jutting, her eyes shadowed. She sees the human body twisted and distorted, bearing great excrescences, and holding holes and crevices which never heal. A starched white overall covering her blue dress, pushing a cart laid out with basins and dressings, she follows behind the nurse, her little hands agile, her face stern with sympathy. She is identifying with her mother and playing a serious part in the business of the world. She is the mother who earns the family living by working in a mental hospital at night and who attends classes in biology as well, while her undisciplined husband drinks at the Moon Street bar and breaks his marriage vows with an unending string of women. For a while the nurse-like female in Frankie triumphs, and she loves, as she has loved Candy, the women with the wounds, the aged defectives with the eyes of children.

In the corner of the ward, 'Old Suzie' sits surrounded by pillows and by bags of scrap material, which in spite of hospital rules she is allowed to have beside her. Her withered and shaking hands employ themselves incessantly, manufacturing dresses for her 'family,' bonnets for the 'baby,' bed-coverings for the 'sick ones,' and even squares of toweling to wrap up those who are going to 'have baths.' The 'family' is made up of a doll with a battered face, a small china ornament formed in the shape of a girl with a dog by her side, and several cardboard cutouts which had been given away as a supplement to a children's magazine.

"Baby is sick," Suzie tells Frankie with a worried expression, as she approaches her bed, "very sick and feverish."

"Why, Suzie, she has no clothes on," Frankie remarks. "Even 'Old Lady' is naked today."

"Old Lady's clothes are at the laundry," Suzie protests. Her eyes, filmed over by cataracts, peer up at Frankie defensively. "She's got to wait till the clothes come from the laundry." She rummages amongst the folds of her bedcovers until she finds 'Baby' and presents her to Frankie with her anxious trembling hand.

"She's sick," she says piteously.

"She'll be all right if you *dress* her, Suzie. The cold won't get at her then."

"But the clothes are at the *laundry*," the old lady quavers.

"Wrap her in a towel," improvises Frankie.

"Will that do, dearie?"

"Sure it'll do. Wrap her up so the cold won't hit her." She watches the slow smile which breaks over Suzie's face, a smile which is half hidden by the clouded eyes and only just touches her lips. Tenderly Frankie helps to find the squares of toweling amongst the covers and to wrap up the battered cardboard 'baby.' One part of her dreams of a life given over to the care of others. She wants to be a doctor, a nurse, a social worker . . .

At the same time, her emotions begin to feed upon protests against the establishment. The free days of the fighting Vivaldos, the group magic of the Floricettes, the interracial activities of the Blue Notes seem far away from her now. The sky is hidden and she is proceeding deeper and deeper into closed worlds. There seems to be about it something inevitable, something foreordained. And she wonders whether the prejudice which she had once felt as a sting had actually meant a profound wound. "I see what I am," she repeats to herself. "I dig what I am—I'm *black!*" And now she wants to get away from this closed-in feeling, this vision of prison corridors which recede endlessly into her future.

She wants to prove nonexistent the many dark faces in the hospital, the implicit degradation of her people, reverting to the ideas of the extremist sects, pondering about violence, cruelty, murder, until her head spins. She dreams about Hitler and his ovens, sees him in her nightmares rise like some monstrous trussed gangster bound in the midst of the chimneys, with a forest of hands raised in salute. At times it is as if she would willingly sacrifice all of her own people to ovens such as this only in order to obliterate her own Negro past.

Because she cannot hate the patients, her rage focuses upon one of the hospital nurses, who does not hide her scorn of 'young colored trash' (especially those having no morals and getting themselves so easily into states similar to Frankie's). This nurse, Negro as she is, becomes a brooding image of Frankie's disapproving self, an alter ego, a light-brown and pock-marked face which looms sadly over a white uniform and watches for some opportunity to catch Frankie breaking the hospital rules. Frankie makes it a point not to answer her questions, and the nurse is so irritated that she tends to follow this persecutor about the wards, as if to force an issue between them.

"Lady," Frankie says one day, turning from the haven of her bed to which she has retreated in anger, "don't you see *anybody* but me?"

The nurse wheels around and marshals the ambulatory patients to take them to the dining room. Her lips tighten ominously, and she forgets to smile at Old Suzie, who childishly clutches at her hand, as she heads the straggling line which advances toward the elevator. This obvious displeasure on the part of the familiar nurse causes a chill to fall over the group, which crowds silently in the hallway, with Frankie, her head in the air, bringing up the rear.

In the dining room the meal progresses without gaiety. Nurse Simpson—everyone understands—is in a bad temper, and Francesca Ford, who is generally the life of the dinner hour, is not talking. The food seems tasteless, and no one cares for the dessert which is tapioca flavored with pineapple, and over which Frankie lingers long after everyone else has finished.

"Don't stand near me," she threatens suddenly as the nurse, unable to control her patience, walks to Frankie's side of the table.

"I'll stand wherever I want to stand," the nurse replies calmly.

"Don't be leaning over my *food*," Frankie mutters. There is some fear in her, not only fear of the hostility she is experiencing, but a primitive fear of magic derived from stories told in childhood. "Don't be spitting all over my *food*," she adds rudely, encircling her plate with her arm.

The nurse is cold and correct.

"Everyone else is through eating."

"Well *I'm* not!" Frankie puts down her spoon rebelliously.

There is a sharp crackle of the white uniform, as the nurse abruptly moves Frankie's plate.

"Well, are you going to get up?"

Aware of the vacuous puzzled faces of the patients, of her enemy standing there, *thinking herself so great* (yet with a face only one shade lighter than her own), Frankie jumps to her feet.

"Yes, I'm up . . . and you can kiss my ass!"

"No I *won't*," the nurse replies briskly, "because it's black as your *face!*"

With a swift movement Frankie has snatched up the water pitcher from the table and broken it over the nurse's head. The nurse staggers against the wall, stunned by the blow, her hands to her face, pieces of glass scattered over the floor, water soaking her cap and her uniform.

One of the patients calls out . . . From the serving room heads are poked into the almost-deserted dining room . . . The nurse staggers and moans . . . Another nurse comes running from the passage.

That evening in the Henry Street Jail, Miss Walton is on late duty and comes into the staff room to take off her outdoor clothes which are wet with the spring rain. She hears the tap-tapping of the typewriter next door, sees the familiar form of Miss McVee's blue plastic raincoat and rubber hat (which last, in a moment of quick vision, she sees flapping around the long blond cautious face, sweetly tinted with cream collage and shades of Wild Rose makeup). The face vanishes. The rain falls. The coat and hat hang there with maddening familiarity. She knows herself again as she seems to have been for centuries in this jail, in the corridors so bleakly and clearly lit, circling the iron-rusted core of cells which clang to the opening and closing of their reluctant doors. And she reads, with the resigned interest of the committed, Miss McVee's note printed on a paper napkin and left on the table under a jar of instant coffee. "HAD TO GO TO MALE SIDE CONFER SHERIFF. PLEASE PROCESS 'DESPERADO' IN CELL 16. INFORM SUPT. THANKS."

She smiles at the familiar staff humor which designates any woman committed for much more than streetwalking as a 'desperado.' She pulls on her white rubber-soled shoes, struggles over her fat thighs to tie the laces, gets slowly to her feet. The long night has begun.

". . . So, it's *you*," she says almost without surprise as she peers into the shadowy cell.

Frankie shifts and turns, peering over her swollen woman's body, her eyes shadowed and bruised-looking, but still child-like.

"You're the desperado?" Miss Walton asks.

"I guess so."

"So— What is it now?"

"I crowned a nurse over at the Bancroft Hospital."

"You *did?*"

"I cold-cocked her with a water jug. She wouldn't get outa my face."

Frankie's voice is sullen, but she smiles self-consciously.

"What else?" Miss Walton lets herself into the cell and sits on the cot.

Frankie's small figure, enlarged as it is, moves back to give her room, but her face thrust aggressively forward alternates between helplessness and bravado.

"She wanted me to finish my meal, and she was leaning over my food. I told her: 'You kiss my *ass*,' and she said: 'No—'cause it's *black* like your face.' Ain't no one can say 'nigger' to me."

Miss Walton stares at her with resigned wonder. She asks her-

self whether somehow, long ago, she might have helped to obliterate the shadow of the bars which now, in the dim cell, stripe
Frankie's face.

"Lot of good it did to attack her."

"She drove me up the wall."

"You *hurt* her?"

"She got a bad *bruise*."

After a moment Miss Walton says: "What about the baby?"

"Well," began Frankie, her voice mocking, "my Daddy always said: 'That girl'll bring home a baby,' and so I did just *that*."

Miss Walton looks helpless.

"At least that didn't happen at Wentworth."

"Not THAT," Frankie says with grim humor, "other things."

"It happened after they let you out?" Miss Walton inquires
logically.

"Yes. Swingin' . . . It happened after they let me out,"
Frankie agrees.

She shifts her ungainly body on the bed. With surprise even to
herself, she remembers that she has been *twice* in and out of
Wentworth, *twice* in Henry Street. She talks to the wall. "I
started hanging in a place called The Burrow. And they have evenings there in a room upstairs, and it's no tea party, I can tell *you*.
You know, you jus' leave your morals outside the door . . ." She
wants to include Miss Walton in this dramatic fantasy, but her
literary efforts are inadequate. After a moment she adds untruth-
fully: "I was gassed . . ."

Between the wrinkles on Miss Walton's plump brow, little angels of goodness peep in and out. She seems the personification of
cleanliness and motherhood, redolent of freshly ironed sheets,
homemade biscuits, and instant hot water. In actuality, she lives in
a rather untidy two-room apartment with a huge alcoved double
bed (beside which are piled up many pocketbooks of detective
stories and science fiction); and here she entertains a grizzle-haired
physical-culture expert with a small amount of Negro blood. This
extracurricular activity makes Miss Walton sympathetic toward
Frankie and adds depth to the experience she has already obtained
in prison. 'We are of the same world,' she wishes to say, but is

afraid of the hypocrisy suggested by so obvious a phrase, and shy about the sense of beauty which she associates with her mountain of a body. *Will she believe me,* she wonders, *if I explain that I am really a confused girl with long golden hair?* She questions instead: "Are you happy about the baby?"

Frankie looks at her.

"No one can speak to me strong enough," she protests with bewilderment. "I want a man to be *mac* . . ."

"*Mac?*" Miss Walton does not know that this word comes from *maquereau,* the French word for 'pimp,' so that the irony of Frankie's use of it escapes her.

"I want a man to be *mac* . . . and to know his own mind. This child's father is a *nothing* . . ." Frankie gazes at the iron door with a smoldering finality. "This child only has a mother."

"Will you look after it?"

"No one's gonna adopt *my* baby," Frankie protests. "It's my heart. I'll bring it up, father or not."

Miss Walton, who has heard such boasts before, questions mildly: "In a prison cell?"

Frankie turns her shining drowned eyes in the direction of the door.

"I'll make out."

After a moment she adds: "They don't give me a chance to *be* anything."

"What do you want to be?" Miss Walton hates herself for the question, and her eyes meet Frankie's, which are still tearful, even as she shifts abruptly on the cot and says defensively: "I'll get through school if it takes me twenty years."

Miss Walton, the officer, rises heavily to her feet, clothed again in the prison's authority.

"Where will they send me?"

"Probably to Paragoula."

There is a silence between them. "They've got you down on the books for assault," Miss Walton says resignedly. "That's two years. They won't keep you here, and since you're seventeen, and pregnant, it's sure to be Paragoula State. For your confinement, they'll send you to the local maternity hospital, and then back to Paragoula to serve your sentence."

"That's *it!*"

Miss Walton hears the note of satisfaction in Frankie's voice and is embarrassed by the echoes of this multiple personality.

She looks down upon the little prisoner and sees the huge stone buildings scattered about the country, opposing their heavy weight to the fragile indecisiveness of their human freight. Like broken butterflies, cropped-winged birds, or fish struggling in nets, these prisoners yearn toward the sturdy stone palaces which curb their frantic movements and allow them room to oscillate no longer. "That's the *real* thing," breathes Frankie's voice.

V

Paragoula—State Prison for Women

The odor of prison. . . . I recognised that this odor would finally be the odor of my destiny.

JEAN GENET, *in Our Lady of the Flowers*

A great arch darkens the fields, covers a double roadway, links itself on one side to a solid nineteenth-century house, on another to a sprawling red-brick institution. Chimneys stick up into the air, and from time to time erupt with the steam and fume of laundries and heating equipment. From the building white-barred windows seem to stare owlishly out at a world which appears, in comparison to the building itself, enameled with the brilliance of tender summer leaves. This is the State Reformatory for Women at Paragoula. The contrast between the building and the sensuous earth, delicious and ominous as are all the contrasts between man's material and nature's, echoes the contrast within the heads of the prisoners themselves, those who can place at will the memory of a mother's kisses or love for an illegitimate child beside such scenes as the dropping of a dismembered body into a lake or the fierce burning of a $2 million school. The harsh jostling of one life upon another, though grating to the ordinary ear, makes a special kind of music familiar to society's outcasts. It is not without reason that those used to conservative melodies and soothing harmonies find this music disturbing.

As Frankie, now at last classified as an adult and sentenced to two years for assault and battery, goes through the prison's admission center, she feels the music as an accompaniment to her alienation, almost as if she were trying to reconcile its strident notes with the store of biblical quotations she has put away since childhood. "FOR EVERY ONE THAT DOETH EVIL HATETH THE LIGHT, NEITHER COMETH TO THE LIGHT, LEST HIS DEEDS SHOULD BE REPROVED."

The admittance procedure, which because it services women

of all ages and those who have committed all kinds of crimes, has an impersonality which makes her breathe faster. Stripped to the skin, washed and disinfected, her possessions sifted, her body invaded—she feels herself revealed in a neutral nakedness, which encourages her to pick up one of those tawdry battered disguises which had, for so long, waited stored in her memory. She tries these disguises one by one (the appealing little girl, straight out of *Uncle Tom's Cabin*, the Topsy who "just growed"; the sullen Butch who, when given a cigarette by one of the matrons, smokes half of it and puts the butt behind her ear; the superior dark-skinned young woman who finds herself in the white man's prison, and remains withdrawn in order to protect herself from contamination). The tone of the passionate letter she had written to her mother from Wentworth (*'I will finish school if it takes me twenty years—and make something of myself'*) seems inappropriate now, and she searches instinctively for a more acceptable role, one more commanding of attention and less arduous. For what she has not foreseen is that Paragoula is a large institution, with great wings where the crowded cubicles are built in tiers around a central well; with many flights of stairs; with dark lower levels of kitchens, laundries and storerooms; with passages along which, at certain hours, flow a sea of faces, faces which not only do not recognize her but which—if they had (so absorbed are they in reflecting back their own necessary images)—could scarcely have been made to change color for her sake. She has forgotten that she, Frankie, is only a small Negro girl in the last undignified stages of pregnancy, with heavy eyes and slightly swollen feet. Here Aunt Jeanette is not important, nor is the fact that she has broken a water jug over a nurse's head. Here she will have to act vigorously if she is to make her mark.

At eleven in the morning, on that wet June admittance day, she is brought by the accompanying officer through the main hall toward the reception center, and Fate—as if it had been watching for her—allows her to see a scene which reminds her of the drama and necessity of violence. When the electrically controlled door opens before her, she feels the hand of the officer on her shoulder for a moment, restraining her and drawing her to one side, and she sees before her in the hall a male guard in the olive-green uniform of Paragoula, holding a struggling girl and propelling her along the passage.

This tableau takes place in absolute silence. The girl is apparently an escapee: she is wet to the skin (it is raining outside) and her thin blue shirt and stretch pants cling to her splendid body, while hair hangs in streaks along her face and one bare arm is stained with mud and emerges from a torn-off sleeve . . . It is her hands which fascinate Frankie, because the officer, who is not a particularly large man, has been forced to handcuff her, and these hands—as she contorts the pendant body in a grim and noiseless battle—are held high above her head. Restrained there for a moment in the passage, Frankie feels her heart thud. It beats to the rhythmic resistance of the captive's body, and her spirit follows that body's maimed progress. She, Frankie, has lived with violence; felt it like an undertow in her Moon Street life. Now here it is in the prison again, clothed in the costume of authority. Her face grows gray, her nostrils and lips darken, old rebellions revive. She yearns for all symbols which might make violence valid: 'ass-whippings'—'cuttings'—'burnings'—'battery acid thrown in someone's face.' She understands, as if she had entered twice through the institution doors, that the riddle of existence can only be solved by compromise, and that since she is here it is here that she must fulfill her destiny.

Throughout the day the work of Paragoula proceeds as usual. Long lines of inmates form for meals, pass through the dining rooms, file out and disperse to work assignments. Living quarters are mopped and cleaned. Offices are swept and dusted. Food is prepared. Clothes rotate through washing machines. But underneath this activity the passages are alive with rumors. In monosyllables the prisoners comment upon the capture of Donna Willey, the blond gun moll who'd been brought in early that morning. They hint that the one who'd run with her, Harriet Brun ('that

silent broad in for stealing and burning cars'), is still at large. No
one says much about the capture; but an undercurrent of feeling
flows, submerged, eddying, present in the lines formed at meal-
times; in the crowded wings at night, where emotion can at last be
admitted and allowed; in the yard where the girls play basketball,
and from which, by turning one's eyes upward and to the left,
one can see the barred windows of the special detention cells (behind one of which 'they'—the establishment—hold Donna Willey).

"The other one's still out," is what someone reports.

"Who is it?"

"That new one. She and Donna met in 'reception' . . . New
to the joint, but pretty strong."

"Maybe she'll make it."

"Maybe."

"Good luck to her."

"You know that Alice took Donna's tray this noon."

"She talk to her?"

"Sure—she says Harriet's got ten bucks . . . Maybe she'll
make it."

"Maybe she can hitch, or hire a taxi—get outa the area."

"Maybe."

As earth-shadows follow the course of an airplane, the quiet
faces urge Harriet on, dog her progress. The faces hide plans and
deceptions, fantasy series of glorious escapes, dream up victories
at knife-point.

"She got a weapon."

"What sort?"

"A knife some kind. Say she worked two weeks in the storeroom. She didn't want for nothing."

"Good for *her!*"

"Ah!" from one of the most cynical, "*she* won't make it."

"Don't be wishing her *in*."

"Not wishing nothing. But be your age, honey, be your age."

"So what? Polly made it in November."

"Was darker then. And she had a night's start."

"True. But don't take the 'J' outa 'Joy.' "

"She won't make it, I tell you."

"Okay . . . she won't make it, you *want* it that way."

———————

Harriet is working in the storeroom. She has been bewildered by her sentence to Paragoula; although it is the logical result of her adoption of the world of fantasy, in which stolen automobiles (with half-empty pint bottles sliding on the leather of the seat beside the driver, and staccato announcements from police cars crackling over the radio) speed forever, never running out of gas. She had truly said to Marie, when they turned the car toward the sunset: "I've never *been* nowhere," and since our appetite grows by what it feeds upon, and since we learn to make maps of our own experience, she had found it natural to mark on hers the names of jails and reformatories all across the country, along with such bigtime sounds as Joliet, Eastern, Marquette, Leavenworth.

In the storeroom, a tall rangy girl regales her with a nonstop panorama of an addict's life: ". . . was in the South 'fore I was here . . . thought I'd go clean, baby, but everyone wants to talk about who's got the best bag, so I forgot about being clean . . . Don't kid yourself, baby, they wrap it in tin foil and get it in a can of powder. My man came up to see me and was he sweet. Tell you he was rocked to his knees . . ." Harriet is preoccupied with the stores she is checking and putting away, but the addict's voice follows her, as if to pad the vacuum which still exists in her life. ". . . just that look's enough. You see it in New York City where you can buy it right outa the drugstore—they got a weight o' snow on their shoulders, those guys—why they's sittin' there on the stoops playing yoyo with their spit. No, baby, that type can't straighten up no more . . ."

Harriet stares at the locks on the door, absorbed in how to open them and what tools will be needed to do it. She has already learned how to manufacture liquor from fruit juice saved from breakfast and sugar stolen from the store. She has picked a warm place near the steam pipes under a grill at the end of one of the long passages, and here she sometimes parks the large wooden trolley which it is her job to push up from the storeroom to the kitchen, so that with the help of Donna Willey (the 'fabulous' blond gun moll who shares her work detail and plays 'chickie' for her) she is able to pry loose the grill and salt away the jars under the floor.

"Harry," the addict says, "*I don't touch liquor . . . I haven't the eyes for it . . . It sickens and nauseates . . . No, baby, that's for you, baby—it takes more than that to turn me on . . .*"

If liquor turns Harriet on, it is something she has always known, but now, on the outskirts of a slow maturity, she has under its influence emotional power over Donna, as once she had had it over Marie; indeed in this prison world where development is asymmetrical, she and Donna can supply each other's wordless needs. Donna, in fact, introduces Harriet to cutting, as long ago Harriet had introduced herself to drinking. If liquor releases Harriet, blood satisfies Donna. And it is Donna who shows Harriet that a knife or a blade has a power beyond its edge, that its mere possession is comforting. By what strange transposition this occurs—the knife the instrument, the blood the release—does not lie within the present story. But the tiny cuts which Donna and Harry give each other in play bind them together like ritual pacts. And Harriet is happy (if so dangerous a link with life can be interpreted as happiness) and agrees readily to plan for an escape from the institution—(out of the hospital window and then over the fence). As if to get training for this experience, she inserts a broken wire into the padlock on one of the storeroom cupboards and extracts certain brassières, panties, nightgowns, and sweaters, none of which she desires for herself, and all of which she gives to the rapacious Donna. Afterwards the padlock appears untouched, and Harriet regards the closed door with affection. She has taken so long to build up her image as a skilled locksmith that this demonstration of skill soothes her ego.

Buoyed up by the hooch she has been drinking the night before, she manages the escape with confidence. As always under such conditions—and perhaps because of them—she feels herself omnipotent; but, as if she were dreaming, unnecessary fantasies cloud her mind, bizarre and violent ways of solving problems not yet faced: 'jacking up' a lady with a knife and stealing her car keys; going into a store with a gun and carrying off for herself and Donna the clothes necessary to disguise themselves. She is still living in the world of crime clippings which had covered the carpet of her bedroom at home, but her hands, educated in her father's yard and made clever from experience, open the special lock on the clinic window—the only window in the hospital without bars—and then help Donna up and over the back fence (against which they both flatten themselves in the darkness, while two dogs bark and fight on a farm in the fields to the south). Harriet has a small pair of scissors in her pants pocket—their only weapon—and Donna has two ten-dollar bills, one of which she gives to Harriet as they huddle panting on the far side of the fence; otherwise they are without the resources of escape: without cars, accomplices, or experience. In a mood of undisturbed calm, Harriet leads the way through a woodland path to nearby Polney, and organizes the ride to Westernport by sending the attractive Donna into an all-night diner to buy a cup of coffee and make contact with the driver of a truck parked outside. Harriet whistles or sings, as she always does when under the influence of liquor, but is clear-headed enough to restrain Donna from hailing a taxi in the quiet, almost empty street. Instead, she pushes her down a side lane, where they both take refuge in a garage. When the cruiser passes nearby, Donna wants to stay hiding behind the pile of lumber, but Harriet, sure that the policeman had seen them and that several men will converge upon the garage at once, leads her through an adjoining garden into another property, where she is already crawling under the fence when she hears Donna's urgent whisper: "Go ahead, Harry . . . go ahead . . . They're coming and I can't get through."

Donna has got stuck in the fence.

Harriet hides behind some latticework and watches her retreat to a toolshed, while half a block away three men get out of the police cruiser. Harriet leaves the latticework and crawls further under the house, flattening her body and peering through the small clumps of lilies which border the house, while the policemen search the garage and then the toolshed and eventually find Donna, who screams immediately: "Turn me loose . . . Turn me loose . . ." She is struggling and kicking until one sleeve is pulled off her shirt, and her face and arms covered with dirt. Later on, one of the policemen reported that he had been forced to handcuff her, and that she had called out: "I'm crazy . . . I'm crazy . . . Send me to the nuthouse . . ."

Harriet watches the officers carry the shrieking Donna to the car, and she lies under the house for a long time, her face close to the earth and buried in her crossed arms. She feels sick and lonely, but her imagination is busy at the same time with those ingenious ideas which absorb the hunted, dreams of omnipotence and escape. It occurs to her that she should double back on her tracks and return to the garage which had already been searched, although her instinct is simply to flee—to run through the yard and along the street, regardless of who may see her. This impulse conquered, she summons up the courage to crawl out from under the house, to run across to the garage and lie down behind a pile of lumber. Here she plans to wait until nightfall. But at six o'clock that evening, when the effects of the liquor have quite worn off, while it is still light, and when she is cramped and sore from her uncomfortable position, she is discovered by the son of the household, who comes to look for the garden hose. In the shadow made by the pile of wood, he sees Harriet, lying on her back, with her arm flexed and a piece of two-by-four clutched in her fist. Her blue eyes are fixed. "One more step and I'll hit you over the head," she threatens, and the boy retreats cautiously. But his father is near the garage door and a neighbor is mowing the lawn next door, and soon the police have arrived again and Harriet is surrounded. She surrenders in a controlled and sullen silence, punctuated only—as one of the officers makes her stand with her hands up against the garage and extracts the scissors from her pocket—by a single low-toned remark: "I can't stand to be locked . . ."

The prison is not necessarily a place of horror. To those reformers who would claim otherwise, it can only be said that so strong a term is not in context. This vast building provides adequate shelter. Good and relatively well balanced meals are served three times a day. From the hot tap the water runs hot, from the cold it runs cold. At least one doctor, several nurses, five or six social workers, several psychologists and a proportionate number of Correctional officers, serve the inmates. Groups of alcoholics meet to discuss alcoholism. Other groups meet for therapy. There are religious services in the chapels. A school functions for four hours each weekday. Recreation is provided. Sports are encouraged. Through the visitors' room pass not only the inmates' relatives, but, for the friendless, Friendly Visitors provided by the community.

Yet the word "prendere" (to lay hold of) from which the word prison derived, suggests that violation at which the flesh shrinks and the ego revolts. It suggests also a shutting away of those fit to be forgotten, a social oubliette, as well as a view of society's ills as ridiculously simple as that of eighteenth-century England, which incarcerated whole families for debt. The ridicule is compounded when one views the prison as a castle, and the crime scene as a muddy moat where nets of insensitive disapproval are thrown to capture the small fish rather than the large, and those frail species which, for one reason or another, have never found their way to the open sea. And as the moated buildings stand, immovable as Gibraltar, equipped and maintained at enormous cost, circled by guards and viewed from afar by army and police, a mystifying screen, spun from the very bodies of those incarcerated within, is woven wraithlike over the stones. This mystification dissuades anyone from tearing the fragile but deceptive mantle behind which the prisoners—in a language formed of signs, foreign words, and expert conmanship—can rebuild reality to suit themselves. Even the humblest prisoners are persuaded to take part in this doubtful game, and, shielded as they are from actual experience, the wine of unreality is fed into their veins.

It is a home away from home that the rejects of society are building in the reformatory: the cleverest superintendent, the

most devoted of staff, can scarcely detect the silken strands of
love and commerce which bind their captive's feet, let alone trace
these strands to their source outside the prison, through industrial
areas where the waters are darkened by waste and refuse, through
slums and ghettoes where they tangle about the feet of innocent
children, through disturbed and delinquent homes, through intricate mazes of corruption and illegal business, and even to the
heart of government itself. There, cleansed and polished, they appear to be proudly clutched in the fists of upright citizens.

And along these communicatory threads, which have their
source in the very center of the maze, news is fed of violent happenings on the street, warnings and shocks of gangland killings,
advice as to the changes in the power structure, propositions for
the future, gossip of 'the life.' In fact, the living breath of this
subculture echoes from the greater depths of the social sea, forms
tiny waves of emotional response, triggers minor alarms within
the prison itself, stimulates fights, punishments, vengeances, and
the growth of unbalanced love affairs—until, at times, even the
breaking of a prison window can be related to that great outer
world, where crime, like other forms of commerce, has its ups
and downs.

That this book is not about prisons, but rather about the fantasies of prisoners, relieves it of the burden of considering the ponderous physical plant, the discipline and mythology, the theory
and practice of penology. It concerns itself, to some extent, with
dreams.

And of these dreams Frankie is already a master. Drawling and
posing in the reception center, she seeks, with the skill of an ac-
tress, to creep under the fragile prison protection. The news, fil-
tering through, that the still-uncaptured escapee is Harriet Brun,
who'd been with her two years ago in the cells in Henry Street
Jail, pleases and alarms her. The pleasure lies in the sense of familiarity, the assurance we derive from seeing old friends in the same
situation as ourselves; the alarm, less tangible, has a flavor of inevi-
tability.

But for the audience around her, Frankie appears all-knowing.
"She ran—and now she'll get two more years put on her . . .

That stupid broad, she going to let herself get *caught!* Well—she so close-mouthed, maybe she'll be hip to get by."

An unkempt Irish alcoholic in the reception center as far advanced in pregnancy as Frankie herself assures her that everyone gets caught.

"They don't have a prayer, dearie. That's for sure. And would I be here, I'm asking you, if I could hold my liquor? . . . I tell you, with one or two inside me, and I'm taking my fists to the policeman . . ."

Frankie regards the woman's hanging stockings and greasy hair with distaste.

"Harry's no alcoholic," she protests, as if Harry were her best friend.

"She's something," the woman says airily, "or she wouldn't be here. All the girls in the kitchen say she was making hooch. Anyway you tell me why she wasn't home where she belongs?"

Frankie protests half-heartedly: "I'm here behind my mother."

"Don't be hard on your mother, God love you," the woman says, shaking her head. "No one'll love you like your own mother, and I never spoke truer words."

Frankie does not answer. Indeed, she thinks, if her mother does not love her, who does?

Two prostitutes take over the conversation, dismissing alcoholism and pregnancy, concentrating on the behavior of their men.

"He hits me again, I'll give Chisholm some business."

"It's all very well to talk, but talk won't cure him!"

Frankie, hearing the familiar sentiments, finds that they no longer stir the old indignation.

"Sure I'll cure him," announces the too-fat woman with the scarred skin, "I'll have his hide . . . This is the second time I'm in for 'pros,' but when I get out I'm going legit . . . and he can get himself another partner."

She pauses. She seems to descend momentarily into a pit of degradation and betrayal. "I'll bury him . . . I'll put him deep under the penitentiary." Her voice is low and vindictive. "He'll be so messed *up*, they'll have to take a *tray* to him."

In other parts of the vast building, interchanges take place which seem no more than emotionless monotones but which bear witness to their buried content as they rise sometimes from calm to hysteria (when one girl, for instance, intrudes upon another in the shower room and hears the second one scream: "Get the hell *outa* here or I'll knock the shit out of you—go ahead—blow it— leave me alone . . .") These interchanges derive from the very depths of those who take part in them, and sometimes have a revealing disembodied quality, blending with the very air, as when an addict, with gentle rapture, her voice low, her body elongated on a bed, recounts as if in a dream the story of her flight from the cops: "I go down and take the bird to New York City . . . I go up to Harlem to buy me a teaspoon of pure . . . I'm walking these streets looking to see who's straight . . . and you know how it is, baby, I see him on the corner . . ."

"Cocaine," someone says, as if not aware that she is interrupting, "cocaine'll make you jump outa the window . . . Cocaine's a light, mellow, crazy high. But heroin's different . . . Pass it by, baby, or you'll end throwing up your gullet."

"Nutmeg," someone says with a note of question, "nutmeg's a nice high."

"Nutmeg'll tear your guts out."

But the last voice is reverent, as that of a gourmet measuring a meal, a wine-taster lifting a bottle.

One of the Negro girls lifts her hand with its incredibly narrow palm and its infinitely graceful fingers (in their turn elongated by sharply filed nails). It is the hand of a priestess, and it tilts in mid-air, so that one sees its pinkish palm and imagines lying there in the rosy center, the sacred seed from the tree in the islands.

"I get so high on *that*, man," she murmurs tonelessly, "so high, man, I'm talkin' to angels."

In one of the cubicles two girls encounter each other with mockingly amorous greetings, and in spite of its ambivalence, their interchange lies like a frail wreath upon the nominal harshness of their surroundings. They are old-timers, and one sees that it is their value to the male which arouses their own sensuousness toward each other, so that only within the cruel protective embrace of their pimps can they turn their love inward, throwing themselves into those postures which are permitted by the cramped confines of the pattern. Within this predetermined position, cruel as an iron cage in a medieval fortress, they manage to extract some human nourishment.

"We've got the same man . . . Dig! . . . We've got no one but each other."

Later one of them picks up her knitting needles, expatiating as she casts on a sweater about the personality requirements of the profession.

"To be a good whore you have to have no feeling. A tramp can't make a good whore because a tramp wants to enjoy herself, and will lie on a bed and forget what the time is. A tramp's out to make the man satisfy *her*. She wants to make him take longer. She hustles for *pleasure* . . .

"I'm a good whore . . . I've been a good whore ever since I learned to get it over with." The little lisp trips up her speech and she is all earnestness as she clicks her knitting needles. "Tricks to every trade," she says portentously. Then she raises her piquant face and holds forth on the weakness of the male.

"If you get them into a highly excited state, they don't know what's what. They don't know what they're doing, those tricks!" She stares over the horn-rimmed glasses she uses for knitting, like an owlish child, like a schoolteacher. "You know there's a way: a hand in the right place—a word. Sometimes I would pretend to be a little coy, but pushing it all the same, getting closer somehow. If you can get a joint between your legs then you gotta good chance to get it over with in no time . . . And he'll say that was the best ever, and how madly excited he was, and all that, when all the time it was '*pure thigh*.'" She laughs hilariously, and the laughter echoes down the passages and comes back and mingles with the silence.

But although it is not night, although the living quarters at this end of the institution are filled with the noises of girls dressing, of showers running, of the swinging doors to the day rooms opening and closing, a silence falls in this cubicle suddenly, deeper than night and filled with fear, as if the two girls went down a muddy incline together holding hands, heads close, sliding, afraid . . . "And this trick was white," one of them was saying . . . "Oh, a *dreadful* white, as if he had no blood in him. Honest to God, as if he'd risen from the dead to come and find me! But there was no business that night . . . I don't know why, but there was just no business, and I was a bit low in funds . . ."

The legend of Jack the Ripper is resurrected from London's East End where, in the gaslit cobbled streets, some strange mad doctor roams looking for prostitutes (those scapegoats of the world) and now he becomes the 'giggling prowler' of Detroit, who wanders the suburbs selling Catholic Bibles, but whose eyes are only for women's breasts, which he longs to mutilate with a small sharp knife.

". . . Although I didn't like him much, I said I'd go with him, and I even thought I'd go with him in his car because if I'm a bit afraid of cars, I'm not like other girls, and I've got more nerve . . . So we drove a bit and he was kinda horribly quiet, and then I asked him to stop, because it was already a trick house I didn't know well. We'd gone way along Evans and I was afraid he wouldn't stop for some reason.

"Well, he did stop—but just before we were to go in the house there was a dark alley, and he pushed me in there and grabbed me by the throat and held me against the wall, and he had this flashlight in his hand, and he was trying to push it up inside me, and he was laughing all the time as if he were *mad* . . . I couldn't move much, I was so paralyzed by his hand I couldn't breathe, and the more I struggled the more he squeezed, and then he dropped the flashlight, and he was so excited that I could feel this mad vibration all over him. I saw he had a penknife in his hand and he was trying to cut my breasts . . ."

Her voice is lost, drifts faint with fear, along an alley. ". . . and a drunk came wandering along, stumbling and absolutely wasted, but here was something human, and I had the strength to break away, and hang onto this drunk and scream . . ."

For a long time the sound of her screams rings out in the tiny cubicle—

Yet all this is cut apart by the bell for supper, is gratefully forgotten and seems to be lost in the normality of a quiet evening, even while they get up from the bed, open the door, and walk slowly, casually, along the passage way, one saying to the other in a low prophetic voice, but with a bland, sad, unaccented conviction: "Death awaits us."

Back in the reception center, Frankie has not heard this last and gloomiest conversation, since it takes place so far away, down so many flights of steps, along such continuous passages, around so many corners—as well as far away in time from her who has never yet seriously seen herself as a prostitute. For like those who are lacking in practical experience but precocious in knowledge of theory, she is intellectually convinced that this will never come to pass. She has still some optimistic feeling that she is destined for higher things.

She breaks in, therefore, on the conversation of the two girls in the far corner with an uneasy bravado, especially since they have now forgotten the more unattractive aspects of the matter and are talking in a calm and desultory way about tramps. "I tell you a tramp can't make it—she can't keep her eye on that dollar bill. Tramps end up under the boardwalk in Coney."

"And where do prostitutes end up?" Frankie demands, eager to relieve her own feelings by asserting herself in front of professionals. "They got no sense, that's what. They give all they make to their pimps. Wouldn't catch me supporting no man, that's for sure."

"You're too fast with your mouth," the older woman contends briefly. A pitying smile plays around her mouth.

Frankie has seen that smile before. But now she is secure in the fact that the men she has found so inadequate can easily be displaced by women. "I don' want to lie up under no man too tough!" she protests airily. "There's plenty more in other places of what they have to give."

"*You* should know," the younger girl suggests staring at her small flat figure in the straight, boyish-looking clothes. She makes a vulgar gesture with her fingers. "Well . . ." Frankie answers as if she had made up her mind to one thing at least. "I know for certain I'm not going on *no* corner, running from *no* police, and going in *no* alley . . ."

It is nearly five o'clock in the reception center's kitchenette, when Frankie runs into Brenda 'Baby' O'Reilly. Pausing, looking over her swollen body as over a year's time, she sees Brenda, healthy and heavy, her black hair cut short, her face unpainted. She is unloading hot food from the wagonette which had been brought up from the central kitchen.

"Baby!"

"As I live and breathe—it's Frankie! I'd known you was here, I'd have come running!"

Frankie makes a sign indicating that an officer has appeared in the doorway.

"The toilet," she whispers.

Brenda drops her lashes with a slight nod.

A moment later the two girls are facing each other in the tiny white-painted bathroom adjoining the passage.

"You look *bad*, Baby," Frankie exclaims with delight.

Brenda smiles and shrugs, glancing involuntarily at Frankie's figure.

"Yes," Frankie admits, "I'm knocked up."

"How'd *that* happen?"

Frankie clings to the role of the experienced Lesbian. "It musta happened when I wuz asleep. This guy kept hitting on me, and before I knew it I was like this." She adds: "Don't worry . . . I'm macking tough when I'm pregnant!"

But the gay expression on her face vanishes as she remembers Oliver's sudden disappearance and, as if straining for some admission of similar betrayal, her eyes look into Brenda's.

"What happened to *you*, doll?"

"I wuz with Pokey . . . Sugar's cousin." Brenda reaches out

and clutches at Frankie's hand. She kneads and squeezes the long dark fingers. The more suffering she has had to endure from her dark partners, the more she feels impelled toward the mystic pleasure and pain which she has learned to associate with this skin color. Like one of Pavlov's dogs, she endures a thousand shocks to enjoy the nourishment she needs.

"Pokey wuz real hard on me, Frankie . . ." she murmurs.

"She *was?* What're you doing teaming up with those tough broads?"

"I don't know . . ." Brenda's voice fades. "Perhaps I'm nuts."

"You're not nuts, Baby. But she's not even your stick! Couldn't you get nothing *better* out there?"

Brenda shrugs her shoulders helplessly. "I took a lotta shit from her . . ." She remembers her flight from Pokey's apartment and murmurs: "I looked for you."

"You didn't look hard enough, Baby."

"I did look, Frankie . . . She was beating my ass something terrible . . ."

"*That* migrant—she come from *Trinidad!*" Frankie declares loftily.

"She gave me no respect." Pride touches Brenda's low monotonous voice. "She don't have to tell *me* what to do, I'm a *woman*, aren't I? . . . She don't know that whippin' a woman went out with high-button boots! She don't have no psychology . . ."

"That Pokey was born in Trinidad, but bred up in Harlem," Frankie declares. "I know her mother and her brother, and I know her *kind*—she's New York slick! They promise the moon and give the boot!"

It has occurred to Frankie that now her opportunity has come to cop Baby. Now that she is in the joint what else is there to do? And surely she has more on the ball than Sugar and Pokey. She remembers Candy's immature ecstasies, and longs to reproduce them on a larger scale, and on Brenda's formidable body.

She reassures tenderly: "Don't worry, Baby, we're both here, that's what counts."

Soberly Brenda says: "I'm all screwed up."

"Well, we're all screwed up." Frankie's voice is light. "At

Wentworth we certainly tore up the place . . . everyone was running in and outa them gates . . ."

"Two girls run from here Tuesday," Brenda informs her.

"Don't you think I know that! . . . I only just made the joint, but I'm sure hip to what goes on . . . One of the girls was Harriet Brun, that broad who was in the cell next to you at Henry Street."

Brenda's face expresses the familiar ambivalence of the delinquent, who is relieved by the capture of a fellow delinquent but pained by her failure to escape.

"They say that the one they caught was hiding in a garage over at Westernport."

"I saw the broad." Frankie shrugs. "They brought her in this morning—and she was handcuffed. Gee, thank the Lord, I never had those bracelets on yet."

The flesh of Brenda's arms is touched by the cold wind of the future. "My mother wouldn't bail me out," she adds bitterly, "and she hasn't come up since I got here. I just wrote her a letter." From inside her brassière she draws out a folded piece of paper and thrusts it into her friend's hands.

"*'Just a few lines,'*" Frankie reads, "*'to say I'm lousy and I hope you are the same. I have about a year to do and maybe I'll be free . . . I'm not coming home. I'll be going to a place by myself . . . I want to thank you for not bailing me out . . . I don't want you or anyone to send me anything except my black dress, black skirt, black heels . . . The only thing I will accept is $5 every other week . . . If you're not here by next Sunday, I'm refusing to work, staying in my room and never coming out . . . You might as well forget that I'm your daughter . . . I'll change my name.'*"

"It's strong," Frankie soothes her, returning the note with its odor of error and tears, "but you sure love your mother, Brenda . . ."

"I don't know. It just gets next to me that she put me in here . . ."

The two girls stand close to each other in mutual agitation.

Brenda wants to embrace Frankie. And Frankie is torn between a desire to show affection and a desire to gain power.

"You're a fox," she murmurs. "I go for you . . . Remember how in Wentworth we thought we were so great just because we'd swap a little spit?" She wants to let Baby know that she is no longer as innocent as she once was. "Remember how gettin' someone into a coat closet was a freak party, and a little bit of hand action—that was *really* something!"

"Sure seems a long time ago . . ." Brenda's voice goes up and down in a melancholy rallentando. "You wuz drawing and writing in the school, remember? . . ."

"Sure I remember . . . Old Papa Do-Do—"

"You've got *beautiful* writing, Frankie," Brenda compliments.

"Thank you, doll . . . Lay it down for me, how'd you leave home?"

"That little old bald-headed Irishman," Brenda refers to her father. "He started in about the colored . . . I tell you, Frankie, I don't know how to *act* around a white man. All a white man can do is give me his money." Obediently she repeats the convenient lessons of the street, though a moment later, pathetically, and with doubt in her voice, she adds (admitting openly to Frankie for the first time, her complete acceptance of 'the profession'), "That's the way I wuz taught . . . when I wuz taught into this life."

"You're the rarest, Baby," Frankie says with gratitude. Here is a white girl who is *really* hooked. "But you don't have to take that whippin' shit from no one . . . There's colored *and* colored . . ."

"I know it." Brenda feels the old calm, but is conscious of the hostility which lies behind her passive front. "I got larceny, Frankie," she confesses, "lots of larceny . . ."

"Okay, Baby," Frankie soothes, "don't be hurting yourself."

"I hear you wuz tight with Candy in the joint."

Frankie fancies that there is a hint of jealousy in Baby's voice, and she smiles, showing her white teeth in the face which seems so small above her enlarged body. "Young girls don't really be kill-

ing me," she drawls. "They don't have no *soul* for me, Baby."
Reassuringly her hands enclose Brenda's shoulders. "I'm not taken
in by broads tryin' to be fly . . ." Then she gazes with melting
dark eyes. "We'll be together, Baby—in the joint and in the
street."

Outside, the officer's voice is heard calling as she walks up and
down the passage, and, alarmed by this intrusion of the institution
world, Brenda darts from the bathroom and rushes agitatedly toward the kitchenette.

"Do you have to take so long in there?" the officer inquires
suspiciously. "The other girls have done all the work . . . Will
you be good enough to help Marilene finish those dishes?"

"Yes, Miss Carter." Brenda looks submissive. "I surely
will . . ."

At this point, Frankie also emerges from the bathroom, perversely ignores the officer and walks off down the passage with an
assumption of great dignity.

"See you later, doll," she calls to Brenda.

The officer halts her with an outstretched arm. "May I ask
you what *you* were doing? Were you two in there together?"

Frankie's tone becomes intensely insulting. "Listen, honey,"
she drawls as Brenda hurries off toward the kitchenette, "ef we
gonna do something, we're not gonna do it when *you're* on!"

That night, just before midnight, Harriet Brun is brought back to
Paragoula. She is taken through the reception center to the locked
cells in the Security wing where she is stripped of her clothes,
searched again for objects with which she might harm herself, and
dressed in a nightgown. Frankie, in her bed in the dormitory near
the Security cells, hears the voice of the deputy and the heavy
tread of the male guard; and although she had had no friendship
with Harriet, whose silence in the block at Henry Street had
effectively protected her from communicating with the other
prisoners, she feels discomfort and despair. (For her Harriet is an
enigma, an anguished voice, a scream which had torn apart a long-

ago afternoon. But this protest is living in her memory, as alive, as green as a leaf picked in midsummer.)

She starts up in her bed, and holds her nightgown against her burdened body, in which the heart of the child about to be born seems to beat with as much alarm as her own.

── VI ──

The Street

Loper (to himself): "The dollar bill is the supreme essence."

As summer ends and winter begins again, time, if measured in maturity, scarcely records its passing. The bizarre imagination of the girls has stripped them of growth and centered them upon fantasy, so that the dependent Brenda still seeks a Nubian master, and Frankie (who has been delivered of her baby, and in spite of protestations, allowed it to be adopted) still looks as she passes through the prison corridors for a line of chorus girls to snap to attention like soldiers. Harriet, kept in her cell for long speechless periods, dreams of machines, and encourages them to mangle her body, until she is given over to dumbness, all cogs and wheels. The memory of Donna returns. She searches frantically for some means to express this link with life, and finally manages to crush the electric light bulb in the ceiling by throwing a plastic cup at it, and to scratch her wrists with the tiny pieces of glass which fall to the floor. Now something in her is satisfied. Now blood flows instead of speech. She is returned to Townsend for further observation.

Those outside the prison have not forgotten those inside. But the parents who have felt themselves rejected find that as the pain lessens, so lessens the concern. With a sense of hope deferred, inertia sets in. Brenda's mother is sunk in weariness, ashamed of Brenda and anxious about her son. She dispatches occasional letters to Paragoula, and at Eastertime, several cards with lilies and crosses, as if hoping that formal recognition of the season will bring about a Resurrection. A lawyer works again for Harriet, but her father has less enthusiasm for her release now that he is beginning to realize that her desire to escape her home is as obvious as her desire to escape the prison.

And in her religious stewardship Frankie's mother is also less ardent, although Opaline writes to Frankie that she doesn't visit the house on Moon Street so much anymore because she can't go "without Aunt Alva starts preaching, and that gets me depressed." In her faithful letters to Frankie, however, Alva is less apt to talk about religion than she is to complain about her husband's undesirable acquaintances, about Bobo's running the streets, and Rosina's getting in with a fast crowd. Without explicit comment, her letters show how hard she finds it to prevent her family from sliding, sliding, down that slippery slope . . . straight into the embrace of 'the life.' *I've had so much trouble— so much trouble. The doctor wants me to have my eye operated on. Your father is getting $60 a month from various ones whom he takes up to visit at Beaver Island and Townsend, but to me that money is tainted. When I tried to rent the downstairs room, Jeanette sent me a prostitute—you can see that you can't trust your own . . . I caught Bo-Bo with that Sánchez boy, and you know what that means . . . He comes and goes and he'll end up on* Beaver. *As for Rosina, she is in with various ones at school, and I had to go up there to visit her teacher . . . Frankie, we nourish our appetites by what we eat, and our minds by what we put in them . . .* BE REAL FOR GOD *. . . If you won't live for* HIM, *if Daddy, Bo-Bo, and Rosina deny* HIM, *yet I must live saved.*

These letters, regularly as they appear, picture life at home as extending rather than opposing the prison life. They suggest to Frankie's subconscious that all is as it was before, that there's nothing to hope for there.

An occasional passionate note comes from Candy (smuggled in by an arrival fresh out of Wentworth), but these, too, strike a note of helpless frailty. "*I want my Frankie . . . I'm so lonely and unhappy . . . If he shows up on the scene, the joy and expectation and delite will be too much to bare . . .*"

. . . And like fading martial music, sounded with more confidence in the past, but now boring and repetitious, with dragged-out chords and tuneless trumpet blasts, there comes the protestation and exhortation of her grandmother, Evangelist Wilhemina Tobey, who no longer tries to visit but whose letters, each more abusive than the last, each more incoherent, regularly herald her coming. They spell out a sad story of mental deterioration ('My grandmother has lost her anointed,' Frankie says sadly), yet hint with pathos at some former courage and purpose. "*I'll take you to court if you don't let her go . . . I don't know what church you have—but I don't care for your stinking church . . . I'm here, the minister of the Lord . . . As for your nosiness and saying that I must go through channels, I say that I go through the channels of the Lord . . . You say you have her record and I say I have the Lord's record . . . I've watched you, and the nosiness of the Negroes on Evans Avenue—I'll come into your low-down stinking place and carry her away.*"

Out in what is called the street, the laws of supply and demand operate as usual.

Beppo has her own rooms on Gorton Place, a grubby little alley running off the upper end of Mackay Street. Close to the ghetto, this address is within walking distance of her mother's apartment and so fulfills Beppo's needs for a firm tie with her family. It is also convenient to the Hotel Chevrolet, where she puts up some of her girls, and where Ana 'Pug Nose' Pulaski has been living now for thirteen months . . . At this hour in the late afternoon on a day in October, the phone rings, and Beppo saunters slowly to answer it to hear a familiar voice asking, "145–0071?"

"Yes," Beppo answers.

"Have you got anyone right now?" the voice questions.

"Yes I have," Beppo answers. "What's your price range?"

"Fifty or sixty," the voice answers.

Beppo sits down, cradling the phone, and leans back in the chair.

"Okay.—Anything special?"

"You know what I like." There is a suggestion of hesitation. "I like someone to work me over good." Beppo has heard this voice almost every week for several years, but there is always something curiously impersonal about it. Its echo penetrates the listening room with a strange even quality.

"The same as usual," the voice says without emphasis.

"I think I've got the person," she assures him with equal calm.

"Good."

"What time do you want her?"

The voice mentions an address on the Hill.

"About five o'clock."

"She'll be there."

There is the click of a receiver being put down.

Half an hour later Maria opens the door of the Delgado apartment, to find her daughter standing on the threshold, laden with bags of fruit.

"It's not Thanksgiving yet," she reproves.

"No—but nearly . . . I thought I'd come up and help you plan." She puts down the bags, pulls out a wooden bowl, and begins to pile it high with oranges and pears.

"Will we have a turkey, Mums?"

"I thought we would. Your brothers will be home from the South."

"A turkey it is then."

Although her mother receives an ADC check each month, Beppo looks upon herself as the one who provides the family extras, and now she decides upon cranberry sauce and 'all the fixins,' lobster salad on the side, martinis before dinner, and what she calls 'burgundy wine' with the main course.

"Where those glasses I got you?" she asks her mother.

"Where you think? They're in the cupboard."

"The red and white ones?" (Six months before, and for just such occasions, Beppo had brought home an expensive set of glasses in red and white crystal.)

"Sure the red and white ones. What you think?"

"Just checking."

"What you going to wear, daughter?"

Although Maria had long ago accepted her daughter's profes-

sion, she had never quite got used to her male attire, feeling that
her daughter and her daughter's beauty had been taken from her,
and that in lieu of losing her altogether she had been forced to
accept—as in a fairy story—this enchanted pseudo male. She is a
little comforted by Beppo's gracefulness, and by the quality of
her clothes which, although always in male form, are made
of brilliant colored silks, of cotton woven with a silver thread, of
black stretch silk and black velour, or of very fine beige doeskin.
But she persists in saying, as she says now, "You wear a skirt,
daughter."

"Maybe, if I can stand it."

After a while her mother adds: "Ana's coming?"

"Ana's coming," affirms Beppo, ". . . if the little broad works
well."

"You abuse that child, and you won't have luck," Mrs. Delgado demurs. If she has accepted Beppo's way of life, she resists
Beppo's extension of it, which, she sees now, tends toward the
keeping of several girls at once. All this has been explained to her
by Beppo herself—the good sense it makes, and how it multiplies
the profits—but although she is as emotionally dependent upon
Beppo as she once was upon her husband, her natural kindness
resists the exploitation of children. Ana 'Pug Nose' Pulaski, whom
she has often seen hugging and kissing one of her stuffed animals
(particularly a woolly bear which Alec had given her), is classified
as a child.

"It'll be tough sledding through the holidays," she warns.
"Men aren't out spending . . . so don't expect too much."

"Well, I'll have to get me a *pretty* girl." Beppo's tone expresses discontent. "This one, I have to throw a bag over her face
to take her out. She's got no class."

"She's white, isn't she?" her mother protests.

In her customary manner, Beppo begins to prowl around the
apartment, picking up objects and putting them down again, the
upper end of her body thrust forward from her hips—her arms,
her flat bangs swinging. "I'm nervous," she excuses herself.

Then she adds: "I'm aggravated."

Her mother is wondering whether Beppo is on drugs again.

"Get a hold on yourself," she warns.

There is a silence and Beppo attempts to reassure her: "Ana will be here and the boys will be here. We'll all be together . . . Okay?" Like any dutiful daughter she gives her mother a quick kiss on the cheek.

———————

But on Thanksgiving Day a thick white snow blankets the windows, and she wakes to a strange discontent. This feast, conceived of as a reward for hard work and frugality, and now celebrating plenty only, stimulates some loneliness and terror. She walks in fear to the window, pressing her bare arms against the glass, trying to look into the street. She sees nothing—only a white holiday silence.

Naked at the window (she seldom, even on the coldest nights, wears pajamas), her tall, narrow figure is brown all over, and her head is wound around with an orange scarf which presses down upon her hair. She is in love with her body, so that she keeps a long mirror on the wall, and in this she now views herself, wrapped still in the fantasies of sleep, her eyes half closed under the turban, thinking of the women who will desire and yield to her. One doctor had expressed surprise that she was so made sexually, with narrow hips and wide shoulders, with breasts and genitals still far from small, but with Fallopian tubes nearly closed, as if adamant against pregnancy. "I'm half man then," she had said, laughing. "It's from all those women hanging on me." And she had given that light and dextrous movement of her lips with her finger, a gesture which takes the place of words, and sounds like the flutter of a bird's wing.

Lost in the mirror's image, she is uneasy for no good reason. To be worshipped by women is only half her aim. She has to achieve this without material loss, and she must maintain an iron control (a little later she is to stab one of her more jealous admirers in the side, and watch her, in a strange posture of pity, bleed on the floor of a sordid hotel room). But behind this compulsive need there is the further one of holding uneasy emotions at bay—

the regrets, doubts, terrors which disturb her quiet. These invade her now, so that the world becomes hushed and sinister, a cold, white desert of remorse. For a while she fights this feeling; but within fifteen minutes she is padding in her bare feet into the bathroom, taking down a bottle from the cupboard, and tilting two 'greenies' into her palm. She swallows them, and sits on the bathroom stool, staring at her feet until she is in that state which she generally describes to herself as being on the fringe. She could not have explained to another person why she fears being shut off from the world and at the same time needs seclusion. But this dual need, this constant necessity to walk a tightrope, has given her a familiar nightmare, never experienced in her bed, but apt to stalk her in her waking moments.

"As if everything had *stopped*," she once said to her mother ". . . As if it had gone *dead*." Sometimes in moments of insight, she feels that it is her own death she fears.

―――――――

Two blocks away, in her room in the far from respectable Hotel Chevrolet, Ana 'Pug Nose' Pulaski has dismissed the last of her men, and has gone to sleep at last with her worn brown bear held tightly in her arms. She is not aware of the falling snow, nor of Beppo's disquiet, nor of the distant drone of the El. She is plunged deep into a sleep, which excludes not only her master, Beppo, but the mechanical love-making and the petty insults to which she had been subjected during the long night especially by a drummer from the South, whom she had first seen as a romantic figure, but who had afterwards cheated her. "He shot me through the grease," she had complained to a colleague in the bar at the Pandora's Box, "an' when I put him down, he said he'd have me busted. Can you *beat* it?"

"What you got such a thing about *drummers* for?" Beppo asks her, when she drops by to wake her up for Thanksgiving dinner. "Don't you know them salesmen are *ridiculous?*" (Ridiculous is one of Beppo's favorite words.)

Ana, still in her short full pink nightie, and biting the nose of her worn brown bear, looks common and unattractive. Everything about her disgusts Beppo who, though living off her earnings for so long, still reserves her better feelings for girls with too much sense to subject themselves to her demands.

"Look, Beppo," Ana pleads, ignoring the question, "look how cute he is. My boogy brown baby. See . . . he's talking to me . . ." She pretends that the bear is kissing her, then tucks him carefully into the blanket and swings her plump legs over the edge of the bed.

"Is it *wrong* to want never to grow old?" she inquires wistfully.

"Oh *Jesus!*" Beppo replies.

To herself she thinks, *Thank God I took the 'greenies.'*

Ana begins talking about her niece. "Daisy's grown so *old* . . . you should see her now. She's thin and everything, and I tell you she lives in a raggedy ole house way over near Morton . . . Ma told me she took stuff for a while, because her husband was a junkie, and she thought it would be a kick . . . But gee, she got *old* an' her teeth are all falling out and everything . . ."

Beppo is disinterested. "Well you're not seventeen yet, so you've still got a few years." Ana, whose attention span is extremely short, goes into the bathroom and examines her pasty complexion in the mirror. Now she tells Beppo that her father doesn't approve of their relationship.

"What's *he* know about it?"

Beppo stretches out in the solitary chair and puts her feet on the bed.

"He don't know nothing . . . That time I went to his apartment, when the sailor beat me up and I got the cut lip, he was nice then, because I cried, and he said I should go back to Ma in the Project."

"So?" Beppo examines her fingernails.

"So I said that Ma crabbed too much."

"What'd he say to that?"

"He says that's why he left, too, because she crabbed."

After a moment Ana adds in a tearful voice, but with some insight: "I think he really left because she's a cripple; and I could hardly stand it myself . . . You know, the way her legs won't bear her up, and she keeps falling over and everything."

"Well, what did he say about you and me?"

"Ah, well—when you and I stayed over his place one night . . . You 'member when you was hiding out from the cops? Well, he said we couldn't come back again, because we fool with each other in bed."

Ana shrugs, and gives a self-conscious smile as she struggles into her slip.

"All right, we don't go back to his fucking apartment," Beppo replies.

The slow process of Ana's dressing goes on. Beppo sees the metamorphosis of the frowzy dumpy little ash blonde in the shortie nightgown into an overdressed girl in a tight blue suit. She watches a glittering glass necklace added to the costume, and sees the rabbit-like mouth made into a red Cupid's bow. She tries to regard her from the viewpoint of a lusty male, but is unsuccessful, so that she finally says in an irritated voice: "Oh for Pete's sake, Pug, let's get going!" To herself she is thinking with a despairing languor: *I wish—I wish I could get really high.*

_____

By the time that Thanksgiving dinner is almost over, the desire to get high has become overwhelming. Taut and restless, she sits at the table, fiddling with the stem of her glass, tapping with her foot under the table. A week before Ana had shoplifted two dresses and five pairs of shoes, and they had been given to Big Charlie, a cocaine dealer, who had promised that he would supply Beppo with cocaine whenever she felt a special need. So far, however, supplies had been short, and now when Beppo left the table to call him, he could only promise her a 'nickel' cap.

"But it's good C," he guarantees her persuasively, "it's good stuff, worth the pound. Better play it slow."

"I'll send for it," she promises him.

The Thanksgiving table, still laden with food and wine, does not restrain her, nor do the remonstrances of her mother and brothers.

"Pug—you hit the street."

"It's a holiday for Chrissakes . . . ," one of her brothers says.

"You sending the girl to *work!*"

"Get going, Pug," Beppo commands.

Ana, as good-humored as ever, gets up immediately, but swaying on her spike heels, she claims that she is 'gassed.'

"Better pull yourself together, or I'll stick your head in the tub," Beppo advises.

When her brother tries to intervene again, she swings around in tight-lipped anger. "Will you shut *up* . . . ? You're bugging me . . . The broad's only going to do an errand."

The family is silent.

In the bathroom two hours later Beppo takes off. The lid is on the toilet seat and she sits on that, her tense back erect, her sleeve rolled up, while the clumsy and inexperienced Ana injects the speed-ball. They are both in their dress-up clothes, but Beppo has changed her skirt for her soft, tight doeskin pants, and over this she wears her high black boots. Under the bare light bulb Ana labors, her underlip caught between her teeth, her long black lashes fluttering, frightened as she has always been by the mere mechanics of the injection, with its business-like and surgical tools. "Slow-ly," Beppo commands, "slow-ly, I wanta get my brush, Baby."

"Oh—ah," moans Ana, "I wish you wouldn' . . . wouldn' make me do this . . . I wish you wouldn' Beppo . . ."

"It's okay, I tell you," Beppo says through her clenched teeth, taking in the agony of her impatience a special pleasure in wounding Ana's tenderness, "just hit me slowly, damn you . . ."

"I am . . . I am . . ."

"You'll *kill* me if you don't."

"Oh I'm being careful, Beppo." Her finger trembles as she alternately pushes and releases the plunger, and as the mixture of heroin and cocaine, stained red with blood, seeps gradually into the vein.

For Beppo it is not *her* vein, or *her* arm. It is as impersonal as some dead body which she is desecrating in a coffin. Like crystals in her blood, that state of regret and tension which she has known all day, that self-hatred which illuminates how short she falls of some standard which she has never glimpsed concretely but has all the same set up for herself, is dissolving now. She knows herself in a purely physical existence. Her entire body, including that arm which Ana still holds, seems to be concentrated marvelously in her stomach, which is hit by the drug as if by some inner-inflicted blow. The ball travels; it invades the back of the neck and strikes there with a force which seems to stun her. She reacts by retching, and leans over the bathtub; but this nausea is mixed with a peculiar delight which expands from sickness into exhilaration, until she seems to feel herself lift from the stool and rise toward the ceiling. Her body at once stretches and races, and the nausea gives way to a joy, which floods her whole being, sweeps over her in alternate waves of heat and chill, coating her teeth, freezing her skin, brushing her over with the menthol-like cold of excessive heat.

"Oh God," she hears herself saying, "Oh God . . ."

In an access of joy, she flings her arms around Ana's waist and draws her body to her, half in that ecstasy of relief with which the drug banishes her despair, and half in some sexual pleasure which falls just short of climax. "Oh Ana . . ." she says with an indrawn sobbing breath, "it's good . . . so good . . . I'm *high*, Ana . . . I'm *high* . . ."

Later as they walk in the street, Beppo takes off her tall black boots and treads in the snow, laughing and declaring that she feels no cold—peeling off her jacket and her sweater, loosening her shirt and half exposing her breasts, throwing back her head in the crisp air and seeming to drink in the whole white night.

Ana, dumb, doglike companion, clutching her cheap fur coat

to her throat, is afraid that if she leaves her Beppo will freeze to death; afraid that if she doesn't go to work, Beppo will beat her. All that she can do is follow along behind, stumbling in the snow on her unsuitable too-high stilt-heels.

And several hours later, when she has been able to persuade two friends from the Pandora's Box to take Beppo to their apartment, and she herself, with the help of a quick drink or two, has recovered enough to stroll under the chilly white lights between Fifteenth and Mayerson, she is so upset that she forgets this area is dangerous for her (because some weeks back, when a certain officer had given her a 'second chance,' she had promised to meet him there and had later forgotten all about it.) So that now, as she accosts a tall young man striding rapidly along the street toward her, she is picked up by the squad car and taken to police headquarters. She knows, as she sits in the car, fumbling with frozen fingers to empty the snow out of her ridiculous shoes, that this time she will probably be sent up to Paragoula.

"Not *my* Ronnie," is what Ronald 'Loper' Robinson's grandmother replied to a policeman who returned Loper to her, one day when he was nine years old, and had been caught stealing a pile of women's raincoats from a downtown store, "—not *my* baby!"

"Yes, ma'am—*your* Ronnie, *your* baby," the policeman said grimly, handing over the boy, whose long face, the brown skin touched with white by the wind and the cold, appeared as sober and stiff as that of a medieval statue carved into the wooden end of a pew.

"How come? How come?" fussed the grandmother, whose ideas of honesty were elastic, but who came from a generation more prone to petty pilfering than to efficient stealing. "How come, Ronnie? What you want with half a dozen raincoat?" The sentimental idea even occurred to her that he had been bent on getting her a Mother's Day present, and her eyes softened as she told the officer that the child had no parents. "I brought him up from the time he was three years of age. An' this the firs' time any officer brought him home for not respecting the law. No sir—ain't been no trouble with this child. None at all."

"There's always a first time," the officer said kindly.

And neither Ronnie nor his grandmother protested further, since he was—as they both knew—'running with the boys,' and even Mrs. Robinson guessed that it was a wonder he had not been caught before. Although she would maintain to the end of her days that her grandson was a '*good* boy,' and go on to prove it by telling how she was getting crippled with arthritis and how Ronnie 'helped her out sometimes,' and how the child's mother was dead and the father 'didn't seem to care,' and how Ronnie was smart in school—all these being reasons for Ronnie being a '*good* boy.'

"And she won't change *that*," Loper would say to his companions later, "not if God comes down."

But by this time he is sixteen, a year after that summer morning in Moon Street, when he had talked to Frankie and Opaline outside the movie theater, Loper is a 'runner' for the numbers, and might have been seen any afternoon after school, sprinting along the streets to pick up the slips from 'Alabama Fred'—carrying, as he often did, as much as five or six thousand dollars in a brown paper bag to hand over to the Controller, (generally to be found at the back of the barbershop on the corner of Moon and Clancy). This chore out of the way, Loper might use the late afternoon to do a little hustling, taking advantage of the hour when feeble old ladies, their welfare checks cashed, tended to go shopping—that crowded hour at the markets when it was easy to lift a good thick steak, and warm it close to the body under a shirt and sweater.

Loper is tall for his age, and he has always been particularly graceful, with bright topaz-colored eyes, wide apart under curved brows, shining like an animal's, and giving, because of the furriness of the eyelashes which surround them, a hint of fox or lynx. He thinks that his illegal activities are peccadilloes, to be expected of someone of his age and temperament; and since he does well in high school, he has the idea that he might like to be a surgeon, imagining himself clad in a white gown, wearing a mask, and cutting delicately with precise instruments in the hushed atmosphere of the operating theater. He thinks he will be willing to abandon his hustling habits for another kind of status and prosperity. But he has had to leave his grandmother, because her possessive adoration has made it difficult for him to move freely in the street, and this independence is dearly bought, since it demands that he hustle regularly to find the rent, or at least pay attention to the unattractive landlady. And so he finds himself, little by little, without the money to manage it, drawn into the responsibilities of a man in the life.

The first apartment he has—a forerunner of more luxurious ones to come—is a testing ground for his sense of decorum. For his sagging bed he begs a piece of red damask from the antique dealer on the floor below. He graciously accepts an old clock from his grandmother. He boosts ardently for several weeks to supply his cabinets with linen, silver, and cooking equipment. And he finds the print of a nude lolling woman in the Furniture Mart in Moon Street, and hangs it above his mantelpiece. He is feminine himself in his love of elegant surroundings, and dreams of sometime when he will have all the material possessions he needs, a time when he can shut himself up in a beautifully furnished apartment, far away from the perils of the street which he seems to court so eagerly.

It is rather as if, long ago, he had been very afraid, so that he looks now for peace and safety. And perhaps it is because of this need for safety that the nude woman above his mantelpiece, whose hips are clouded in a blue bedcover, whose negligent foot is dangling from the edge of a bed, is not so much a form of womanly beauty as she is an extension of himself. His love for women, which is a real enough love, is also a passive love, and seeks to suck hungrily at female breasts. A lassitude, a weakness overcomes him. It is as if he had never exercised moral force. As if a whole world of energy and light had been denied him.

In his sixteenth year—at that time when Frankie, pregnant, and only a little older than he is, has been dismissed by the youth board because of the assault on a nurse at Townsend—Loper, who is still going to high-school parties, meets at one of them a precocious white girl who is his senior by more than a year. Her bold brown eyes seem to taunt him, and she moves closer, so that Loper is crowded against the window sill. "I've heard of you . . ." is all that she says to him.

. . . He has had many adventures with girls, but so many of them have been hasty, immature episodes, fumbling conquests in hallways, 'gang bangs,' or sordid matings for personal gain (such as the sessions with the landlady in lieu of rent) that he still has a certain ignorance.

Meeting this girl on the next afternoon, and walking with her in the summer heat toward the wilting park, he seems to hear her flesh breathing under a light transparent dress. He desires her so much that he can scarcely endure her presence, and slowly as they walk she becomes reptilian, an elusive contractile creature whose red tongue darts out of her mouth to touch her equally red lip, whose body seems to vanish as they walk, slipping into the shrubbery, appearing and reappearing before his bewildered eyes. Yet through these fantasies he knows that she is a woman, and he stops her on the path and murmurs clumsily: "I'll show you my apartment . . ." while he thinks clearly: *She's beat—she's a beat bitch.*

In the apartment he pulls nervously at her clothes, and they fall on the bed together, where they tangle for a moment like machines out of control. He is kissing her white shoulders and struggling to get close to her, rearranging her limbs as if she were an inanimate object, and burying himself in her with moans of satisfaction. Again she is that reptilian creature whose movements elude him, but she draws back a little into the endless reaches of her body, trying to preserve herself from his onslaught.

"Come on," she is murmuring, arched back from him, but with her wet kisses on his shoulders, "come on . . ." He smiles into her flesh, sleepily embracing her.

"What's wrong?" she says, alive and awake. Her lips run over his throat in a necklace of tiny peremptory kisses. ". . . What's wrong?"

"Nothing's *wrong* . . ." He smiles. "*Nothing* . . ." He cannot express his deep content.

But she is elastic, wriggling, contracting. "Come on . . . don't play . . . *love* me . . ."

"I'm through," he murmurs.

"Don't *tease* me." There is a sharp threat of fear in her voice. ". . . You're *kidding* me!"

"No." Loper lifts his thin brown young body from her warm curves and looks at her with sleepy puzzlement. "I'm through."

"What!" The cutting amazement penetrates him like a knife, and the girl flings herself away from him, spread hopelessly on the red damask. He sees her eyes staring at him, wide open, hostile, dark and hard as obsidian. "Is *this* what I came up here for?" There is an ominous pause, and then she spits out at him—"SHIT!"

Loper feels a hurt unlike any he has felt before. His hopeful body is discarded and spurned. He feels his skin shrink and grow tough, even while he holds inside himself an aching wound.

The girl is getting up, rearranging her clothes, throwing herself around in rage and contempt. While Loper sits on the edge of the bed with his head bowed, he hears her final comment before she strides out, slamming the door. "Let me go out and find myself a MAN!"

When her footsteps, echoing and re-echoing (on the steps in the street, around every corner, in the park where the girls are still laughing and beckoning), have died away, he gets up and locks the door. Then he sits on the crumpled red damask of the bed and cries with his head in his hands.

———————————

Loper's closest friend was Chub, a dark, plump, studious Negro boy, who had raced him for top place in earlier school grades, and then pulled well away in high school, while Loper, busy running with the boys, dallied in the middle of the class. Loper thought with respect and affection of Chub, but now that school was over and Chub had gone on to Howard University, he knew that he would be effectively separated from him, and that others could be elevated to first place: boys like Larry and Salvatore Luigi, the two Italians who had forced Frankie when she was drunk with

Wild Rose wine; or King Whitfield, the tall boy who had sung in the Blue Notes, and turned out Brenda 'Baby' O'Reilly. These three friends were in excellent positions to tell him about women.

"It's the money, man," King advised. "You got something they need, and they pay to get it—that's what you got to know."

Loper, wondering whether he had this something, remained sunk in doubts of his manhood. He sought substitutes for virility, his eye on a billiard ball, his hand on a watch in a department store, and he returned always to the thought of the girl who had left him with such bitter and contemptuous words.

"I'm walking along, and it's hot and humid, and this broad had the most maddening habit of looking sideways at me . . ." he tried to explain to King. ". . . I tell you that when I mounted her I was so excited . . ." He implored King with his puzzled wide-apart topaz eyes. King laughed, dismissing it.

"Why didn't you kick her in the butt?" was all he had to contribute. Loper knew that King's coarseness was not desirable, that he wished a different kind of life for himself, but a lazy perversity kept him there where his friend was, a green bill in his tenacious hand.

"Never . . . never . . . *never* give it to a broad without expecting something in return," King advised.

But Loper, even while he worried (*I was not capable, and if you're not capable, life smacks you in the face*), set up for himself a slightly different set of values. He thought of the things he wanted—an apartment on the Hill, overlooking the city and the river, a Cadillac in the garage, wall-to-wall carpeting, elegant clothes. He absorbed King's philosophy, but he expressed it differently. "The dollar bill is the *supreme* essence," he said.

Linking the word 'essence' with the dollar was not without its suitability. As certain celibates obsessed with storage and containment will guard their precious essences against wastage, so these men of the street hoarded their sexual energy. They expended it only when the female (like a deer heckled by a stag), becoming emotionally and sexually desperate, opened her pocketbook in return for the response to her open legs. Loper absorbed this cold wisdom, and tried to balance it with his love for women, their beauties, their generosities, their foolishness, their caprice. Long ago, when he had been sheltered, nourished, and served by his tiny adoring grandmother, he had realized that women meant safety for him, that they presented an implacable emotional front to the rigors of the world. Now because his success depended upon his boosting skill, and upon what he was able to do in those rackets which needed speed, nerve, cunning, and judgment, he was required to really earn his money. And there could not fail to be something infinitely seductive about the thought of women earning it for him. In a trance he waited, passive, his masculinity withheld.

On the stairs to his apartment one day he met the homosexual who had given him the length of red damask, and whose somber eyes seemed to say: 'I'm gay—what are we to do about it?' Loper, who had lost his directness when he traded his male virginity for a bicycle and a twenty-two, paused for a moment.

The statement close to a question, the man said: "Saw you with a fine broad."

"Ain't nothin' to the chicken but the bill." Loper laughed.

"Got some *spare* time," the man said, "you come on up to me."

Loper hesitated again. Then he replied with smiling deliberation: "But it's chicken still." The man nodded and passed on.

That afternoon, after his usual play, and with what seemed like the direct intervention of Fate, Loper won a small but adequate amount on the numbers. He knew that his moment had come, and he took the late plane to New York City.

———————

He has been so obsessed by the whole question of women and the future that he scarcely notices the plane trip. He is challenging the world to assess his value. He touches his taut muscled arms and legs as if to try them out. He glances at his image a thousand times, in every street mirror, in every men's room, in the glittering space behind every bar. He seeks to see himself as others see him, to judge what effect he has, to present himself now to Harlem in a new role, and to start all over again. He is being asked, as one of his knowledgeable friends would have expressed it 'to put his balls on the line.' He knows 144th Street because his aunt had once lived there, and he knows the bars because King had once taken him to some of them and explained their uses and limitations. The Theatre was only for those with money to spend: it was a status bar. The Orpheus was for the professionals, and as King explained it to Loper 'I'm not ready for that yet man.' The Trinidad was for hip squares; for those who liked to make the scene, but might not be good for anything else, unless there were special inducements. Loper has chosen The Trinidad, because he feels safe there and his presence won't be challenged. He likes the photographs of the Negro singers and dancers who have climbed out of the ghetto and made the bigtime. He likes Angel, the barmaid, who wears a tiny red plastic bow in her stiff glossy hair and gives him a whisky sour without asking for identification.

He notices the girl who sits on the other side of the big circular bar—a bar which, although it is supposedly not for professionals, seems to say 'Look who's sitting here!' She blends with the mirrors and the afternoon shadows, but he sees that she is sharp-featured with a light-golden skin and big limpid cowlike brown eyes. He notices that she has adequate breasts which jut under a silver-colored sweater (. . . So are the first scenes of our adult lives imprinted upon our memories . . . He was to see long afterwards the gesture she made as she raised her glass to him, while Angel put an unsolicited drink at his elbow, and said, with a jerk of her head, "She ordered it.")

A moment later he asks her: "With whom am I drinking?"

"My name is Jennie."

"And mine is Ronald—they call me Loper."

She regards him soberly. "What do you do, Loper?"

"I hustle," he answers after a moment's hesitation.

"What's your racket?"

Her eyes were on the far wall, where the mirrors jostle with their reflections.

"Almost anything." His smile is modest.

"Good as *you* look," Jennie says, "you shouldn't have to do *anything*."

Loper, sitting back on his stool, is a little uneasy at hearing her use a gallantry which he himself might well have employed.

"Not *anything* . . . ? Well I like to eat."

She sways her body in the silver sweater, and leans slightly toward him. "Don't you have a woman?"

"No," Loper replies softly.

They look at each other.

"Perhaps . . ." She is tapping against her glass with one long brown finger weighted by a purple-painted nail. "Perhaps, you'd like to have a drink with me in some more private place?"

"Such as?"

"My apartment?"

Loper nods, and she slips decisively off the stool and gathers up her gloves and pocketbook.

"Let's go."

There is a silent walk across Harlem to Seventh Avenue, a walk during which each step is freighted with sexual purpose. It is a walk not unlike the pilgrimage on that hot day in North City, when the restless girl had accompanied him to the park, her tongue touching the red portal of her lips. Jennie also turns to look at him as they walk, but soberly, her eyes placing him in one scale and herself in another balancing the two of them in the ghetto's weighing machine (where so many clamor to sit in the scales of justice). She keeps her head high, picking her way in gray high-heeled suede shoes, as if she despises the ordinary street, and strolls on a pavement spread with dollar bills.

Inside the apartment (three carpeted rooms), she still seems to walk on that same richness of color. She produces a bottle of Scotch and offers him a drink, saying gently: "I think I'll take you under my wing." Loper suddenly unsure of himself, would like to escape, but she holds him there with a merciless calm eye, like the sun full in the heavens. He can only raise his drink to her and smile wisely when she says: "You're not the type who has to go out and scramble for an egg."

"You don't think so?" He is dominated by the need to pretend that *he* is in command of the situation.

"No—I don't think so."

He arranges himself carelessly on a skimpy chair with sharp modern corners, "Why—if I may ask?"

"Sit here!" She has discarded her jacket and he sees that the silver sweater stretches up, encloses her breasts, then lovingly clasps her round neck. Now she pats the sofa beside her.

Loper moves over and sits where she suggests. Idiotically he sips his drink and says: "This is good."

She smiles.

"So you hustle?"

"Yes—I hustle."

"That's how you scramble your eggs . . ." She pauses and smiles again so that he notices the makeup at the corners of her wide mouth.

"You see," she adds significantly, "it's one thing to have to go out and scramble for an egg—it's quite another thing to have an egg already scrambled."

"I suppose."

He doesn't dare to take his topaz-colored eyes from her own large brown ones, feeling that by concentration alone he will be able to understand what she is suggesting.

"You could scramble the egg right here at home . . ." Her voice tails off and she puts down her empty glass, indicating the bottle.

"Help yourself . . ." She moves toward a closed door. "Excuse me for a moment."

He hears again the roar of the traffic below, that ravenous ceaseless and frightening voice of a city which is ten times larger than the one he is used to, a voice which penetrates the strongest building, and appalls those human beings who, dreaming of security, have themselves created this many-tongued monster. When Jennie comes into the room again, she is naked except for a tangerine-colored half-slip, which she has pulled up so that it makes only a flaming band around her thighs. Her face wears still the same calm reflective expression which it had worn when she was dressed in her smart gray suit; and she advances toward Loper until she is quite close to him, as if she were offering her nude body to him and saying: "You see how lucky you are—this is what I am giving to you . . ."

Afterwards when he has put his arms around her and drawn her toward him, she adds with a small half-tight smile: "I want to test your social capabilities."

In Jennie's bedroom Loper has his first lesson in female sensuality. He learns that a slow and deliberate approach to love-making has its uses and beauties, even while that very precision quiets and limits his natural desires. Striped by the light through the Venetian blinds, washed continually in the roar of the traffic, their two bodies varying in a permutation and combination of positions, this prostitute of thirty-five and this ghetto boy of seventeen practice all through the afternoon. It is like a ballet lesson in which the steps are often falteringly and imperfectly achieved, with Loper's more clumsy movements reproved by an insulting rigidity on Jennie's part, with a successful 'pas de deux' rewarded by a kiss on the mouth. From time to time, Loper notices that his partner's arms and throat smell of expensive perfume, and he feels that this is an air he must breathe forever, just as each time his long narrow feet touch the leaf-green carpet (the color of money) he experiences a swift, electric thrill. He is sure that he has at last achieved a pinnacle of skill, and looks down now upon a conquered woman. But this romanticism is swiftly checked when he encounters the expression in Jennie's eyes, as she says—when he rises from a hasty and what he has felt to be a bold foray into that mysterious forest between her legs—her voice dry and sardonic: "Okay—the old college try—you did your best!"

––––––––––––––

The nature of the battlefield upon which he was now required to serve was different from what he had imagined it to be. Jennie's was the first female body which had adequately responded to his, and soon he was able to penetrate and possess, to feel extreme pleasure and to experience himself giving it. Yet to bear arms for this lady he was asked to control that very masculinity which she had fanned into life, and to further deaden sensibilities blunted by his life in the street. In those early days and nights, when her dark and limpid eyes, which with one glance across the bar at The Trinidad had chosen him as a man worthy to represent her, looked into his, he often found himself ready to drop all other supports and drown in their depths. But recalled from such forgetfulness, there came each day a moment when he was conscious of the clock, when—in spite of his wild entreaties—she would walk coldly about the room, fixing herself up for his rivals.

The situation in the world which these two inhabited was not unlike that which existed in the wilds—when male animals fought for the females, with only the strongest, the cleverest, getting to first base. There in the world of nature, the sleekiest and most perfectly formed females were carried off by their male counterparts, and in reproducing their kind, they perfected the race. But in the malformed city ghetto, where money rather than sexual instinct predominated, the prettiest women were habitually pursued by those who had a different form of exploitation as their aim, and who therefore could not allow their instincts full rein. It was ironic that Loper, in bed with Jennie, must be alert not only to satisfy her femininity but to keep in mind the next day or the next weeks, and that later part of the evening when his purpose would be to guide toward her the highest bidder—whether old, infirm, perverse, or pathological—or even (and this hurt him most) those young males like himself often of a different color, but seeming, in their intemperate ardor, rivals to himself. It was ironic that Loper should find the competition for women in his world as stringent as in nature's own; that the older and more successful pimps were not above lengthening their arms with the help of a gun ('an equalizer,' as the cowboy phrase had it), and that these overdressed cocks of the ghetto were accustomed to subdue their women with the ferocity of their bird namesakes, or as male minks (who, seizing females in copulation, would sink their teeth clear through their pelts). Yet in this sharp and obsessive struggle, man had managed to reverse the order of reproduc-

tion itself, so that if children were born, they were sure to be the
children of the trade, fathered often by the least balanced of the
population, the dullest witted, the most inadequately endowed.
Subconsciously Loper knew, as he was taken through the sexual
hoops of strong-willed Jennie's training ring, that the irony was
more poignant in the ghetto than it was in the generalized and
open vice world. He might flaunt his exploitation (and at this
point he was almost more exploited than exploiting) by pretending that he was 'stripping Whitey'; but he knew that Negro girls
as attractive as Jennie had less chance to marry well than their
white counterparts; that they were hunted from childhood, as
animals are hunted for their skins, trapped by the wiliest and
often the most handsome men of their own race, and then turned
over to the trade.

During the first weeks of his apprenticeship as a pimp, Loper
wooed Jennie. He caressed her with a desperation born of the
despair of possessing her, his youth and inexperience providing
him with a constant flow of passion and excitement, making it
harder for him to admit to the absurdity of his wooing and driving him, the more she educated him in love-making, toward
greater torments of jealousy.

He did not see himself as a child of history. Had he been able
to read about the matriarchal societies which had flowered in the
fertile lands of Asia Minor and in many parts of the Africa from
which his ancestors had come; from those lands stretching indeed
from Spain to Japan, where the 'magna mater' had been worshipped in the form of Arditi, Tergatis, Demeter, Cybele, Isis, and
where such high value had been placed upon sexual intercourse
that it had been freely and devoutly offered to God, he might
have understood better that he was only one of a long line of
males, inheritor of the fierce patriarchal societies (the Semites, the
Mongols, the Ayrans) who had displaced the yoni with the lin-
gam, desecrated the temples of love, denied the sacred birth, and
shut women up in tombs, harems, and houses of prostitution. He
might then have turned to Jennie and wooed her in a different
way, with more security and less ambivalence. But his background being what it was, his inheritance being that of the slave,

the patriarchy and the industrialized society, he could only balance as best he could the impulses which warred within him, and perform his part in that grotesque cabaret, which he had watched from babyhood, and of which he now learned—upon Jennie's bed —the further and more controlled movements.

———

It was their custom to share one pair of pajamas, so that Loper would parade around the apartment in the *eau de Nil* crepe de Chine bottoms, and Jennie, like a pretty page, would wear the monogrammed top which matched them, finishing off the costume with a pair of white-satin feathered mules. Loper liked to see her on Sunday—her day off—relaxing in this outfit, with her cloud of loose curly hair over her shoulders, indulging like a young wife in amorous play, making a specially good breakfast which they would eat together in bed. On such holidays she would only occasionally let drop some slight reference to the life, as if she sensed that he did not like it, but still felt it better that he should learn to put up with it. Her dark eyes, which he now felt to be her most expressive feature, would often cloud with some emotion he could not read, but which, thinking back on it years later, he felt referred to her own early training, to that harsh knowledge gained when she was 'turned out,' when she'd been through all those experiences endemic to the life, been 'Jonah'ed,' played-on, 'Georgia'd' . . . until she might wryly call herself larceny-hearted, a description which derives from 'larceny' or 'theft' but has as well overtones of 'malice' and 'bravado.'

On one such Sunday, Loper said to her: "I love you, baby," and turning to her in the kitchen he picked her up, and carried her to the bed in the other room where he deposited her amongst the covers, and playfully pretended to beat her with a little satin pillow which she used as a neck rest.

Something about the incident touched Jenny. She gripped his wrists and, gazing up into his face, she said seriously, "I love you too, daddy."

"And so . . . ?"

"And so . . ."

She was still holding his wrists. "Tomorrow I want to show you something . . ."

"Because you love me, baby?"

Shadows fled through her dark eyes—fear, long-repressed anger, weary knowledge. But these were replaced by a cautious bland kindness, and she sat up a little, and released his wrists, but then thrust away his hands again as they began to explore her breasts. They were business partners, she seemed to say, and as the older and more experienced of the two, she intended to be the teacher. Yet she implied also that as a woman, she must do it her own way, and that due to his eager youthfulness, she must do it soon . . . He scarcely realized yet that she operated from within the terrible context of danger. Danger to herself and her interests —danger to her future with Loper—danger much multiplied should either of them be involved, by accident or design, in that violence which is natural on the street. Upon Loper's tempering much depended, and she could not count on a green boy who might show emotion at the wrong time, flinch before a knife or a gun, or fail to get respect from the older and more rapacious hustlers. In Jennie's world there was no room for sentimentality.

"For us both," she said now.

"What's the show?" Loper asked.

"It's a show, daddy . . . That's about what it is. I'm gonna bring a trick here tomorrow."

Decisively she swung her legs over the bed and said: "Come." She walked over to the second door to the bedroom, which was shut off by a bamboo curtain, and indicated the alcove to one side of it.

"Tomorrow when I bring a trick to the house I want you to be standing here. I'll bring him up the back stairs through the kitchen, and I want you to be here. Around five o'clock. Give or take ten minutes."

Again Loper asked stupidly: "What's the show?"

She had always insisted before that he be out of the apartment if she intended to bring home a customer, and since this pushed the commercial aspects of their relationship into the background, he had been grateful to her for it. Now her tone was brisk, and she no longer looked at him. "It's just a trick of the trade. Certain things you should understand . . . You're my man, Loper, I turned you out." He was reluctant and puzzled. "Okay, baby—if you say so."

The next afternoon at five o'clock, it was almost dark in the street outside, and in the alcove beside the bamboo curtain, where he could see into the bedroom without being seen, Loper felt a fluttering in his stomach, such as he had experienced in school before examinations. He was afraid to smoke because that might betray his presence, and for the same reason he took off his shoes, and occupied his time by padding quietly to and fro in the living room, and listening for the opening of the downstairs door.

Suddenly there came the slightest ping of the bell, as if a finger had touched it lightly, and then withdrawn without pressure. A moment later he heard the tread of feet, and Jennie's voice, light and high, and a deeper voice, murmuring spaced comments. It was like being in the theater, Loper thought, and waiting for the curtain to rise . . . Later the whole scene had indeed the quality of a stage, all of it—music, movement, dialogue, tuned to a distant view, yet rooted within the very center of Loper's feelings, and twisting them strangely, so that Jennie's admonitions to remain silent became scarcely necessary, so paralyzed were his emotions. The shaded lamp switched on, and he glimpsed Jennie's hand, with the ring he had given her (a pearl set inside smaller pearls) on her little finger—and then her body, dressed in the silver-gray suit she had worn on the first day they met, swimming to and fro, striped by the slats of the bamboo curtain, swimming like a fish, to and fro in the room . . . The man was out of focus, his figure blurred. Sometimes he appeared to be over near the door, and Jennie's voice seemed to be luring him toward her, tenderly, carefully, with patience.

"You goin' to take your things off?" she said seductively. "Will I hang your coat?" And through the slats she saw her hand again—the more treacherous because of his ring on her finger—reach out toward the man's voice . . .

He was a white man. Loper saw the back of a plump reddish-pink neck. He heard a voice command, a little hoarsely: "Take *your* things off, too," and then Jennie's silver shadow darted to the other side of the room, and she was speaking across distance. "Baby—" Why must her voice linger like that? . . . "Baby, we've got time. I know we settled on fifteen dollars, but now we're here and we could *really* go to town . . . I can't do much for you for fifteen, baby, but how I'd love to do *everything* . . . I tell you something, baby . . ." Her voice drifted closer to the man, was freighted with heavy promise, dragged out slowly, "I *love* white men—that's the truth I'm telling you . . . It's always *white* men I want, know that, baby . . . ? Know that?"

. . . After a long time, Loper, who had involuntarily shut his eyes, heard her disjointed murmurs. "Eh . . . ? For ten more dollars, that's only twenty-five? You want to, baby?" There was some sort of argument. "I've only got twenty-five . . . You said . . ." "Yes, but now we're here, and plenty of time . . . For ten more, that's thirty-five, you can french me . . ."

Loper's face was burning, his body rigid in the darkness . . . He could see through the curtain into a brilliantly lit den, where Jennie, who in all this time had taken off nothing but her blouse, lured the naked frantic man into complete and detailed recognition of her charms. He saw her face, in sudden full view, avid as the man's own, and tilted back, so that her nostrils and her slightly open mouth seemed to speak without words, to repeat the silent message of her outthrust breasts where the nipples were dark and erect, as they had so often been for Loper himself.

With pounding heart and clenched fists, he saw her retreat a little, luring the eager man to the bed, yet preventing him from coming closer . . . He saw Jennie's lips move almost imperceptibly, promising everything, begging. He saw her hands move to push down her skirt, heard her whisper, as if reluctantly: "Baby, you're generous—I know you're generous . . . I don't go with everyone . . . This is not for everyone. I need money bad . . . I need stockings and the rent's due . . . I need fifty dollars, baby . . . Okay . . . ? Look at these stockings, baby . . ." Loper saw her leg and thigh. ". . . We'll do everything, baby." The brown body, almost naked now, arched toward the white groping hands. He heard her voice: "Okay, it's fifty . . . that's right? . . . Thank you for being so generous . . . Oh, *baby*, I'll show you something . . ."

"She *means* it . . . The bitch *means* it . . . no one could act like that . . . She *likes* white men . . . She's buking me . . . *using* me . . ."

His eyes narrowed murderously, he felt a cold rage obliterate the sight before him, and he felt that in another moment he would rush in and throttle this male intruder, who now, oblivious to everything, mounted Jennie in a frenzy. Loper opened his eyes again to the wild motion on the other side of the screen . . .

In a few seconds it was over. The exhausted man moved slowly, lay still.—Loper stood immobile in the dark alcove, stranded.—The man began to dress, and the woman on the bed stretched, her task done.

Afterwards in the living room, she came and placed her hand on his shoulder.

"Don't touch me," Loper said.

She took away her hand and murmured: "Well—now you see. This is how you are able to wear $100 suits and keep pocket money. I had to be sure you were with me."

He threatened: "Don't say anything to me, bitch."

The darkness in the room deepened. She said lightly, with a tired flatness: "I was afraid of that . . ."

"Don't think . . ." With a great effort, Loper managed to keep the tremor out of his voice. "Don't think that just because you Jemima'd up to him like that, that I went for that shit." He saw her turn with a gesture of discouragement.

"You heard him talk, daddy: he was out of Tennessee."

"What you tryin' to do, con me?"

Jennie's voice came, soothing, cajoling in the darkness.

"*Baby*, you know how them old 'Boss Charlie' whiteys are . . . ?"

～

Loper got up and went out, closing the door carefully.

Outside in the cold street, with the traffic moving senselessly past, something like grief choked him. "*She* did it—the whore. *She* did it to me." He was not clear as to what she had done. But he knew that he was in a trap of some kind, that he dared not show his anger. Some unrealized hope was dying. He turned to look back at the dark windows of the apartment. The light had not been turned on and perhaps she was sitting by the window. But in the bedroom he imagined her body brilliantly illuminated, tauntingly displayed . . .

Afterwards—pretending always that it was more convenient to pay for an extra apartment—he would refuse to allow a girl to bring a customer back to the bed which he customarily shared with her. He was never to risk again the sight of that living tableau.

When the sun rises on the Paragoula State Reformatory for Women, it rises, too, upon North City, some fifty miles away. It rises upon the southern side of the Hill, where the houses cling somewhat drunkenly together, and upon Moon Street and Evans Avenue, Mackay Street and South Spring Street. It rises upon the little park behind Moon Street bordered by the dilapidated school attended by Frankie and Opaline, Beppo and Loper, and upon the back of the red-brick brewery which has been deserted since the famous beer battles of 1944, and is now the favorite meeting place for teen-age gangs.

The sun rises on this little park, leaving a prostitute passed out at the root of the only tree, one eye closed and bloody (where a pimp had pummeled her because she refused to leave her current man, and join his own stable). It rises upon the addict who walks the streets with pain gripping his bowels and stands immobile on the corner, not far from a house where a boy walks through the doorway and throws his 'bag' under the stairwell because he hears the cop beating at the door upstairs. It is an early sun, but means the end of the day to many weary night workers, toilers in crime as others are toilers in factories, their faces glossed with that varnish of fatigue, saying nothing except "I've done it . . . It's done now . . . I've earned my way for another day," saying it as if they already were placed in their coffins, and were suggesting, as Loper often did, "*A broke man is a dead man!*"

In the early morning hope rises and a man tells his wife that he had a dream about the numbers ('I played 306 last week and now a 7 is due to show . . . I dreamed it, baby, and I want you to put half a buck on 7, and if 7 comes out, play the rest on a 3, and if there is a 3 well, baby, bring me *mah money*'). And a boy tells his brother about his enemy in school ('He gave me a dirty look, Alec —a dirty look . . . I hate him . . . I hate the ground he walks on . . . When I fight with someone I don't see him and I agitate myself. I tell you that's what started me stealing, and maybe I'm not smart at school, Alec, but I'm smart at stealing').

Hope rises because everyone can think of something to be grateful for. The Syrian law student up all night with his books, and staring over these roofs held so tightly in the grip of his less moral countrymen, sees the little Syrian girl downstairs lounging in the street with her stomach swollen, and he remembers a time not far back in history when Syrian daughters who lost their virginity were—for the sake of the family honor—killed by their own fathers. And reading his lawbook, which defines a wayward child as "a child between 7 and 17 years of age who habitually associates with vicious or immoral persons, or who is growing up in circumstances exposing him or her to lead an immoral, vicious, or criminal life," he wonders if the little girl downstairs will end up in the reformatory, and rationalizes that there the conditions, if not perfect, are better than they were when the male members of a family could conveniently cut up such a female into small pieces.

One of nature's most effective miracles lies in the fact that light is spread equally: that the sun rises upon the towers and domes and campuses of North City (center of culture, birthplace of civil liberties, home of political savoir-faire) as it does upon the gray acres of the East and South, the crowded shabby warrens around Moon Street and the neon-splashed criss-cross circle at Spring Street and Evans Avenue. It touches lovingly the sedate mansion in which a former governor—corrupt custodian of the years of adolescence of Frankie and Brenda, Beppo, Ana, and Harriet—rises to have breakfast, as it does the little diner where King and Loper watch the sky grow lighter. It disregards the ethnic convulsions which take place under the roofs it touches, and, blind to change and history, to threats of war, to faces moving into conflict, it proceeds with slow and inexorable movement higher into the heavens.

Loper has been up all night—he had walked out on Jennie when she objected to his tangling with other prostitutes, women whom she described as not worthy to touch her, wearers of vulgar clothes and artificial hair, cheaters and liars, users of obscene language. In spite of the fact that he had agreed with her completely as to her own superiority (Isn't that why he had been so enthusiastic about her in the first place?), he has taken great pleasure in flaunting his interest in other women before her, hoping to wound her so severely that she will understand that he has at last learned the lesson of indifference. For all his resentments, he now demands payment. For the hurt of the bit in his mouth. For that memorable night when the scene in the bedroom had been burnt into his brain. For the times when he had lain silent on the bed as she made her cold preparations to depart. He puts it in a different way.

"That broad tried to have *me*," he explains to King as they sit together at the all-night diner on Evans Avenue. "She wasn't satisfied being my *woman*, she wanted to *own* me."

"You let them get away with that, you gone, man," King assures him. They order scrambled eggs, sausages and coffee, while the street outside grows lighter, while the faint colors of morning strike through the grease-dulled windows.

"Jennie has a rep on the street . . . and naturally I got a few shots," Loper says complacently. "That any reason she going to curb me?"

"You're right, man," King assures him again. "One thing dem

vets'll do is buke you. Baby, you gotta be watchin' out for trick-eration!"

"It's a poor rat has only one hole," Loper comments.

King chuckles, pulling his plate toward him, pushing the silk scarf around his neck, leaning over the booth with his huge enveloping arms. He has grown in the last few years (from those early days when he had turned out Brenda O'Reilly,) into one of the most up-and-coming pimps on the Avenue. He likes to hear this story from Loper, as he likes to hear reiterated his own old triumphs. He is reassured by Loper's emancipation, as poor children are by the story of Cinderella.

An hour or two ago in an apartment off Mackay Street, King had provided Loper with a further demonstration of control. One of his girls was claiming that he neglected her, and that Friday night was *her* night.

"No such thing as *your* night, bitch," King had said to the sullen dark girl in the tight tawdry yellow dress. Roughly he had swung her around by her arm, put his face close to hers and said, with a gesture of menacing tenderness: "*Your* night is when I get there." The girl's face set into a dumb defiant stare . . .

Now King asks Loper: "What Jennie say, man? How she put it?"

"She say I have to be *hers*. She say she wants me to *herself*. . . . She bitches if I talk to another woman. She knows that Fanny digs me, man, and so she bitches if I pass the time of day with Fanny . . ." (*Talking like this Loper is momentarily alone with Jennie. He murmurs to her, and Jennie opens her mouth as if to swallow nourishment for the rest of her life. In a victorious fatigue, the moon sinks into a bed of blood-red flowers. He thinks of how it has been since he left her. He thinks of the dark, heavy, good-natured girl he has been using as a temporary source of income. Her body is as lumpy as a sack of potatoes. In order to make love to her he has had to choke down distaste, to keep himself in control. He has been worn out with the effort. Fatigued. Deadened . . .*)

He murmurs aloud: "Bitch!" with a touch of viciousness.

"Sure are—all of them!" King chuckles, wiping his broad shining lips.

They light cigarettes, and stretch out their legs under the table, waiting for that time, not more than an hour or two away, when they will stretch out at last in their beds.

"Hear Frankie's up at the joint? . . ." King says.

The institution at Paragoula expands to include them for a moment, as if underground passages had been built all that distance to Moon Street. There Brenda 'Baby' O'Reilly walks like a white bride, thinking of her ebony lover. There Frankie, disappointed student, struts with a Scout-like emblem pinned to her shirt. There Harry, returned from Townsend, but for one reason or another back in the secluded cells (so poetically called 'Secure'), climbs into her dream car; and there, the electrically controlled door opens at last to receive little Ana 'Pug Nose' Pulaski (who had beaten the rap last Thanksgiving, but now is sent up at last, bedraggled in her finery, her locks dyed black and touching her plump overpainted cheeks, which give a last touch of innocence to her weary open mouth). Only Beppo is not in the joint, and, no longer supported by Ana's indecent earnings, is seen (dressed in her tight suede pants, high boots, and open silk shirt) roaming wolf-like through the bars, night after night.

"Yes—Frankie's there all right."

"Glad to know it," Loper says with a smile. "She came out of Wentworth twice, didn't she? Something about attacking Whitey . . . ?"

"Yes, she broke a pitcher on a matron's head. Now she's at Paragoula and I hear she was knocked up."

"That *so?*" Loper feels a vague surprise, not because Frankie has graduated to a real prison, but because she has asserted her femininity through pregnancy.

Aloud he says: "Funny—she always seemed to be one of the boys. She sure could fight."

"Never could figure it out." King's eyes are glazed over with fatigue and repletion. "Some of these broads act as if it doesn't mean anything to go with a feller. Even that little Brenda I turned out . . . She was here on the street with Pokey."

"Pokey?" Loper is bent on knowing every girl in the life, on making a human map of Moon Street and the Avenue.

"She's a Butch," King informs him, "big black nigger Butch. Operates down in Spring Street . . . I turned Baby out, and she's a real woman, I'll say that for her. But she's in Wentworth and I'm on the look-out for her when she gets out—and man, before I can get my eyes on her, I hear Pokey done copped . . ."

"A streak of freak," contributes Loper.

The two men sit silently. Through the smoke of their cigarettes forms appear and disappear, images of the past still enveloped in the freshness of childhood memories. A certain yearning, a certain love of home touches them, as if their confused dark world had been daubed here and there with color.

"Louise is pregnant again . . ." King says.

"Ain't that a bitch," sympathizes Loper.

King stubs out his cigarette and comments that the little white girl—the one Beppo had on the street, the one from the East City Project—was up at the joint too.

"Oh yeah?" Loper looks puzzled. "I knew Beppo from way back when she used to hang with Frankie's cousin, Opaline . . . Who's the little broad?"

"I don't know her name, but she's a new turn-out. She only got six months. She and Frankie should hit the street about the same time . . . Frankie got two years, but she's doing eighteen months."

"That so?" Loper's interest revives. "Frankie and I always were tight. When we wuz both in the Vivaldos, I used to tell her 'I'm going to be your pimp.' "

"Test her out, man," King advises. "Send up a kite."

"A kite! . . . Hell, I'll go up and see her."

"They won't let you *in* man." King speaks with the weary assurance of one who, in order to further his own ends, has made many trips up to Paragoula. "You have to be a *relative*." Loper taps reflectively on the table, and pushes his empty coffee cup to and fro.

"*You* get to go up?" he questions.

"Not this time," King replies regretfully. "They got wise to *me*. But I might make a message to Turkey, and Turkey could sound out Baby, and Baby's tight with Frankie . . . It's worth the chance."

"That's right." Loper is glad he's back in North City where he knows everyone. He is as eager as any businessman to carve out new markets. "It's worth a chance."

But King warns him about Ana. "Far as I know, she's fresh meat, man."

"Sure . . . but could she be turned out?"

King glances at Loper's confident face and throws back his head, so that the dark cords in his throat contract with a controlled amusement. He says with admiration: "Anyone can do it, bet *you* can, man."

He extracts a pair of dark glasses from his pocket, puts them on, and prepares to emerge—disguised—into the world of daylight. He has become so used to these glasses that ordinary light seems to hurt his eyes.

Loper, as if in imitation, pulls out dark glasses also. "You'll slide a note on Turkey?" he asks.

"Sure thing," King assures him, "I'll let them know up there we're out here waiting for them."

They sit immobile, hunched up in the booth gazing out into the street, their eyes blank.